The World of Engineering

The World of Engineering

JOHN R. WHINNERY

Professor of Electrical Engineering
University of California
Berkeley, California

McGRAW–HILL Book Company
New York · St. Louis · San Francisco
Toronto · London · Sydney

THE WORLD OF ENGINEERING

II

Prologue

The Profession of Engineering *

It is a great profession. There is the fascination of watching a figment of the imagination emerge through the aid of science to a plan on paper. Then it moves to realization in stone or metal or energy. Then it brings jobs and homes to men. Then it elevates the standards of living and adds to the comforts of life. That is the engineer's high privilege.

The great liability of the engineer compared to men of other professions is that his works are out in the open where all can see them. His acts, step by step, are in hard substance. He cannot bury his mistakes in the grave like the doctors. He cannot argue them into thin air or blame the judge like the lawyers. He cannot, like the architects, cover his failures with trees and vines. He cannot, like the politicians, screen his shortcomings by blaming his opponents and hope that the people will forget. The engineer simply cannot deny that he did it. If his works do not work, he is damned. That is the phantasmagoria that haunts his nights and dogs his days. He comes from the job at the end of the day resolved to calculate it again. He wakes in the night in a cold sweat and puts something on paper that looks silly in the morning. All day he shivers at the thought of the bugs which will inevitably appear to jolt his smooth consummation.

* From Herbert Hoover, *Memoirs of Herbert Hoover*, vol. 1, *Years of Adventure*, The Macmillan Company, New York, 1951, pp. 132–133.

v

On the other hand, unlike the doctor his is not a life among the weak. Unlike the soldier, destruction is not his purpose. Unlike the lawyer, quarrels are not his daily bread. To the engineer falls the job of clothing the bare bones of science with life, comfort, and hope. No doubt as years go by people forget which engineer did it, even if they ever knew. Or some politician puts his name on it. Or they credit it to some promoter who used other people's money with which to finance it. But the engineer himself looks back at the unending stream of goodness which flows from his successes with satisfactions that few professions may know. And the verdict of his fellow professionals is all the accolade he wants.

Preface

This book is designed to tell something of the profession of engineering, and is directed primarily to those students who are just beginning it or are thinking of it as a career, and to their counselors. We hope it may be useful to any others interested in the profession. Engineering can be a most rewarding career because it influences the whole structure of our civilization. It can also be an exciting one because of the rapidity of change in the tools used by engineers and in the products and systems they turn out. It is also a varied profession with opportunities for persons with a range of talents, including the most analytic and the most inventive, and with the ability to work with people and society in using to best advantage the products of the profession.

It is impossible to describe the complexity and scope of such a profession in a single book. The rapidity of change and the variety make especially difficult jobs for the authors of the several chapters. The examples they use to make specific points may well be major innovations at the time of this writing but "old-hat" or even obsolete by the time the reader picks up the volume. Nevertheless, these may be thought of as "snapshots" of the state of the art, of a present problem, or of an ingenious solution, and as such will remain valid after there are new problems or better solutions. In this light, the excitement, creativeness, and dynamicism of the profession can be seen, and the reader himself can supply the current examples.

The book is purposely not divided along classical lines of engineering: civil, electrical, etc. Although we do not wish to minimize the contributions of these subjects or their probable importance for some time to come (more will be said of this and the usual divisions in Chap. 1), we have decided to use a more functional grouping to stress the increasing interdisciplinary effort among graduates of the several fields in solving some of our current large problems and the growing unity in the bases of many of these classical divisions. This grouping is also used because the usual divisions are described in many excellent orientation volumes.* In deciding upon an unconventional grouping, the editor recognizes that it becomes even harder to give proper perspective to the several problems and proper relative coverage to the different divisions of engineering that contribute to these problems. Our colleagues will notice and be disappointed in many omissions and certain distortions of emphasis that result. To the extent that these mislead the prospective student, they are serious. So we must make clear that this is not, in spite of the title, the whole "world of engineering." It is a sampling written by persons of international reputation who have contributed to the fields about which they write. To the extent that the book inspires the student with aptitude for the profession to read further or to consult with experts in the several areas, the goal is achieved, and the lack of completeness is necessary and unfortunate, but unimportant.

JOHN R. WHINNERY

* See the Bibliography at the end of Chap. 1.

Contents

The World of Engineering

1

The Profession of Engineering

by John R. Whinnery

John R. Whinnery is a native of Colorado who received his B.S. and Ph.D. degrees in electrical engineering from the University of California at Berkeley. He worked at the General Electric Company, Schenectady, from 1937 to 1948, at the same time teaching part time in company educational courses and war-training programs and lecturing at Union College.

In 1946, Dr. Whinnery joined the faculty of the University of California and is currently Professor of Electrical Engineering at Berkeley. His administrative assignments there included positions as Director of the Electronics Research Laboratory, Chairman of the Electrical Engineering Department, and Dean of the College of Engineering. On leaves from the university, he worked for the Hughes Aircraft Company, the Ramo-Wooldridge Corporation, and the Bell Telephone Laboratories. In 1959, he held a Guggenheim Fellowship at the Federal Technical Institute in Zurich, Switzerland. He is author or coauthor of texts and papers on microwaves, electron tubes, and quantum electronics, and has been active in professional societies and government advisory committees.

His hobbies include camping, hiking, and the writing of children's stories.

2   *John R. Whinnery*

IT IS THE PURPOSE of this book to tell something of the profession of
engineering and the pride and excitement it inspires in the contributors
to this volume. Engineering is a creative profession, whether one person conceives in a flash of brilliance the heart of a new defense system
or works diligently within a group to bring into production a simple
product used by everyone, but does it better and more economically
than before.

The reader has lived with change so long that he is likely to be blasé
about the technical marvels of our age and the planned additions to
them. The longest suspension bridge in the world is now open for
crossing. Plans for the world's tallest buildings have just been an-
nounced. Commercial jet travel, which is less than five years old at
this writing, is so much a part of our lives that a busy executive forced
to fly cross-country in a prop plane would feel a kinship with the
Wright brothers if not with the Donner party. Yet supersonic commercial airliners to cut present flight times in half are now on order
in at least three countries. Communication and electronic computation capacities have doubled about every thirteen months for at least
this five-year period. The well-publicized achievements of our space
program and the classified achievements of defense have brought a hundred items that would have been considered miracles a decade ago.
And one can name others.

Many people and many professions have played a part in these
achievements. Scientists (often long ago) discovered the first principles. Other scientists worked with engineers in the application of
these principles to new and difficult problems. Bankers and brokers
arranged the financing. Management experts helped to coordinate the
efforts of all, especially in the large projects. But no one would minimize the essential part played by engineers in the development of these
dramatic changes or in the job of keeping our existing technological
society from grinding to a halt. If we sometimes overstress the role of
the engineer, it is only because this book is about the world of engineering.

WHAT IS ENGINEERING?

As we will stress often, "engineering" represents a variety of activities difficult to define in a few words. It is, in fact, the purpose of the
book to develop some picture of these activities. However, the definition
set down by the Engineering Council for Professional Development is
an excellent short statement to begin with. It is:

Engineering is the profession in which a knowledge of mathematical and natural sciences gained by study, experience and practice is applied with judgement to develop ways to utilize, economically, the materials and forces of nature for the benefit of mankind.

When the author was in school, it was very popular to say that an engineer was a person who could do for one dollar what any fool could do for two. The epigram had point in that it stressed the economic aspect of engineering. This is important whether one is attempting to shave a few tenths of a cent from a mass-produced transistor or to save a billion dollars on an antisubmarine detection system. Nevertheless, the truly new designs of engineering—the Golden Gate Bridge, a printed circuit board for the latest-model digital computer, or an antisubmarine missile—could not be made by an intelligent layman, let alone a fool, given all the resources of Fort Knox and all the time short of that necessary to educate him as a competent engineer for the job.

We should also not forget the origin of the word. As originally defined it meant an "ingenious person," and the cleverness, resourcefulness, and inventiveness implied in this word are still at the heart of the best engineering and should always be.

Finally, we shall stress some of the characteristics of the profession, which will be developed in the book along with some of the activities. Perhaps the most important is the *opportunity* for service to our society. If you have not yet read the words of Herbert Hoover in the Prologue, it is suggested that you do so now. These are the views of a man who had the privilege of serving his country through engineering, business, and government, and who reached our country's highest executive office. The statement expresses eloquently the spirit of the profession we would like to describe. Other characteristics are those of change and of variety. Both have been mentioned, but will be stressed again.

THE MATTER OF CHANGE

We probably have few five-year-old readers, but you who are reading very likely have five-year-old children, relatives, or pets. We referred in the second paragraph of this chapter to some of the engineering developments that were completed during this arbitrarily selected period, and it may help to think of them in relation to the short lifetime of your five-year-old.

To develop this point, consider the laser, which generates very intense beams of coherent light. It was proposed by Schawlow and

Townes in 1958 and was first demonstrated by Maiman in 1960. Within six months, commercial models were advertised for sale, and now dozens of companies are concerned with research or manufacture of these devices. Hundreds of other laboratories are studying the use of this tool in medicine, chemistry, warfare, precision machining, materials research, and communications. All manned space flights took place during the five-year period mentioned, and the successful communication satellites were launched during the latter part of this period. Nuclear reactors for large-scale power production first found their economic place in large utilities during this period.

Lest the reader conclude from the above that all problems have been quickly solved, we may remind him that the transportation system of our country has worked itself into a critical condition during this same period, and that the air and water resources of some of our most beautiful and important cities are rapidly being used up. More generally, all new advances, such as the laser or nuclear energy, open up new fields of application that could not have been imagined before their demonstration, and others will follow these.

As we noted in two examples above, some of the new developments and the rapidity of the changes have brought problems as well as increased enrichment, health, convenience, leisure, and safety to our lives. It would be easy to say that the problems are for social scientists, economists, and politicians, and it is true that experts in those fields must face them. The engineer should respect the special knowledge and skills brought by those experts, but he must also be concerned to an increasing degree with the problems and be willing to work in his proper place with all of society to solve them. If little more is said about this aspect in the book, it is because the subject requires a book in itself. Meanwhile, change will continue, and the optimists will be optimistic about the value of the new developments while the pessimists will be pessimistic about them. As good engineers, the writers of the various chapters try to be realists, but they are not pessimistic.

VARIETY IN SUBJECT MATTER

In spite of omissions, the chapters of this book will give some view of the variety in subject matter to be found in the profession of engineering. Those who have thought a good deal about the profession, talked with teachers, and studied college catalogues may find the titles puzzling. They are not the most common way of dividing engineering. The professional societies and the majority of college curricula are still formed about divisions such as chemical, civil, electrical, mechanical, industrial, metallurgical, and others to be noted below, each with a great deal of pride in their special place in engineering. If one follows engineering, he will very likely enter one of these fields, and may even now have a favorite one selected.

The departure from the usual manner of subdividing engineering is purposeful, as explained in the Preface. The most important reason is to show that which is common to all branches of engineering and the interrelations among them. Such interrelations and interdisciplinary efforts have always existed, but they are growing. The rate of growth is such, in fact, that some schools have given up the divisions at the undergraduate level and list only a common engineering curriculum with a reasonable number of electives. Still others have adopted new divisional titles (perhaps a bit like those of this book). But even though the majority of students will select one of the classical divisions, it is hoped that the groupings here will give a fresh point of view and show the increasing team efforts by graduates of many of the curricula.

Because the classical curricula still exist in the majority of colleges, and because the professional societies built around them continue to contribute to the stature of engineering, we would like to list these divisions and to describe some of the specialties and their relations to the subjects of this book.

CHEMICAL ENGINEERING

Engineers in this field are concerned with the systems and processes of our important chemical industry. They are usually closely associated with chemists, but in addition to the chemical reaction itself, they must be concerned with fluid flow, heat transfer, control, and the systems-engineering job of a large plant that may be needed to produce the desired product economically. Chemical engineers play a major part in space engineering, systems engineering, energy sources and conversion, bioengineering, and materials, to mention some of the chapter headings of the book.

CIVIL ENGINEERING

This field was historically the first of the present major divisions. It is still one of the most important to our country in that it is concerned with major projects such as buildings, dams, transportation networks, water resources, and sanitation. Its practitioners enter into most of the subjects of the book, and with new materials and techniques for design, there are major opportunities for imaginative graduates interested in contributing to any of these systems. Specialization may be

Figure 1   Model of a chemical processing plant. Exact scale models are valuable aids for acquainting young engineers with design and operating procedures. (Allied Chemical)

in structures, hydraulics, transportation, sanitary systems, or other options. Architectural engineering, offered in some schools, is usually closely related.

ELECTRICAL ENGINEERING

This subject was originally concerned with power systems and electrical machines, but especially since World War II has changed subject matter completely. This change is usually described as an emphasis on electronics but actually embraces many fields, including systems, computers, control, networks, energy conversion, solid-state electronic materials, and others. Spurred by the defense and space industry, it is now the largest in terms of enrollment in most schools. Thus students with electrical engineering backgrounds will also be found in all of the subjects treated in this book.

MECHANICAL ENGINEERING

This part of the profession has a fine tradition going back to the dynamic and thermodynamic design and analysis of the mechanisms of our industrial society. Modern mechanical engineering is still concerned with these objectives but embraces systems engineering and control, and has also been revolutionized by today's new materials and tools for design. Mechanical engineers contribute in a major way to space projects, energy conversion, and systems, and in some degree to most of the subjects to be discussed. Mechanical engineering has developed many other important branches of the profession. Electrical engineering was the first of these, but is now well separated. Others sometimes found within the department and sometimes as separate departments include aeronautical, agricultural, industrial, and nuclear engineering, theoretical and applied mechanics, and naval architecture. Each of these will be defined briefly:

Aeronautical or aerospace engineering   Aeronautical engineering became an important specialty concerned with the design of aircraft; it stressed the aspects of structures and power plants for flight, with the related fluid dynamics. Now, whether or not it is a major part of mechanical engineering, its emphasis is much more on the problems of space vehicles and systems.

Agricultural engineering   There are many opportunities to apply the techniques and methods of precise engineering to agriculture, and the marvelously productive agricultural system of this country owes much to the existence of this field. It is often associated with mechanical engineering because of the ingenious and well-known mechanisms of modern agriculture, but the larger field utilizes a wide range of subjects such as fluid flow, electronics, and climatology.

Industrial engineering   Specialists in this field are concerned with proper design of the industrial process itself, which requires attention to the materials and tools of manufacture, the economics and management aspects of the process, and especially the interrelation of man and machine in the manufacturing system. Recently the very powerful tool of operations research, and corresponding use of the high-speed computer, has made it possible to be very much more quantitative in optimizing industrial systems.

Nuclear engineering   One of the important applications of nuclear energy has been through the nuclear reactor, and so this field is a part of the study of general power sources. However, in the larger sense nuclear engineers are concerned with all aspects of nuclear devices for which practical applications can be found. Nuclear engineering is usually a specialty only at the graduate level and is now most often separated from mechanical engineering.

Applied mechanics (or theoretical mechanics)   This is, in a sense, at the heart of mechanical engineering in that new methods of analysis are sought for the problems of mechanics, in fluids as well as solid bodies. It is nevertheless a separate department in many places, and an option or field of graduate specialization in nearly all others.

Naval architecture   As with aeronautical engineering, the special aspects of fluid flow, power plants, and structural design are stressed, but here in relation to ship design. There are only a few programs in the country, some only at the graduate level.

METALLURGICAL AND CERAMIC ENGINEERING

These are often separate curricula, but the trend is for unity in attacking the problem of new materials of all types in a more unified manner under fields which may be known as materials science and engineering. New materials have made possible lighter and stronger structures for civil engineers, higher- temperature materials for mechanical engineers, and the solid-state devices of modern electronics. Many problems in all fields, and especially in space, electronics, and nucleonics, are still limited by the properties of available materials. Thus the student in

Figure 2   Process control room for making phenol, a starter product for the manufacture of nylon. (Allied Chemical)

this field has a chance to contribute to the majority of the topics to be covered in the text.

MINING, GEOLOGICAL, AND PETROLEUM ENGINEERING

These fields also were originally separate curricula (usually in schools of mining) but are tending more toward unification as minerals engineering. Many new and exciting methods from physics and chemistry are available to supplement the classical geological emphases on minerals and petroleum exploration. Similarly, new methods for developing and reducing deposits are designed to meet the changing needs for various resources. The result may be that a whole new source (such as the ocean) will become economically feasible for exploration. Geological engineering, which combines aspects of geology and several fields of engineering, is important to all projects concerned with soil and rock mechanics—highways, tunnels, dams, and mines.

ENGINEERING SCIENCE (OR APPLIED SCIENCE)

Science is a major part of all engineering programs, and a part which has been increasing recently. However, there are curricula which stress the scientific aspect even more. The chief advantage of these is that students who like both the sciences and engineering can have more of a combination than can be obtained from either the engineering or the science program alone. The programs are often designed for students who definitely plan on graduate work, and the graduate study can usually be in either science or engineering after completion of one of these programs. Since they are often experimental or even "honors" programs, a considerable variation can be expected in programs of this name from school to school.

These are not all the subjects one can find in college catalogues, or even in lists of professional societies, but they represent the majority of divisions in the conventional breakdown. With the unconventional breakdown to be followed from here on, they should demonstrate the variety in fields, which was the point of this section.

VARIETY IN TYPE OF JOB

In addition to variety of subject matter, engineering careers cover a tremendous range of activity. Once the "image" of the engineer was a bronzed young man leaning on a transit, or a worried draftsman biting

Figure 3   Modern data-processing equipment, used in management and engineering problem solving and in process control. The control unit is in right foreground, memory tape units in the rear, and print-out apparatus at center. (Allied Chemical)

his pencil over a drafting table in a large room with dozens like him. These pictures always represented poor technique for surveying and drafting, but if they ever indicated the center of activity for the engineering graduate, they do not any more. Although these are tools that *some* engineers will use at times, and others will supervise the use of, portraying that use as a representative activity of the engineer today is about as accurate as saying that the chief activity of a skilled surgeon is sewing. Unfortunately these images remain as symbolic of engineering in the minds of some parents and counselors.

The difficulty in presenting a single accurate and updated image is just that there is such a range of opportunity for different types of activity. Thus it is a difficulty only to those of us who are trying to tell you of the profession, but a rare opportunity for variety to the engineering graduate. There are indoor jobs and outdoor jobs; there are careers with stress on theory, others on laboratory experiments, and still others on dealing with customers or personnel. There are increasing opportunities for travel all over the world. There is a very great demand for engineering graduates competent in management.

Very roughly, the types of activities may be divided into research, development, design, applications engineering, management, and the teaching of engineering. At the research level, the engineer will work with pure scientists, and the activities of those trained in engineering or science may be indistinguishable. The work here is often individual or carried on with a few colleagues, but the results must be presented and defended both within one's own organization and to the professional or scientific societies. The goals are very broad and ideally may be any development resulting in new knowledge, but they are usually directed to some imagined use.

In advanced development, the work is more likely to be a team effort, the team frequently including physicists and mathematicians as well as engineers. There are goals to be achieved with varying degrees of specification (i.e., size, weight, accuracy of the system), and there is usually a time scale. However, the manner of achieving the goal may be seen only vaguely or not at all in the beginning. The development problem is solved if there is found at least one good way of meeting these specifications.

Design is to a very large degree the characteristic activity of the engineer. Here the desired goals are known and the specifications given, although trade-offs may be allowed within certain limits, for example, between cost and purity of a commercial chemical. To class a problem as design rather than development, there should be reasonable assurance at the start of at least one possible way to reach the goal, although the best one may not be known. The ingenuity of design will be in comparing several possibilities and determining the "best" of several known alternatives, hopefully devising a solution better than would have been predicted beforehand. Cost and time are always at issue in this process. It may be an individual process for small units and even some large structures, but it is almost always a group effort for large systems.

In the applications areas, one may be concerned with final testing, installations in the field, discussions with customers on future needs and their solution with your company's products, or the proper use of installed equipment. Travel and the ability to work with people are characteristics of this part of the spectrum, but the technical knowledge required is not at all trivial. It often combines elements of all the other activities, with a bit of puzzle solving thrown in when complicated systems do not work as planned.

All of the above areas may be entirely analytical, with work at a desk or in a computing center, or entirely experimental, with work in a laboratory or at a testing site. Most often the work is a combination of these. And, of course, the above divisions are artificial; actual jobs tend to be combinations or gradations between the areas mentioned. In a small company it is typical to find one person performing all of the above functions to some extent; in a large one he may perform a single specialty from one of these areas. In neither case is it necessary to find oneself "in a rut" if one's full talents are not used, for there is at every level a dearth of good talent, and a ready acceptance of even the youngest of persons with ideas and an ability to achieve goals.

The opportunity for engineers in management positions has been growing, and technically educated persons with management interests and skills are very much needed in the organizations with a large scientific and engineering content. The importance of the project manager with a broad knowledge of engineering will be stressed in Chap. 9, entitled "The Engineering of Large Systems," with special examples also given in Chap. 8, "Space Engineering." Research and development laboratories must be managed by persons who have enough knowledge of their subject to maintain the respect of those reporting to them. Civil engineering and consulting firms from small one-man consulting offices to large ones such as the worldwide Bechtel Corporation are traditionally headed by engineers. Many utilities and chemical plants are also. However, the rapidly growing electronics and aerospace industry has publicized the need for engineers in management at all levels, and this principle is now clear in all dynamic industries.

The teaching of engineering can also be a most rewarding career for some of you, but no description of this will be given as you will have direct contact with that part of the profession in your school work, and if you are interested, any professor will be glad to tell you of his rewards and problems.

SUMMARY OF PROFESSIONAL ENGINEERING

A good way of summarizing the diversity of fields and stressing the various activities of the professional engineer has been given by M. P. O'Brien:

The ultimate objective of engineering work is the design and production of specific items of "hardware"—a bridge, a factory, a ballistic missile, a digital computer—each designed to fulfill an operational objective, and novel to the extent that each meets a new or different set of requirements. The term "design" as used here connotes the bringing into existence of something which did not previously exist. Reproduction of identical items is a manufacturing process, not engineering design.

Achieving this objective involves many intermediate items of "soft ware"—feasibility studies, computer programs, theoretical and experimental work, data on the properties of materials, reliability analyses, and so forth—but these are means to the engineering objective of hardware, not ends in themselves. In skeleton form, the essential features of the engineering process are:

1   Identification of a feasible and worthwhile technical objective and definition of this objective in quantitative terms.
2   Conception of a design which, in principle, meets the objective. This step involves the synthesis of knowledge and experience.
3   Quantitative analysis of the design concept to fix the necessary characteristics of each part or component and to identify the unresolved problems—usually problems of materials, of component performance, and of the interrelationship of components.
4   Exploratory research and component tests to find solutions of the unresolved problems.
5   Concepts for the design of those components which are not already developed and available.
6   Re-analysis of the design concept to compare the predicted characteristics with those specified.
7   Detailed instructions for fabrication, assembly and test.
8   Production or construction.
9   Operational use, maintenance, field service engineering.

A very broad view of the overall needs should be maintained at every step. This was well stated by Sadi Carnot, who wrote in the concluding paragraph of his treatise on the second law of thermodynamics:

We should not expect ever to employ in practice all the motive power of the combustibles used. The efforts which one would make to attain this result would be even more harmful than useful if they led to the neglect of other important considerations. The economy of fuel is only one of the conditions which should be fulfilled by steam engines; in many cases it is only a secondary consideration. It must often yield the precedence to safety, to the solidity and durability of the engine, to the space it must occupy, to the cost of its construction, etc. To be able to appreciate justly in each case the convenience and economy which present themselves, to be able to recognize the most important from those which are only subordinate, to adjust them all suitably, and finally *to reach the best results by the easiest method*—such should be the power of the man who is called on to direct and coordinate the labors of his fellow men, and to make them concur in attaining a useful purpose.

EDUCATION FOR ENGINEERING

Education for engineering starts with a standard college preparatory course in high school. Electives are usually taken in science and mathematics, but the humanities, foreign languages, and English courses are in no sense of second importance. Mechanical drawing courses are recommended by some schools because they improve space visualization, and shop courses may be of similar help if the student has done no building or tinkering as a hobby, but these are not engineering courses and should not be thought of as such. The most important single indicator of probable success in a college or university engineering program is the record made in mathematics, on the basis of courses which are not too abstract but have a reasonable stress on applications of the mathematics. For those who are mechanically inclined but poor at mathematics (and immune to special help in this area) a technical institute program should be considered. For those in doubt, some of the aptitude tests which can be arranged through most high schools may be of help.

In starting the college or university program in engineering, the student may or may not have in mind the particular field of engineering he wishes. The first year or so is nearly the same for all fields, so even if asked to state a preference, he can usually change in this period without loss of time, and even into the third year without serious loss. Such is the case because this period in a typical program is spent in stressing physics, mathematics, chemistry, the humanities or social sciences, and only basic or introductory courses in engineering itself. The student should pick a school of high standards, but should not be made to believe that there are only one or two of these in the country. There are literally hundreds, as proved by the records of their graduates in industry or in graduate work at other institutions. In many states the two-year colleges (community or junior colleges) provide excellent engineering education for the first two years, with transfer to the best colleges and universities possible at the junior level without loss of time. Where electives are allowed, it is recommended that the student take the most basic courses possible. These may be in mathematics or the sciences, but can also be very fundamental courses in the engineering department where the added motivations of application are included. However, he should not take courses with the thought that he is becoming a specialist in a *narrow* field at the undergraduate level. Such specialization is better achieved in industry, in graduate study, or in extension courses after graduation.

The engineering major typically receives the Bachelor of Science degree after a four-year (or in some schools a five-year) program, and a few years ago it was assumed he would then go at once to a job. Now all students who can qualify for graduate work must seriously consider it. Dr. Terman in Chap. 11 stresses the increasing importance of such work for all who can qualify. We state categorically that every student should go just as far as his talents warrant. Financing may be difficult, but since there are increasing numbers of scholarships, assistantships, and cooperative programs with industry, it should not be used as an easy excuse for not undertaking the appropriate graduate work, either before, with, or after the first engineering job. If academic qualifications do not justify formal graduate work, there are still many job possibilities in most of the categories described and many informal ways for continuing to learn.

It is usually fairly easy for persons specializing in one field of engineering to undertake graduate work in another branch because of the flexible requirements at the graduate level. These combinations often have great advantage because so many modern problems are interdisciplinary. The choice of school for graduate work is important, and is vital at the doctoral level.

Finally, we would stress the importance of the humanities and social science courses in a program. Clearly, one cannot take all courses a humanities major has and also build the base for science and engineering. But even with a few courses the student can form an incentive for continued reading after graduation and for conversations with those in other disciplines. In the narrow sense, this is important because in the end he will have to work with and sell his ideas to persons educated in many fields, but in the broad sense it is necessary in order to become a good citizen as well as a good engineer. This includes the consideration of social as well as technical needs in one's engineering designs.

SCIENCE AND ENGINEERING

One of the most difficult choices for high school students generally interested in technical subjects is the choice between engineering, mathematics, and sciences. The basic education for engineering in high

Figure 4 Electron microscope, used for resolution of particles too small to observe in a light microscope. Electron microscopes are used in materials study, as shown here, in bioengineering, in quality control, and in microcircuitry. (Monkmeyer)

school is the same as that for preparation in the sciences, and the student has courses in sciences and mathematics but none in true engineering. Yet he must usually state his preference before entering college or a university. Fortunately the crossovers are not so difficult if the first choice is wrong, since the first two years of an engineering curriculum largely build the science and mathematics background. Even later changes are possible, and there may be special advantages at the graduate level for a person majoring in physics or mathematics, but interested in their applications, to undertake graduate work in an engineering department.

Ideally, science is the search for new knowledge, and engineering is the solution of certain problems of our society with the use of science, mathematics, experience, and the social sciences as its tools. Practically, there are all sorts of combinations and gradations. Large systems and new fields especially will have engineers and scientists working together both at research and the design levels. Still, you are faced with the choice of how to start, and about the best that can be suggested is to consider your motivation toward the two ideals. If you are interested in problems that science and mathematics courses permit you to solve and find yourself motivated toward more of these subjects because they will give you help in solving additional and more complex problems, you should find the presentations of the engineering curriculum geared to your motivations and engineering the rewarding career we describe. If on the other hand you find the proofs and abstractions of mathematics the interesting part, you should very likely plan a major in mathematics; if you find the *why* of the laws of science much more interesting than any possible application, you should plan a career in science. Aptitude tests may help, and if your choice remains a toss-up, look up one of the engineering science or applied science programs mentioned.

THE NEED FOR ENGINEERS

In the last few years there has been much publicity concerning the need for more engineers. Starting salaries of engineers have been for several years the highest of those for any profession placing graduates in sizable numbers. The reason for this need has been the strong technological base of our society. The estimates for future needs have come from projected growths, studies of national goals, and knowledge of the number of engineers trained in Russia and other countries with which we are competing. Our economy is such, and world conditions change so rapidly, that no one can be sure these predictions will hold in the short term. However, unless there are major changes in world conditions, and goals that could not be predicted or planned for, the need will exist in the long term. We have mentioned a few of the unsolved problems of this country, and it is believed that we must also take a much larger part than we have in giving engineering assistance to the developing nations of the world.

Quite apart from numbers, there is no question about the need for engineers of high quality at any time. It is the thesis of our contributors that you should study for this profession if you are convinced it is the correct one for you regardless of temporary conditions. If you do not have aptitudes for it, you should not undertake it regardless of any current stress on needs. We only reiterate the wide range of aptitudes that can be useful in the profession and the desirability of obtaining correct information about engineering in making your decision.

SUBJECTS OF THIS BOOK

It has been noted that the subjects of this book are samples from engineering but are neither the usual divisions nor the whole of engineering. A few thoughts about the selection may be useful before the reader begins. Energy and materials are in one sense the raw materials of all engineering, and their efficient use is one definition of engineering. Exciting new developments are occurring in both areas. If there had been nothing in this century but the use (and misuse) of atomic energy, it would on this ground alone stand as one of the most significant centuries of history. Chemists, chemical engineers, metallurgists, ceramic engineers, solid-state physicists, and electronic engineers have worried together to improve old properties of materials and discover new properties for exploitation. The story of resources is at one level closely related to materials, but it is a broader subject, and in the areas

Figure 5   Integrated circuit for space, military, and commercial computer applications is as small as a single conventional transistor. The device shown contains three transistors and four resistors within the square silicon chip in the center. The actual size of the chip is ☐. (Monkmeyer)

of water, air pollution, and land use may well be one of the most significant subjects for our civilization.

The past century since Bell and Morse has seen communications divorce from transport and grow beyond imagination. With the still more recent developments of electronic computation and control, these elements have combined with others to produce a society entirely dependent upon communications and automated processes, both in its civilian and defense segments. Biology is of obvious importance to living beings; it was once largely a qualitative science but it is now quantitative, permitting engineering approaches to biology which promise one of the most interesting and significant areas for discovery and design in the future.

Large structures were among the first engineering works and, for much of the history of engineering, have been its symbols. They are still important. The new materials, as well as new tools of analysis such as the high-speed computer, open new dimensions for the structural engineer. Since structures are usually conspicuous, it is desirable that they also be esthetic. Architect and engineer must work together, or one man must combine the talents of artist and engineer. The story chosen for this subject is a highly personal account of one engineer's solution of problems in construction under the special seismic and soil conditions of Mexico. The solutions were esthetic and ingenious, but also required the tools provided by a modern graduate program in civil engineering.

Space engineering needs no new press agents, yet it is one of the modern wonders of the world. The ability to escape the gravitational field of this planet has been imagined so long and achieved so recently! And it has been achieved by solving problems of great variety and utilizing contributions from persons trained in all disciplines. Thus it is a perfect example of the engineering of large systems. However, that is a broader subject with its own special techniques and problems, so a very thorough treatment of the general attack on large systems continues in a separate chapter.

The last two chapters are of a different character. One is concerned with women in engineering careers and is self-explanatory. The other describes the effect of growth industry, with its high-level engineering talent, on a community. The industry-university relationships which result are stressed. This is in a sense a different aspect of the sociological impact of today's engineering, but may in the end be one of its most significant ones.

We have stated that chemical, civil, electrical, mechanical, and other engineers take their part in the above examples. But in many respects even the divisions made here are interrelated. Let us consider just one example. The subject of control is mentioned in the title of one chapter, and the example given there is naturally related to the communications and information-processing aspect of that chapter. The concept of a closed-loop or *feedback* control system was well known by mechanical engineers through the governor on James Watt's steam engine. Sophisticated analysis of such control systems really began with the electrical engineers' feedback amplifiers and servos, and the application of these devices to military systems became vital during World War II. The mathematician Norbert Wiener then contributed still more powerful methods of analysis for such systems. Extensions of these, with the tool of the electronic computer, have led to extremely complicated and versatile control systems in the two decades since. The most sophisticated man-made control systems are in space engineering applications, but the principles have been applied to control of nuclear reactors and other energy sources, chemical engineering and other materials processes, communications and computers, and at least in peripheral fashion to resource and structural engineering. The control systems of space were qualified as the most sophisticated "man-made" systems because those of the human body still beat them in many ways. The understanding of the biological feedback control processes has in fact played a major part in formalizing the new field of bioengineering, and has already affected medicine on the one hand and engineering application of control systems to inanimate systems on the other.

Thus we have seen one example of a single tool permeating, unifying, and in many cases revolutionizing all the fields we will discuss. Other examples will appear in the development and they would be found no matter how the subject of engineering is divided.

BIBLIOGRAPHY

HOOVER, T. J., and J. G. L. FISH: "The Engineering Profession," Stanford University Press, Stanford, Calif., 1950.

MC GUIRE, JOHN G., and H. W. BARLOW: "An Introduction to the Engineering Profession," 2d ed., Addison-Wesley Publishing Company, Inc., Reading, Mass., 1951.

SMITH, R. J.: "Engineering as a Career," 2d ed., McGraw-Hill Book Company, New York, 1962.

Energy Sources and Energy Conversion

by L. Talbot

Larry Talbot was born in New York City and received his B.S., M.S., and Ph.D. degrees from the University of Michigan, the last degree in engineering mechanics with specialization in fluid dynamics. He served as Instructor and Research Assistant in the Aero Research Center at the University of Michigan. In 1951 he joined the University of California, and is currently Professor of Aeronautical Sciences in the Department of Mechanical Engineering at Berkeley. He has made many research contributions on shock wave structures, free-molecule and slip flow, viscous-interaction phenomena, low-density plasma jets, and other aspects of fluid dynamics. His work in energy conversion has been in the field of magnetohydrodynamics.

Dr. Talbot has acted as consultant on rarefied gas dynamics for the Sandia Corporation, the Atomic Energy Commission, the Ingersoll-Rand Company, the General Electric Missiles and Space Vehicles Department, the Litton Industries, and the Bendix Aviation Corporation, as well as for other companies and government agencies. His many guest lectures include a series sponsored by NATO in England, France, Holland, Belgium, and Germany.

Golf, skiing, and mountain "walking" are included among Dr. Talbot's main hobbies. On his most recent trip to Europe, this last hobby led him to a walk up the Matterhorn—with guide.

THE ENERGY REVOLUTION

When primitive man succeeded in controlling fire for his warmth, food, and protection, he achieved the first milestone in man's continued quest for greater control over his environment. From the earliest dawn of civilization to the present, the advances in man's comfort, and often his knowledge, have been closely linked to his successes in harnessing new sources of energy for his desired uses. The domestication of beasts of burden multiplied manyfold man's muscle power and made possible construction, farming, and transportation on a larger scale than he could achieve unaided. When he learned the art of constructing and navigating sailing vessels powered by the kinetic energy of the wind (and often aided by the broad back of the oarsman), he began his first serious explorations of the globe and his first ventures into commerce and intercourse between nations.

Without doubt the most important milestone in the history of man's utilization of energy sources was the development in the late eighteenth century of a practical device which for the first time made possible the use of the chemical energy of wood and coal to drive all kinds of industrial machines. This device was the steam engine. Although the idea of using a fluid to absorb heat and by subsequent expansion do work (the principle of all heat engines) was known to Hero of Alexandria, it was not until after James Watt's innovations between 1760 and 1790 that the steam engine became an efficient heat engine.

With the steam engine came the *industrial revolution* and, as we shall see, the beginning of what might be termed the *energy revolution,* a concerted and ever broadening attack on the energy resources of the planet. In the period between 1830 and 1860, reaction and impulse turbines for extracting the potential energy of water stored at high heads were developed. These developments were followed closely by the achievements of Otto, Daimler, and Diesel between 1874 and 1895, which led to practical internal combustion engines that could operate on liquid hydrocarbon fuels, such as oil, gasoline, and kerosene. At about the same time, Parsons developed the steam turbine, and not long after this, at about the beginning of the twentieth century, the first steam turbine–driven electric power generating plants went into operation.

We see about us today the fruits of the industrial and energy revolutions. Energy is being devoured in tremendous quantities by automobiles and airplanes, by more and better-heated homes and with multitudinous electrical appliances, and by vast manufacturing and processing industries. Not only has the per capita energy consumption risen steadily, but the population has climbed along with it. With more people and more energy demand per person, it is inevitable that we should ask: What are our energy resources? How long will they last? What new energy sources should we be investigating and exploiting?

These are not easy questions to answer. Even though exhaustive studies have been made, such as those listed in the Bibliography, one finds that the answers arrived at involve a great deal of guesswork and extrapolation, and are subject to considerable uncertainty. For this reason, and because of our limitations of space, we shall here discuss these questions in only very broad outline, and will restrict our discussion to the United States. However, since the United States is estimated to possess about 15 percent of the total world reserve of fossil fuels (oil, coal, gas) and to account for about 37 percent of the present total world power consumption, the figures we shall present are in a sense representative of the world situation.

ENERGY CONSUMPTION NOW AND IN THE FUTURE

We will be talking about vast quantities of energy. A unit of energy which has been found convenient for such discussions is the Q which is defined as 10^{18} Btu. (Recall that the *British thermal unit*, or Btu, is defined as the heat necessary to raise by one degree Fahrenheit the temperature of one pound of water, and 10^{18} represents a billion billion, that is, 10 followed by 17 zeros.) To give a physical idea of the size of the Q, it represents the heat liberated by the combustion of 38 billion tons of bituminous coal. To give another example, if we had 400 million automobiles, each with a 100-horsepower engine, and ran them all at full throttle night and day for an entire year, we would consume an amount of gasoline equivalent to about one Q of energy.

A graph of the *accumulated total energy* consumed in the United States from 1800 to 1960, and extrapolated to A.D. 2000, is shown in Fig. 1. The United States passed the 1-Q total-consumption mark about 1940, and if the hypothetical extrapolation to the future is valid, we should hit the 10-Q mark a little after A.D. 2000.

The *annual* United States energy consumption in 1962 was about 0.03 Q. Of this, roughly two-thirds, or 0.02 Q, was supplied by oil and natural gas, and the remaining third by coal. Water power and wood combustion accounted for roughly 5 percent of the total, and surprisingly, wood was about five times as important as water power as an energy source.

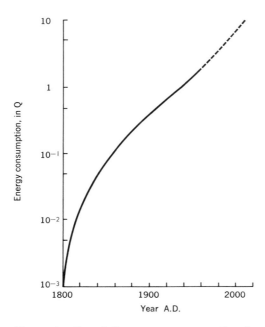

Figure 1   Cumulative energy consumption in the United States, in *Q*. (Adapted from Putnam, "Energy in the Future," D. Van Nostrand Company, Inc., Princeton, N.J., 1953, Fig. 9-12.)

The way the United States "energy pie" is presently cut up is of interest. This is shown in Fig. 2. One sees that the energy expended in electric power generation (mainly from steam plants operating on coal) is about 15 percent of the total energy consumed. About 30 percent goes for comfort heating of homes, office buildings, and factories. About 10 percent goes for *process heating*, that is, heat expended in refining, manufacturing, etc. Approximately 20 percent of the total is consumed by automobiles, and the remainder is accounted for by work-producing devices of various types, such as reciprocating- and jet-engine airplanes, tractors, diesel engines. The division of energy usage is of interest in its own right, but it will be of primary concern when we consider the possible new forms of energy which might become available, and what kinds of devices will be needed to tap these new energy sources.

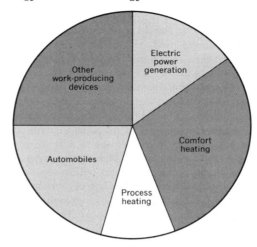

Figure 2   The United States "energy pie."

OUR FOSSIL FUEL RESERVES

We have seen that oil, natural gas, and coal provide almost all the energy consumed in the United States, and that this consumption now is at an annual rate of about 0.03 Q. How much oil (we shall lump natural gas with oil) and how much coal do we have, and how long can they be expected to last at the rates we are expected to consume them in the coming years?

According to some geologists, there is more oil and coal in the earth than we shall ever need. But the amount that is economically recoverable at, say, no more than twice the present costs of mining and drilling is quite limited. Typical energy estimates for economically recoverable reserves are about 0.5 Q for oil gas, and about 6.0 Q for coal. Thus, at our present rate of consumption and assuming no importation, the United States oil reserves might last only about 0.5/0.02 = 25 years, and our coal might last 6.0/0.01 = 600 years. These estimates do not account for the steady trend of increased annual consumption shown in Fig. 1. If the 1960 figures on population growth and the consumption per capita are extrapolated to A.D. 2000, one finds that the annual fossil fuel consumption might rise to more than 0.1 Q per year and at this rate, the estimated present United States oil-gas reserves would last only 7½ years! Of course, we can produce oil and gasoline from coal, at roughly a yield of 1 Btu of liquid fuel for 2 Btu of coal, so we should really consider the combined coal and oil reserves. Thus, if we used coal alone to meet both our liquid and solid fuel needs, then at the present rate of consumption our coal reserves might run out in about 120 years.

The numbers we have been talking about are very rough estimates based on assumptions, extrapolations, and pure guesses too numerous to mention. The estimated life expectancies of our fossil fuel reserves may be too small by as much as a factor of 10. But if the numbers are at all correct, they indicate that with our present pattern of energy consumption, we might face oil shortages within the next few decades, and perhaps coal shortages within the next few hundred years.

If we assume that this is true, what can we do about it? What are some of the possible short-range solutions to the problem? Are there any promising long-range ones? If we continue to increase our standard of living and continue to live "high on the energy-hog," as it were, then answers for these problems will have to be found. Finding them may involve engineers and scientists in possibly the most significant and challenging research and development since the start of the industrial-energy revolution.

INCREASING OUR EFFICIENCY OF ENERGY UTILIZATION

One of the first things one asks with regard to prolonging the life of our fossil fuel reserves is whether they can be utilized more efficiently. The prospects for significant gain here are not bright if the pattern of energy consumption continues essentially as it exists today. About 60 percent of the energy we consume goes into the production of work by heat engines (internal-combustion engines, steam turbines, etc.). The efficiency of a heat machine, that is, the fraction of the fuel energy which we get out as useful work, is governed by a fundamental thermodynamic law, known as Carnot's theorem. It states that the maximum efficiency e_{max} of conversion of heat into work cannot exceed the value [1]

$$e_{max} = \frac{T_{max} - T_{min}}{T_{max}} \tag{1}$$

where T_{max} is the maximum temperature at which heat is added, and T_{min} is the lowest temperature at which heat is rejected. (Heat *must* be

[1] The temperatures in this formula are absolute temperatures, found by adding 460° to the Fahrenheit values. Thus 70°F = 530°R, where R stands for Rankine.

thrown away in a heat engine cycle, as for example, in the exhaust steam from a steam turbine or in the exhaust and cooling water of an automobile engine. It is an unfortunate but inescapable fact of thermodynamic life, known as the Second Law, that heat cannot be converted completely into work in any heat engine.) In practice, the efficiencies achieved fall far short of the maximum efficiencies given by Eq. (1). Typical values are around 25 percent for optimum operation of an automobile engine, 35 percent for a diesel engine, and 40 percent for the most modern high-pressure (5,000 psi) steam-turbine power plant. Improvements in these heat engine efficiencies are possible but hard to achieve, since they invariably involve higher operating temperatures (higher T_{max}), which in turn mean better high-temperature materials. Process and comfort heating, which account for the remaining 40 percent of our energy consumption, is more efficient, and efficiencies here can get up around 50 to 60 percent. The overall average efficiency of energy conversion in the United States is estimated at about 30 percent. Thus, unless we produce a substantial portion of our work requirements by devices other than heat engines, we cannot hope for dramatic improvements on the total overall efficiency of energy conversion. Nevertheless, with our huge energy consumption, one percentage point of increased efficiency can mean large dollar savings, so engineers today continue to work hard on ways of bettering heat engine performance.

One modern approach to station power generation which seeks to increase thermal efficiency is the *magnetohydrodynamic (MHD) power generator*. Basically, an MHD generator operates on the same principle as a conventional electric generator. In the latter, when a conductor, usually copper, is passed through a magnetic field, an electric current is induced in it. In the MHD generator, a stream of ionized, electrically conducting gas replaces the copper conductor. The gas flows across a magnetic field, and the current induced is drawn out in an external circuit, as shown in Fig. 3. To make a gas a good electrical conductor, it must be heated to very high temperatures, in excess of 6000°F, even when the gas is "seeded" with small amounts of an easily ionized metal vapor such as potassium in order to enhance its conductivity. This heating could be accomplished through the combustion of coal, kerosene, or other fossil fuels. Only part of the power potential of the hot ionized gas can be obtained from the current induced by the magnetic field. The gas, still hot after passing through the magnetic field, can then be used to generate steam and produce additional electrical power by means of a conventional steam turbine-electric generator arrangement. The theoretical efficiency of MHD power generation is higher than that of conventional steam power because the use of an ionized gas permits a higher maximum temperature, and in the case of MHD generators, overall efficiencies approaching 56 percent are hoped for.

The MHD generator is not yet a practical reality. The high temperatures involved, which from a thermodynamic point of view are necessary for high efficiency, pose many technical problems in electrode design and materials which are not yet solved. Very high magnetic fields are necessary, which appear to be obtainable on a large scale only by using superconducting coils cooled to near absolute zero temperature—a curious marriage of hot and cold which presents additional technical problems. Moreover, the MHD generator produces direct current, so that conversion to alternating current is necessary to integrate MHD power into existing electrical power systems.

Despite all these problems, hopes have been expressed that practical MHD generators will be operating within the next ten years. One line of current thinking is that they will be used as *topping plants,* combined with conventional steam-turbine power plants, to provide electric power at times of peak demand. From an economic point of view, it is estimated that the greater capital investment necessary for an MHD-generator plant would make MHD electric power, despite its higher efficiency of generation, cost about the same as power produced today in conventional steam plants in the United States. However, in countries where fuel costs are higher and capital costs lower, economic savings might be achieved by using MHD generators, provided the hoped-for performance of the MHD plant is realized.

Figure 3   Direct-current magnetohydrodynamic generator. (Adapted from R. J. Rosa and A. Kantrowitz, "Magnetohydrodynamic Energy Conversion Technique," AVCO Research Report No. 86, April, 1959.)

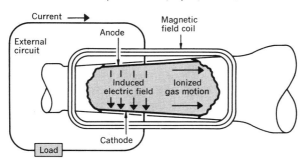

ATOMIC ENERGY AS A NEW SOURCE OF ENERGY

The first controlled nuclear fission chain reaction was achieved in Chicago in 1942. In the little more than twenty years since that historic event, the technology and science of fission reactors have advanced to the point at which today's private power companies are building multimegawatt atomic power plants which they consider economically competitive with coal-fired plants.

Most of us are familiar to some extent with the basic ideas of the atomic power generator, as exemplified by the schematic diagram of Fig. 4. The nuclear fuel is usually some mixture of uranium 235 and uranium 238. (Natural uranium is a mixture of these two isotopes in the proportion 99.3 percent U^{238} and 0.7 percent U^{235}.) The U^{235} is capable of sustaining a chain reaction. When the nucleus of a U^{235} atom is penetrated by a neutron moderated to the proper energy, the nucleus, which is in a precarious state of equilibrium, may fly apart into smaller fragments which are lower–atomic-weight elements and elementary particles. In the process of this fission, additional neutrons are released (between one and two per fission) which are then available for fissioning other U^{235} atoms. The key to the energy release is Einstein's famous law of the equivalence between mass and energy, $E = mc^2$, where m is the mass and c the speed of light. When a uranium atom fissions, the fragments turn out to have less total mass than the original atom (the whole, in terms of mass, is greater than the sum of its parts). The mass difference is accounted for by the energy released in fission in the form of radiation and kinetic energy of the fission fragments. Ultimately, much of the liberated energy ends up as heat. In an ordinary chemical reaction such as the burning of coal, the energy released corresponds to a mass loss so small, about one part in 40 billion, that it is undetectable. But when a uranium atom fissions, the mass loss is much greater, so much so that the fission of 1 pound of uranium releases energy equivalent to the combustion of nearly 1,500 tons of coal.

The heat produced in the fission process is transferred within the reactor to a circulating liquid coolant, often a liquid metal such as sodium. Outside the reactor, the coolant passes through a heat exchanger, and in so doing boils water to produce steam. The steam thus generated goes to a turbine to produce electrical power. In effect, then, the nuclear fission reactor operates in much the same way as a steam power plant, except that the heat is supplied by energy released in nuclear fission rather than in the combustion of coal.

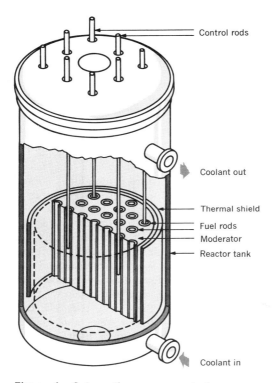

Figure 4   Schematic arrangement of a power reactor shows uranium fuel rods, moderator, thermal shielding, and reactor vessel. The coolant carries off heat developed by fissioning U^{235} atoms. Control rods hold reaction at a proper level by absorbing excess neutrons. (Adapted from Skrotski and Vopat, "Power Station Engineering and Economy," McGraw-Hill Book Company, 1960, Fig. 21-1.)

The main advantage of the nuclear reactor is that a single charge of nuclear fuel may generate power for several years before it has to be replaced. Although U^{235} is not plentiful in nature, it is a fortunate circumstance that the relatively abundant U^{238} can be converted within a reactor through neutron capture to a chain-reacting element, plutonium 239. This process is known as *breeding*. Similarly, natural thorium can be bred into chain-reacting U^{233}. It has been estimated that the world supply of natural uranium and thorium is equivalent in energy to more than *twenty* times the world's coal and oil, so it is conceivable that nuclear reactors may gradually replace coal-fired plants as coal becomes more uneconomical to mine. Today, despite the much greater first costs of a nuclear plant and the problems of radiation shielding and radioactive waste disposal, power produced over a period of years by nuclear fission may become cheaper than coal power in many locations where coal transportation expenses are high.

The practicality of electric power generation by atomic fission in large power stations is firmly established. But electric power generation accounts for only about 15 percent of our energy demand. What about the other 85 percent? Assuming that our fossil fuel reserves are as limited as some current estimates indicate, will we be able to fill the breach with atomic energy when coal and oil supplies begin to dwindle? Can we use nuclear reactors to heat our homes, run our automobiles, trucks, and airplanes, and provide heat for refining and manufacturing? To some of these questions, such as home heating by central-station reactor-generated electricity, the answer is undoubtedly yes, but to others the answer is clearly negative.

Nuclear reactors, unless adequately shielded, emanate deadly radiation. Shielding is bulky and heavy, and therefore reactors are practical only where large size and weight can be tolerated. A reactor is practical in a submarine or ocean vessel, but not in a small motor launch or airplane or automobile. In addition to the shielding problems, there are other hazards involved in the operation of nuclear reactors which make unlikely their safe use by the general public. As far as private transportation is concerned, the thought of thousands of nuclear-reactor-powered automobiles being demolished on the highways each year, strewing radioactive materials about, is too horrifying for even the most sanguine of visionaries to contemplate. Even apart from the hazards, the nuclear reactor is basically not an ideal power device for automobiles because it is suited more for steady power demand than for the intermittent on-off service required from an automobile. For this same reason, nuclear reactors are unsuited for use in commercial and private airplanes, although arguments have been made for the military utility of a nuclear-powered airplane which could stay aloft for indefinite periods of time without refueling.

ATOMIC BATTERIES AND THERMOELECTRIC DEVICES

If, as some predict, nuclear reactor power stations begin to supplant coal-fired ones, then we shall be faced with an immense problem of fission-product disposal. Several disposal techniques are currently in use. One method is to store the wastes underground for a long enough time to allow the radioctivity to decay. In another method, fission products are sealed in containers which are then encased in concrete blocks and sunk in deep parts of the ocean. It would be nice if a large-scale use could be found for fission products, which would both provide additional payoff for the nuclear reactor and lessen the disposal problem. Atomic batteries conceivably could accomplish this end.

Many types of atomic batteries which convert radiation and heat energy into electrical energy are being investigated in laboratories today. We shall mention only one, the thermocouple battery, which is probably the simplest to understand.

When two dissimilar strips of metal are joined together at both ends to form a loop, and the two junctions, called *thermocouples,* are kept at different temperatures, a current flows in the loop. This is the *thermoelectric effect,* and represents a process which, from the power engineer's point of view, is highly desirable, namely, the direct conversion of heat into electricity without moving parts. At first glance it might appear that, with such direct conversion, the efficiency of thermoelectric power generation would not be limited by Carnot's theorem. But in fact heat is added at the hot junction and rejected at the cold junction of the thermocouple loop, and the theoretical thermoelectric generation efficiency is identical to that of a heat engine operating between the same temperature limits. In its simplest form, the atomic battery consists of a thermocouple circuit, with one junction heated by the energy liberated from a reactor-produced radioactive isotope, such as polonium 210. Connecting an external load to the battery terminals closes the circuit and permits current to flow.

Thermoelectric power sources are still in their infancy, and a tremendous amount of development work will be required if ever they are to assume a prominent role in energy generation. At present, these power generators run at much lower efficiencies than what is theoretically attainable. Nevertheless, they have already been used with atomic heat sources in some satellites, and have been used with simple kerosene heat sources to power radios. Possibly what will make the thermoelectric device practical will be an ingenious combination with some form of semiconductor current multiplier. Work in this direction is being pursued in many laboratories. Other thermionic devices, such as *plasma diodes* and certain semiconductors, which we do not have space to discuss here, are also being investigated today.

FUEL CELLS

The direct conversion of chemical energy into electricity without the intermediate generation and flow of heat is very desirable, because one is then not limited by the restrictions on maximum efficiency imposed by the Carnot theorem. It is not surprising therefore, that a tremendous amount of effort is being expended on the development of devices which might achieve this end. Thus far, the most promising of these devices appears to be the *fuel cell*.

Basically, the fuel cell is a device in which the energy liberated by a chemical reaction appears not as heat, but instead appears immediately as an electric current flowing under an impressed voltage. In appearance, fuel cells have many features in common with conventional storage batteries, except for the important distinction that the fuels which undergo reaction in the fuel cell flow continuously through the cell.

Many different fuels have been used in fuel cells. In some cells the chemical reaction can be achieved at essentially room temperature, in others high temperatures are required. To illustrate the basic principles of operation, we will consider the low-temperature hydrogen-oxygen fuel cell in which these two gases react to produce an electric current and water.

A schematic diagram of a hydrogen-oxygen fuel cell is shown in Fig. 5. It consists of two porous electrodes, typically made of carbon impregnated with suitable catalysts, immersed in an electrolyte which might be a concentrated solution of sodium or potassium hydroxide. The hydrogen side is the negative side, and the oxygen the positive side. On the negative side, the hydrogen gas diffusing through the carbon electrode reacts at the electrode inside surface with negative OH^- ions in the electrolyte to produce H_2O and free electrons e^-. The reaction is

$$H_2 + 2OH^- \rightarrow 2H_2O + 2e^- \tag{2}$$

The free electrons flow through the external circuit and constitute the electric output of the cell; the water produced goes into the electrolyte.

On the positive side of the cell, air or oxygen diffuses through the electrode. The electrons which arrive from the external circuit react

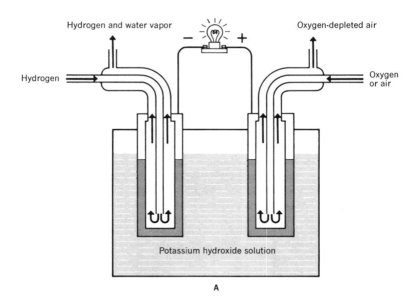

Hydrogen and water vapor

Oxygen-depleted air

Hydrogen

Oxygen
or air

Potassium hydroxide solution

A

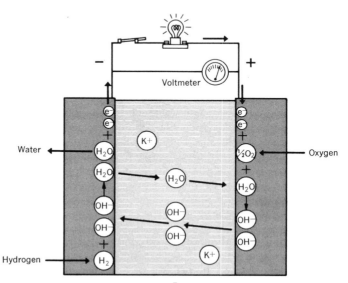

Voltmeter

Water

Oxygen

Hydrogen

B

with the oxygen and with water in the electrolyte to produce OH^- hydroxyl ions. These ions then diffuse through the electrolyte to take part in the chemical reaction at the hydrogen side. The migration of the OH^- ions through the electrolyte provides the current which closes the circuit within the cell. The reaction at the oxygen side is

$$H_2O + \tfrac{1}{2}O_2 + 2e^- \rightarrow 2OH^- \tag{3}$$

The electrolyte and the catalysts in the electrodes promote the reactions but do not actually take part in them. However, the electrolyte becomes progressively more diluted by the water generated in the reaction.

Low-temperature and -pressure hydrogen-oxygen cells have the disadvantage of typically producing only about one kilowatt of power per cubic foot of volume, and hydrogen is an expensive fuel. This performance can be bettered by as much as six times by operating at high pressure and somewhat elevated temperature. The Bacon hydrogen-oxygen, nickel-electrode cell which operates at up to 250°C and 800 psi can produce as much as fifteen times the power per pound of a conventional lead-acid automobile battery. Efficiencies as high as 75 percent have been obtained, much greater than the best heat engine. Like the conventional battery, the fuel cell is a low-voltage, direct-current device, delivering somewhat less than one volt per cell, so many must be connected in series to provide the voltage required for most direct-current machines.

Considerable effort is being directed today toward developing fuel cells which operate efficiently on cheap fuels, such as natural gas, gasoline, or coal. Operation with these fuels requires temperatures above 500°C, and presents additional problems not found in lower temperature cells. To date, performance of high-temperature fuel cells has

---

Figure 5   (A) A hydrogen-oxygen fuel cell consists of two porous carbon electrodes (dotted areas) and an electrolyte such as potassium hydroxide. Hydrogen enters one side, and oxygen the other. Both gases diffuse into the electrodes, reacting to form water. Liberated electrons flow through the circuit. (B) When the circuit is closed, the gases and electrolyte react to produce a flow of electrons. A catalyst embedded in the electrode dissociates hydrogen gas molecules into individual atoms, which combine with hydroxyl ions in the electrolyte to form water. The process yields electrons to the electrode. Electron and ion flow produces the desired current. (From Leonard G. Austin, Fuel Cells, *Scientific American*, pp. 73, 74, October, 1959. Reprinted with permission. Copyright © 1959 by Scientific American, Inc. All rights reserved.)

been poor in comparison with the hydrogen-oxygen cell. Of course, the fuel economics of tomorrow may be quite the reverse of today; hydrogen produced by electrolysis of water conceivably could one day be cheaper than hard-to-find oil and natural gas.

The proponents of fuel cells envision their eventual use in a variety of applications. Suggestions have been advanced for their installation in large nuclear power stations to provide electricity at times of peak demand. At times of low power demand, excess reactor power could be used for the electrolysis of water, thus providing the hydrogen necessary for the fuel cell operation at times of peak demand. As in the case of MHD power, the direct-current output of fuel cells would have to be converted to alternating current.

If a satisfactory high-output fuel cell or a high-output, rapidly rechargeable battery can be developed, we might very well see the return of the electric automobile. The electric automobile is in principle quite attractive for several reasons. Electric motors are simpler, quieter, and more efficient than internal-combustion engines. Moreover, they do not produce air pollutants. A demonstration that fuel cell–driven mobile transportation is at least within the realm of possibility was pro-

Figure 6   An experimental farm tractor developed by Allis-Chalmers, powered by 1,008 fuel cells. (From Eric Eltham, The Fuel Cell: Promise or Threat to the Petroleum Industry, *World Petroleum*, November, 1961.)

vided by the Allis-Chalmers Company with their experimental tractor powered by 1,008 hydrogen-oxygen fuel cells, shown in Fig. 6.

The prospects appear bright for the eventual widespread use of fuel cells. But much development and engineering will be required. As one researcher has put it, "Fuel-cell development is not a field for the faint-hearted."

ENERGY FROM THE SUN

Our energy balance is very much like a bank account. When this planet was created, probably of material cast off from the sun, the earth received its fission-fuel inheritance. Much later, the sun added to our inheritance the fossil fuels. We are living on this inheritance today. But we also receive a steady "income," at a rate of about 120 watts per square foot or about 50 Q per year in continental United States, from the sunlight which falls on the earth. Among other things, this income evaporates and elevates the water which is the source of our hydro-electric power, produces the wind which drives our sailboats and wind-mills, and provides the energy for the food we eat and the vegetation which some day may be transformed into new fossil fuels. Our daily income is in fact much greater than all our energy needs. But since we have not yet discovered how to manage our bank account prudently and live within our income, we must continue to dip into our inheritance.

We have not yet succeeded in meeting our energy expenditures with current income because thus far all the methods we have for capturing large amounts of the sun's energy are woefully inefficient. As an example, we may consider the amount of energy that can be recovered by making use of the natural photosynthesis occurring in plants. As is well known to racing enthusiasts, alcohol is an acceptable motor fuel. It can be obtained by fermentation of many different plants, such as corn, potatoes, sugar beets, various grains, etc. About the largest yield is obtained from sugar beets, which produce at maximum about 300 gallons of alcohol per acre. This, unfortunately, is but a trifling amount when compared to our *daily* gasoline consumption of 170 million gallons. The best photosynthetic yields achieved to date apparently have been with a species of single-celled algae called *Chlorella*. In a pilot plant built in the early 1950s, it was found that these algae, when grown in water, absorbed and converted up to 2 percent of the solar energy falling upon them—a yield about twenty times better than the photosynthetic efficiency of sugar beets. Even so, an area about equal to the state of Indiana would be required to grow enough *Chlorella* for fermentation to satisfy our current motor fuel needs. Evidently, the prospect of supplying motor-fuel alcohol by photosynthesis is rather dim, in terms of what we know about it today. If *Chlorella* farming on a large scale were ever seriously considered, some differences of opinion would undoubtedly arise as to which state or states should be swamped by seas of algae for the good of the rest of the nation.

More promising are the possibilities that many of our future homes may be heated by solar energy, and that small devices will be powered by solar cell–generated electricity. Solar cells, which have already found widespread use in satellites and space vehicles, are now reaching efficiencies between 10 and 15 percent, so that in bright sunlight they can produce well over 10 watts per square foot of irradiated area. With this kind of power output we are not going to be able to run automobiles, but, on the other hand, a 1,000-square-foot solar cell panel could easily provide enough battery-charging current to meet the electrical needs of a normal household, if the climatic conditions were reasonably favorable. A 1,000-square-foot panel could also provide the power necessary to boil roughly one pound of water every two minutes, which suggests that solar cells might ultimately be useful in certain arid areas to distill salt water. Of course, the figures cited show only the technical feasibilities of the various applications. Before any one of the proposed schemes could become a reality on more than a laboratory scale, much engineering development would have to be done, and what is most important, the scheme would have to be more economical than the available alternatives.

Probably, hydroelectric power generation will continue to be the most significant use of our daily income from the sun. At present in the United States, hydroelectricity accounts for roughly 20 percent of the station power generated, or a little over one percent of our total energy consumption. The trend, however, has actually been away from water power in recent years. In 1940, for example, 33 percent of our electricity was hydrogenerated, and in 1920 the figure was 40 percent. It has been estimated that if all the hydroelectric resources in the United States were actually developed, they might be able to supply about 5 percent of our total energy needs. Clearly, hydroelectricity will not provide the solution to a fossil-fuel shortage. It will, however, continue to be an important power source in the United States, and even more so in certain other parts of the world. It is quite possible, for example, that the industrialization of the African continent may depend crucially on the development of its hydroelectric potential.

THERMONUCLEAR POWER

If we are unable to find ways to live on the sun's "income," perhaps we can here on earth mimic the sun's method for producing its tremendous energy output. Such is the goal of thermonuclear power, or as it has more dramatically been put, "taming the H-bomb."

The nuclear reaction which is responsible for the sun's energy and for the explosive energy release of the hydrogen bomb is the *fusion* or *thermonuclear* reaction. The fusion reaction is the opposite of the fission reaction referred to previously, because in the fusion reaction two light nuclei combine, or fuse, to form a heavier one. But the energy released by this process is governed by the same law as the fission reaction, Einstein's $E = mc^2$ equation. It seems that when two nuclei of certain of the lighter elements are fused, the result is a nucleus of less total mass than was contained in the two nuclei before fusion. As in the case of the fission reaction, the mass defect appears as liberated energy. Fusion reactions are more energetic than fission reactions; typically more than ten times as much energy is liberated per fusion than per fission.

There are many possible energy-liberating fusion reactions. We shall discuss only one—the deuterium-deuterium (D-D) reaction—not only because it is one of the best understood but also because it is by far the most important for power generation. Deuterium is an isotope of hydrogen and differs from the latter in that the deuterium nucleus contains a neutron in addition to the proton of the normal hydrogen atom. The most abundant source of deuterium is natural water, in which this element is found in the form of deuterium oxide, D_2O, sometimes called "heavy water." About 3 out of every 20,000 water molecules in the ocean are D_2O molecules. Our supply of deuterium is therefore, for all practical purposes, limitless.

In a fission reactor, all that one has to do is to bring enough U^{235} together (the critical size) to prevent excessive leakage of neutrons, and the chain reaction "goes." The fissionable fuel does not have to be preheated, nor do any special temperature-insulation precautions have to be taken, because by carefully controlling the rate at which neutrons produce new fissions, almost any level of power generation can be maintained. The fusion reactor is another matter altogether. To fuse two deuterium nuclei together requires a tremendous kinetic energy of impact. The kinetic energy of gas particles increases with their temperature, and to produce fusion one must achieve the temperature which exists in the interior of the sun, over 100 million°C. In brief, the

40   *L. Talbot*

problem of the fusion reactor is to heat deuterium to this very high temperature, and to hold it together for a sufficiently long time to permit the fusion reaction to take place at a controlled rate. Somehow, also, the energy liberated in the fusion process must be harnessed as useful power. In a hydrogen bomb, fusion temperatures are produced by the explosion of fissionable material, and the fusion reaction is likewise an explosive liberation of energy. What is necessary is to change in some way the fusion "bang" to a "whimper," so to speak. In view of the differences between the fission and fusion processes, it is not surprising that, whereas the fission reactor preceded the atomic bomb, the H-bomb has not yet been "tamed."

How do you heat a gas to 100 million degrees? And even if you could get a gas that hot, what would you hold it in? Physicists and engineers working on thermonuclear power are today searching for the answers to these questions. Many different and novel devices have been built and tested, and more are on the way. All these devices, however, have one essential feature in common—the use of magnetic fields to confine the hot gas.

To understand the essential ideas of magnetic confinement, we must first understand what happens to any material when it is heated to the very high temperatures we are concerned with. At these temperatures, all matter becomes gaseous. More than that, it becomes completely ionized, in that the electrons surrounding the nuclei of the material are torn off and the gas becomes a mixture of free electrons and positively

Figure 7   Confinement of a hot plasma by a magnetic field "bottle."

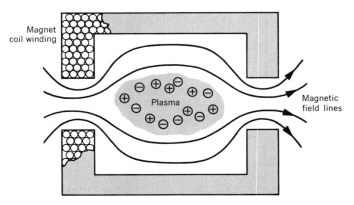

charged ions. Such an ionized gas is termed a *plasma*. Except for the fact that it is gaseous, a plasma has many things in common with a metal such as copper. In particular, both are excellent conductors of electricity, a fact we noted earlier in our discussion of magnetohydro-dynamic power generation.

The principle of magnetic confinement of a plasma can be illustrated by the example of what is sometimes called a "magnetic bottle." An idealized version of such a bottle is sketched in Fig. 7. We imagine that in some way a plasma has been created within the region surrounded by the magnetic field lines of the coil. Recall that this plasma is a gas composed of ions and electrons. Let us consider now what might happen if either an electron or an ion tried to get out of the plasma region by crossing the magnetic-field lines.

It is a fundamental law of electromagnetism that when a charged particle moves across a magnetic field, a force F (called the Lorentz force) is exerted on the particle in a direction perpendicular to both the magnetic field B and the velocity v of the particle, as shown in Fig. 8. The equation, which is a consequence of Ampère's Law, reads

$$F = qvB \qquad (4)$$

where q is the charge on the particle, taken positive for an ion. The units here are mksc (meter-kilogram-second-coulomb), but that need not concern us now. It is in fact this law which explains the electric field and current produced in a magnetohydrodynamic generator or in a wire conductor when it is moved across the magnetic field of an electric generator.

When a charged particle tries to cross a magnetic field line, the Lorentz force F acts in such a way as to make the particle circle around the line. Electrons circle in one direction and positive ions in the other, but both are trapped by the field lines and are unable to cross them. Ideally, then, the only way the particles can move unimpeded is along the field lines. They may leak out the ends of the bottle, but we can minimize the leakiness of our bottle-stoppers by forcing the magnetic field lines closer together there. Even better, we can eliminate the ends of the bottle altogether by joining them to form a torus, or doughnut. In practice, the confinement of a plasma by a magnetic field involves additional complex processes, but the basic ideas are the same.

Magnetic confinement makes it possible to isolate a hot ionized gas from the material walls of a container. Without magnetic confinement, there would be no hope for controlled thermonuclear power, because

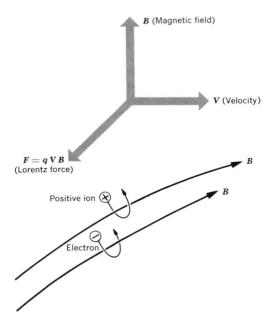

Figure 8   Forces on moving ions and electrons in a magnetic field.

no material is known which can withstand the temperatures necessary for the fusion reaction.

In addition to its confinement function, the magnetic field may be used to heat the plasma. We may imagine the field lines in Fig. 7 to behave in much the same way as a bundle of rubber bands under tension, being bulged outward by the pressure of the plasma which they surround. If the magnetic field strength is increased, a procedure equivalent to increasing the tension in the hypothetical rubber bands, the field lines will tend to become straighter. The volume surrounded by the field lines is thus decreased and the plasma within this volume is compressed and heated. This process, which is called *magnetic pumping,* is incorporated in more complex forms in many of the thermonuclear devices currently being investigated.

Scientists are today still a very long way from achieving a controlled fusion reaction which produces a net-positive energy yield. Schemes which have been tried, and ideally should have worked, have failed because of a variety of complicated plasma phenomena, not all of which are yet understood. Much additional basic knowledge of the properties of ionized gases in magnetic fields will be required before reliable predictions of plasma behavior can be made. Even if a controlled fusion reaction should be achieved, there are as yet only the vaguest of ideas concerning how the reaction might be harnessed to provide useful work. This is an entire new area of technology whose surface has not even been scratched.

But the potential payoff for fusion power is tremendous, and justifies the effort which is being expended upon it today. The supply of deuterium in our oceans is limitless; thus fusion power would represent a truly permanent solution to man's energy needs. Moreover, fusion

Figure 9　Increased demand for high-temperature nuclear fuel materials has led to the investigation of the physical properties of a number of metal and ceramic fuels at temperatures up to 3000° C. In the vacuum chamber shown in this photograph, measurements are made on samples by heating them to high temperatures. Properties such as melting point and emissivity are determined with this equipment. (Ewing Galloway)

reactors are not expected to produce significant amounts of radioactive waste, so that with them one would not have the waste-disposal problem which will surely be a major problem of the next centuries if fission-reactor power takes over the present role of coal power. If one wished to indulge in some long-range speculation, one might imagine a civilization of the future in which all energy came from the sea; fusion-power-produced electricity and fuel cells run on hydrogen produced electrolytically from sea water. It is amusing to contemplate that the ocean, which was the cradle of life on this planet millions of years ago, might thus someday be man's ultimate sustainer.

THE ROLE OF THE ENGINEER

Our discussions of some of the proposed energy-conversion devices of the future have led us through a wide range of scientific and technological subject areas—from biological photosynthesis through steam turbine technology and electrochemistry to nuclear and plasma physics. When faced with the awesome body of scientific knowledge which is represented by all these areas, one may well wonder whether the engineer as we know him today is not a vanishing breed whose functions will gradually be taken over by physicists, chemists, and representatives of other basic sciences. To such a question the answer must be that this is assuredly not the case—quite the contrary—if anything, the particular and special talents of the engineer will be needed more than ever before if our future energy needs are to be successfully met.

What distinguishes the engineer, however scientifically or research-oriented he might be, from the "pure" scientist is that the engineer has the ultimate goal in mind of building something or making something work, or of making something work better than it has before, or of manufacturing it more economically. Often the fundamental scientific information necessary to achieve his goal is available, and his function is to assemble and apply this information in an imaginative and ingenious fashion. In many instances, however, the need for additional fundamental understanding may lead the engineer along the path of "basic" research. Though he may then at times appear indistinguishable from the pure scientist, there remains the important difference that at the end of the trail the engineer perceives, however dimly, an object, device, or system that his efforts may help to perfect.

Many of the energy-conversion systems we have discussed are reasonably well understood in regard to the basic physical phenomena which govern their operation, although in some cases important gaps in our understanding still exist. Yet almost all of these devices are still in the laboratory stage. Some undoubtedly will remain there permanently. Engineering developments and technological advances will be the decisive factors in determining which of these devices ultimately emerge from the laboratory and come into general use. And engineers will surely play key roles in these developments and advances. But to do so, engineers may have to cross many of the traditional boundaries which have in the past compartmented the engineering profession. Tomorrow's engineer may have to be part chemist, part physicist, part electrical, mechanical, and civil engineer, if he is to cope with complex systems such as those we have been discussing. For today's engineer, whatever his interest, there remain countless challenging design problems associated with the ever-changing complexion of the energy system we now use, which is such an important part of our entire economy.

The space program being pursued by the United States today affords us a good preview of the possible shape of things to come in power systems engineering. With the exception of thermonuclear power, all the energy-conversion devices we have discussed here, and many others that we have not had space to mention, are under active study and development in the search for power sources to meet the special needs of space exploration. For this reason, though his goals are in the sky, the space engineer's most significant victories may in the end be celebrated here on earth.

BIBLIOGRAPHY

AUSTIN, L. G.: Fuel Cells, *Scientific American*, vol. 201, no. 4, pp. 72–91, October, 1959.

AYRES, E., and C. A. SCARLOTT: "Energy Sources: The Wealth of the World," McGraw-Hill Book Company, New York, 1952.

LANSDELL, N.: "The Atom and the Energy Revolution," Philosophical Library, Inc., New York, 1958.

PUTNAM, P. C.: "Energy in the Future," D. Van Nostrand Company, Inc., Princeton, N.J., 1953.

SKROTZKI, B. G. A., and W. A. VOPAT: "Power Station Engineering and Economy," McGraw-Hill Book Company, New York, 1960.

Space Electrical Power, *Astronautics and Aerospace Engineering*, vol. 1, no. 4, May, 1963.

3

Materials Science and Engineering

by W. R. Hibbard, Jr.

When Walter Hibbard received the 1959 Yale Engineering Association Award, he was cited as a "scientist and engineer, metallurgist of international reputation who has carried over into his industrial research affiliation a continuing interest in the teaching of youth." Following his baccalaureate from Wesleyan University, Middletown, Connecticut, and the Doctor of Engineering degree from Yale, he served as Associate Professor in the Yale School of Engineering. In 1951 he joined the General Electric Research Laboratory, and is currently manager of the Metallurgy and Ceramics Research Department. He directs more than 100 scientists and engineers on fundamental and applied topics in physical and chemical metallurgy, ceramics, and materials application and evaluation.

Dr. Hibbard is a Fellow of the Metallurgical Society of the American Institute of Mining, Metallurgical, and Petroleum Engineers and has served as president of that Society. He has been a director of the Engineers Joint Council and is active on many other professional, government, and educational boards.

In 1957 Dr. Hibbard was selected as a member of the exchange delegation of United States metallurgists visiting the U.S.S.R. He is active in civic and school activities in Schenectady. His hobbies include golf, swimming, bowling, and work with Little League and Babe Ruth League programs.

IN THE BEGINNINGS of technology, the keystones of the early eras were the increasingly versatile use of materials. The Stone Age is identified with man's ability to fabricate useful articles from stone, such as hatchets, arrowheads, and stoneware. The Bronze Age is identified with bronze weapons, utensils, and art. The Hittites were the early exploiters of iron and steel. Wood and bamboo were the first fiber-reinforced plastic composites; clay and stone were the first ceramics. As cultures developed, their manifestations often took the form of structures, objects of art, weapons, or machinery—evidence of their advancing skills.

As technology progressed, utilizing new forms of energy in new ways for new purposes, new materials evolved that were largely dependent on the economics of materials sources, the skill of the materials craftsmen, and the importance of the resultant products to the safety and welfare of the population. Materials disciplines were oriented toward each type of material just as engineering disciplines were oriented toward each type of energy utilization or design. These orientations were keyed to technological needs, since the availability of a material was dependent mostly on the economy and skills needed to obtain it rather than the skills needed to use it. The use frequently followed the material development. On this basis during the nineteenth and early twentieth centuries, materials availability and development kept pace and even led technological development in other fields.

During the late nineteenth century, it was discovered that metals, as well as minerals and other inorganic materials, are crystalline solids. Certain mineral specimens are agglomerates of many small crystals which grow together during their formation. If a plane surface is cut and polished through such an agglomerate, the crystalline character can be observed under the microscope after suitable etching (i.e., chemical action of a selective, usually dilute, slightly dissolving solution). This microstructure, as is shown in Fig. 1, is seen as a grouping of polygonal crystals outlined and bound together by crystal boundaries. All crystalline solids such as metals, alloys, ceramics, and inorganic salts have this type of crystal structure. The size and shape of the crystals are determined and can be controlled to advantage by the conditions under which they form from the liquid or gaseous state and by subsequent treatment in some cases. In the case of metals, the blacksmith changed the size of the crystals in a horseshoe by the temperature of his forge and the severity of his hammer blows.

In the early twentieth century, the discovery of X rays led to a technique for measuring the size and orientation of atoms in a single crystal and the orientation of crystals in a crystalline aggregate. Certain types of crystal structure are inherently ductile or forgeable; cer-

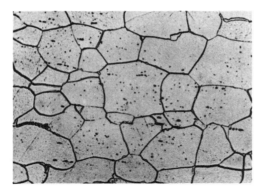

Figure 1 Photomicrograph showing single-phase polycrystalline material. Polygonal or equiaxed grains of high-purity iron etched (magnification, 500×).

tain types are ferromagnetic or ferroelectric. In addition, these properties are affected by crystal size. Thus the scientists had techniques in optical microscopy and X-ray analysis to relate the structure of a crystalline solid to its properties. Through trial and error, intuition, and a large amount of experience, the scientist began to create a phenomenological picture of how to make materials and control their properties so that they might be increasingly useful.

The science and engineering of metals, ceramics, glass, plastics, paper, and textiles, and also of chemistry in general, progressed remarkably independently, although all were basically dependent upon the sciences of chemistry (for development of processing and identification of structures) and physics (for the development of properties and related phenomena). Science was almost entirely diagnostic or analytical; i.e., on occasions it could explain the success of a new material after it was developed and used.

Early in the second quarter of the twentieth century, the internal-combustion engine had started to tax the capability of available steels, and the steam turbine was becoming limited by the materials used in its construction. But there were ways around these problems through design or cooling.

However, materials needs became acute during World War II. Aircraft development required stronger and lighter materials for airframes and stronger, high-temperature–resistant materials for engines. The nuclear developments required a whole new category of materials previously undeveloped. Rallying to the cause were many scientists, who concentrated on the science of weaponry and logistics. Thus, new eras began to evolve in which a system was conceived without the materials to implement it. These scientists were not biased by having been previously associated with a single material specialty. They sought the best material for the purpose intended with a convergency of function and a divergency of materials outlook.

The field of materials science had its origins in the increasing realization that similar broad scientific principles applied to the physical or chemical behavior of all solids and thus to the origin of properties, the response to environments, or the reactions occurring during materials preparation and processing. For example, ionic conduction occurs in glass, ceramics, or certain polymers. Magnetic phenomena are similar in metals, ceramics, or certain organic compounds. The principles governing strength are similar in glass, ceramics, metals, polymers, or textile fibers. There are broad generalities relating composition and structure, as determined by processing, to physical properties. The discovery of new phenomenological principles can lead to new materials in several of these categories.

Figure 2 Relation between grain size and Brinell hardness in alpha brass.

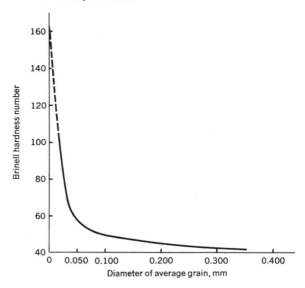

With the technological developments associated with the jet age, the nuclear age, and the space age, there evolved a new breed of materials engineer. This engineer was concerned with the development, manufacture, fabrication, and utilization of materials in a specific technology. The nuclear materials engineer was concerned with the processing of uranium and plutonium into useful systems together with all the other materials needed to contain, control, and utilize the nuclear reaction. The space materials engineer was concerned with new fuels to propel space vehicles, materials to contain and control the burning fuels, and materials to resist very high temperatures of reentry, very cold temperatures in space, very low vacuums, and very high speeds. There were new requirements for compact systems of communication, energy conversion, monitoring, and guidance.

A new phenomenon occurred. Physics and chemistry began to predict types of atomic and molecular structures and their size, shape, and distribution; these predictions often pointed to the new and unique properties of another material before that type of material was in fact discovered. Chemistry began to reveal how to synthesize the materials which did not yet exist in nature.

This novel relationship between science and new materials can be best understood by a series of examples of man-made or synthesized materials with new and desired properties.

The domain model of magnetism identifies ferromagnetic materials as being made of atoms with a specific net magnetic moment or spin. When there is no external magnetic field, the atoms align themselves into subdivided volumes or domains with equal and opposite moments which exactly counterbalance each other; thus, the net magnetic moment is zero. With a soft magnet such as iron, under an external magnetic force, the appropriately aligned domain will grow in volume at the expense of its neighbors so that there is a net magnetic moment in the same direction as the external magnetic force and characteristic of the types of atoms involved. The interface between domains is of finite thickness. It was recognized by physicists in the late 1930s that if iron particles could be made smaller than the thickness of the interface between domains, the particles could not contain more than one domain. Thus they could have a permanent magnetic moment and could become permanent magnets whose direction of magnetism could not be changed by simple domain interface movement, but would require the collective rotation of the atom spins—a much more difficult phenomenon. The required particle size is approximately the same as that of smoke particles: 100 to 1,000 angstroms. In the 1950s, a tech-

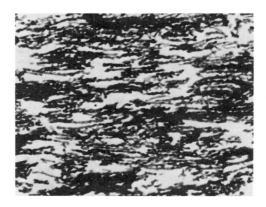

Figure 3 Photomicrograph showing a fine particle of iron.

nical team consisting of a physical chemist, a physical metallurgist, and an electrical engineer discovered that by electroplating iron into mercury such particles could be made. Materials engineers were then required to learn how to make these particles in sufficient quantities, how to remove them from mercury, and how to preserve them in useful shapes. Today, single-domain iron particles are commercially available and are used in several unique applications, particularly where small compact magnets are required.

The development of this model, together with new techniques for observing the structure of materials, led to the realization that the same phenomenon occurred in certain permanent magnet alloys of long standing. Alnico, an alloy of aluminum, nickel, and cobalt, was discovered and used long before World War II. The application of domain theory has led to Alnico magnets twice as strong as those previously available. These magnets are particularly important in speakers for communication systems.

Superconductivity, discovered in 1911, is an important scientific phenomenon. Certain metals and alloys, when cooled to nearly absolute zero, lose all of their electrical resistance. Under these conditions, a direct electric current induced in a superconducting circuit will continue indefinitely without any resistance losses. Superconductors become normal conductors (with resistance losses) when heated above their critical temperature or when exposed to a magnetic field above

Table 1   PROPERTIES OF FINE–PARTICLE MAGNETS

Material	Grade	B_r, gauss	H_c, Oersted	$(BH)_{max}$
Elongated iron	Commercial	7,900	560	$2.2(10)^6$
	Best laboratory	9,140	765	$4.3(10)^6$
	Theoretical limit	14,300	3,600	$38.5(10)^6$
Elongated iron-cobalt	Commercial	9,000	850	$3.6(10)^6$
	Best laboratory	10,800	980	$6.5(10)^6$
	Theoretical limit	16,300	4,100	$49.9(10)^6$
Alnico alloy	Commercial	12,700	650	$5.5(10)^6$
	Best laboratory	11,800	1,340	$11.0(10)^6$

a critical field (Fig. 4). Both the critical field and the critical temperature are characteristic of the specific metal or alloy concerned and are
monotonically related.

Figure 4   Superconducting properties as a function of
a magnetic field.

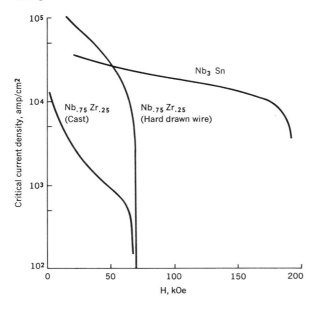

The critical fields of available superconductors were at first too small to be useful in electromagnetic circuits. The highest critical field was associated with an alloy of niobium and tin and was only a few thousand gauss. During subsequent years, a model of superconductivity was evolved which included considerations of the paramagnetic character of a superconductor, i.e., the repelling of a magnetic field. In particular, studies concerned the surface layer of the material in a magnetic field, both at interface, where the superconducting state interacts with and repels the magnetic state, and in the subsequent intermediate state, while it was being driven normal by the penetration of the magnetic field.

It was determined that although the magnetic field is repelled, it also penetrates into the superconductor a finite depth, producing a high-energy state in the material. If the superconductor is in the form of filaments thinner than this penetration depth, these filaments will remain superconductors in magnetic fields manyfold more intense than the bulk critical field. Subsequent studies have developed the relationship between composition, structure, and properties.

It remained for a team consisting of physicists, metallurgists, and chemists to prepare quantities of niobium-tin wire which were found to remain partially superconducting (i.e., in the intermediate state) in

Figure 5 Photomicrograph of Nb_3Sn wire. (Courtesy of Research Information Section, General Electric Research Laboratory, Schenectady, N.Y.)

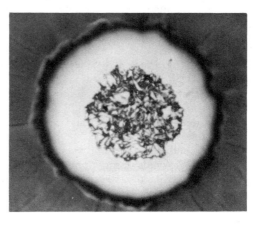

magnetic fields as large as 80,000 gauss (Fig. 5). The development of these and other alloys has led to additional understanding of the importance of the filamentary structures identified in the earlier theories and models. Large magnets with fields above the point at which iron cores are useful (about 20,000 gauss) were made from water-cooled copper coils at a cost of many hundreds of thousands of dollars. Now magnets with larger fields over 100,000 gauss have been made from high-field superconductors at greatly reduced costs. These magnets are important as laboratory equipment related to scientific investigations and, specifically, to the development of magnetohydrodynamic power generation.

Many problems remain to be solved, including the understanding of hysteresis losses resulting from alternating currents and of techniques for economic low-temperature refrigeration, before high-field super-conductors can be applied to rotating electrical equipment such as motors, generators, alternators, etc.

Optical properties also benefited from the new science of materials. Aluminum oxide is a commercially available ceramic used as an electrical insulator (dielectric) and for high-temperature strength. It is normally a white opaque material which is brittle at room temperature, and is made by pressing and sintering (heating) the powdered form. Studies of its structure under the microscope revealed that its opaqueness is the result of millions of tiny voids which occurred during the sintering of the powder; i.e., the spaces between the powder particles are trapped during the sintering process. Voids can be removed by a process called diffusion, which involves atom transport into the voids. Motion of the atoms is a temperature- and specie-dependent process which can be analyzed quantitatively so that the rate of void removal can be calculated. It was discovered that at the temperatures where sintering resulted in strong subparticle bonding, the rate of particle coalescence was so rapid that the tiny voids were trapped within the particles at too great a distance from the crystal boundaries or void sinks for their removal in reasonable lengths of time. It was also discovered that magnesia was uniquely effective in controlling the rate of coalescence. Magnesia atoms by their slower transport characteristics vastly reduce crystal growth and retain the crystals at a size close to that of the powder particles. The crystal boundaries are retained near the voids, and thus diffusion distances are short enough to permit the removal of the voids during normal sintering. As a result, aluminum oxide can be made dense, stronger, and transparent to direct normal light. The new dense alumina is useful as envelopes for high-tempera-

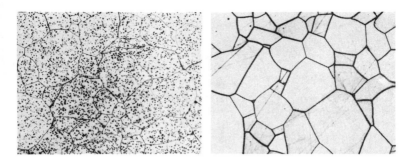

Figure 6 Photomicrographs of sintered structures of ceramics. (*Left*) Porous sintered Al_2O_3. (*Right*) Dense sintered Al_2O_3. (Courtesy of Research Information Section, General Electric Research Laboratory, Schenectady, N.Y.)

ture lamp bulbs and for other high-temperature windows. In addition, synthetic sapphire can now be made directly from powders rather than by a costly melting process.

Important advances in electronic components resulted from significant research discoveries related to semiconductor materials. Semiconductors are those elements and compounds with electric resistivity of about 10^5 ohm-cm, which is intermediate between that of metals (about 10^{-5} ohm-cm) and that of insulators (about 10^{10} ohm-cm). This class of materials has been known for many years, and certain metal-semiconductor systems have been used for electric-power rectification, i.e., changing alternating current to direct current. With the development of the quantum mechanical theory of solids and specifically the application of band theory, it became theoretically apparent that semiconductors such as silicon and germanium had band structures which would lead to unusual electronic conduction characteristics. Specifically, the addition of certain impurities generates either mobile electrons (donors, n type) or electron holes (acceptors, p type) of useful lifetime. In order to realize these intrinsic characteristics, it was necessary to obtain single crystals of semiconductors and to remove all impurities which caused these conduction occurrences in a random and uncontrolled manner. This achievement required a tolerance in silicon of only one impurity atom in 10^9 and in germanium of only one impurity atom in 10^{12}.

A purification method known as *zone refining* was discovered. In general, most impurity atoms lower the equilibrium melting and freezing temperatures of solids. In addition, melting and freezing occur over a range of temperatures such that, under these conditions, the portion to freeze first will be purer than that which freezes last, and the reverse is true in the case of melting. According to these mechanisms, if a narrow slice of the material is melted locally and the resulting molten zone is caused to move along the axis of a cylinder of a solid, an impurity-rich layer (which melts first and freezes last) will also move along the cylinder with the molten zone. By many such "passes" of a narrow molten zone, zone refining occurs to an extent which produces the ultra-pure silicon and germanium. This innovation permits the revelation, control, and use of semiconductors. In addition, melting and solidification techniques were devised which produced single crystals, and which achieved the introduction of controlled numbers of specific-impurity atoms in specified small volumes of material. The mutual stimulation of materials discoveries and theory led to the discovery of many new devices, e.g., the *p-n* junction which consisted of *p*-type material in continuous juxtaposition to *n*-type material. These discoveries, as well as the development of understanding, led to new miniature components such as the transistor and the tunnel diode which can be used as amplifiers and oscillators; i.e., they perform the same functions as do certain vacuum tubes, but are smaller in size and require less power. These developments and their extensions have revolutionized the electronic communications industry. Small portable radios, TV sets, and other devices which operate on primary batteries are now readily available.

In addition, the purification and crystal-growing techniques have had profound influence in other areas of science and engineering. Certain single crystals of controlled purity form the heart of devices in which *l*ight is *a*mplified by *s*timulated *e*mission of *r*adiation. The so called *laser* is made from high-purity optical-quality aluminum oxide (sapphire) to which chromium is added to provide the exciting atoms to form single ruby crystals. This device produces an intense coherent (parallel) beam of light of a specific wavelength.

Laser devices resulted from studies of resonance characteristics of atoms under certain types of stimulation. Such an assemblage of atoms can be excited (pumped) by light or radiation from a lamp of appropriate energy so that some atoms hop to a state higher than the next intermediate state. Then a signal of wavelength related to the two excited states will stimulate more emissive transitions (i.e., to a lower unfilled energy state) than absorptive transitions (to a higher unfilled energy state). Thus, with dominant stimulated emission, an amplified, intense, directional, monochromatic light is achieved. As a result, amplification can occur in direct relation to the specific energy difference. Lasers can be made with semiconductor *p-n* junctions, e.g., gallium arsenide. Excitation occurs at the junction by the injection of electrons (or holes) achieved by intense electric currents.

In addition to visible and infrared light waves (photons), similar amplification can be achieved with radio microwave radiation, i.e., a maser, and also with sound waves, i.e., a phonon maser.

These devices constitute a new class of quantum mechanical amplifiers resulting from new understanding of the behavior of materials, new ability to obtain materials of unusual quality with carefully controlled impurities, and a recognition of how to combine this knowledge to achieve new devices.

Science has made rapid strides in understanding the strength of crystalline solids—metals, ceramics, crystallized glasses, and crystalline polymers. The strength of such materials is many hundreds of times less than that calculated from elastic theory. As a result, it was postulated in the 1930s that imperfections in the crystal structure, such as dislocations and atomic vacancies, exist to weaken the materials.

In a perfect crystal, free from dislocations, deformation occurs elastically primarily to strains as large as 2 to 3 percent increase in length. These strains result from the collective motion of atoms until the interatomic bond is ruptured. In materials with an *elastic modulus* of 10^6 (elastic modulus is the slope of the linear relation between stress in pounds per square inch of cross section and strain in percent), a breaking stress of 5×10^7 lb/in.^{2} should result. Materials with a modulus of 10^6 yield at stresses of apparently 10^3 lb/in.^{2} and strains of approximately 0.1 percent. The presence of a dislocation (which can be envisaged as a low-angle crystal boundary) can permit a row of atoms to be displaced by individual atom movements across the dislocation at stresses equivalent to the strength of the line tension holding the dislocation in situs (the diffusion of a low-angle crystal boundary during crystal growth). These stresses are usually one thousand times smaller than the elastic bond strength. Strengthening can occur from changes in structure which increase the line tension of the dislocation or impede its motion.

Twenty years later such imperfections were actually observed microscopically, but meanwhile a series of theories and models came into existence to explain many phenomena observed in critical experiments.

These theories were a useful basis for developing new materials from an approach of enlightened empiricism—a method that prescribed a less than random approach toward problem solving. Finally, it was determined that by making filaments a few microns in diameter the devastating effects of dislocations could be avoided and experimental bits of very strong metals, ceramics, and semiconductors could be made with elastic strengths approaching their theoretically calculated strength. For example, iron filaments have been made with breaking strengths of nearly 2 million lb/in.² compared with 20,000 lb/in.² for comparable bulk material. Amazingly high strengths were measured for filaments of copper, silicon, glass, and aluminum oxide. Engineering has not yet succeeded in making these materials available in useful amounts and forms. More about this development will come later in this chapter.

The most dramatic results of the dislocation model have occurred in particle-strengthened materials. A great volume of knowledge developed largely between World War I and World War II indicated that many materials contained more than one kind of crystal; i.e., they

Figure 7 Strength of iron filaments as a function of diameter.

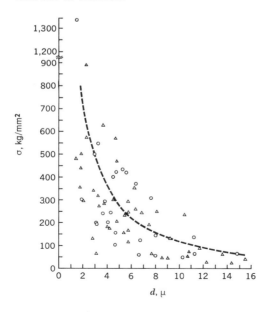

were multiphase materials. The properties of these materials often followed something like the law of mixtures; in other words, they were intermediate between the properties of the two kinds of crystals or phases in relation to the relative amounts of the two phases.

For example, tungsten carbide is one of the hardest materials known, but it is also too brittle to use as a cutting material. A composite of tungsten carbide crystals surrounded by a thin, ductile, binder layer of cobalt has resulted in the synthesis of a new cutting material which is used on our most effective tools today.

Other properties can be enhanced by the careful synthesis of multiphase materials. Since weakness in crystalline solids is due to the presence of dislocations which move readily in materials, strengthening will result if dislocation mobility is curtailed. Fiber studies have shown that high strength results from fibers too small to permit the presence of dislocations. In addition, if a material is saturated with particles of a second phase too small in size to permit the passage of dislocations, the material will be further strengthened. Thus strengthening will be particularly apparent at temperatures near the melting point of the matrix material, where free dislocations are particularly mobile and materials are particularly weak. An ap-

Figure 8 Photomicrograph of tungsten carbide bonded with cobalt.

propriate particle size for this strengthening is several tens of microns in diameter, and an appropriate particle spacing is several hundreds of particle diameters.

It remained for a team of colloid chemists to selectively reduce colloidal dispersions of nickel and thorium oxides to form thorium oxide dispersions in nickel; this process increased the strength of nickel at room temperature by a factor of 10 and formed the strongest nickel alloy yet developed at temperatures of 2000 to 2400°F, near its melting temperature. The fine dispersion inhibits easy dislocation mobility and crystal growth which result in weakness at these temperatures.

Even greater strengthening can be realized by reinforcing materials with fibers. The reinforcing fiber should have a higher elastic modulus than the matrix. The matrix should be sufficiently ductile so that it may yield without fracture, and thus transfer the stresses uniformly to the fibers. Glass and plastic scientists have combined to develop continuous-glass-fiber-reinforced plastics composites. They consist of a bundle of carefully oriented glass fibers with a modulus of 10^6 encapsulated in a polymer. Strengths as high as 250,000 lb/in.^{2} have been developed. On a strength-per-density basis, these materials are stronger than steel. They have replaced their natural antecedents of bamboo in fishing rods and poles for pole vaulting. They are also used as bodies for automobiles, hulls for boats, and in a variety of filament-wound pressure vessels and space-vehicle parts.

The understanding of strength in these filament-type composites is based on utilizing the strength of high-modulus continuous filaments which retain their elastic strengths to high strains due to the protective and stress-distributing characteristics of the ductile matrix. From these principles, the strength of certain composites can be

Table 2   PROPERTIES OF SOME PRESENTLY AVAILABLE STRUCTURAL MATERIALS

Property	Filament-wound glass fiber-resin composites	Steel	Titanium
Density	0.08	0.285	0.163
TYS, psi	250,000	220,000	180,000
TYS/density, in.	3.12×10^6	0.77×10^6	1.10×10^6
Modulus of elasticity, psi	8.5×10^6	30×10^6	16×10^6

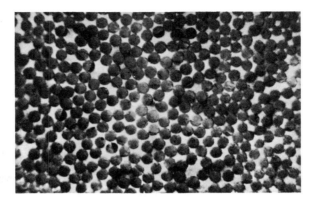

Figure 9 Photomicrograph of glass fibers in plastics. Filament-wound Fiberglas is an artificial two-phase material. Seen magnified approximately 415 diameters in this cross-sectional view, the glass fibers appear as small gray circles against the lighter background of epoxy resin, the supporting matrix.

accurately calculated for specific combinations in which the filaments are not touching, the matrix-filament bond is good, and the filament size and strength are uniform. It has been discovered that equivalent strengthening can result from short fibers, provided the length-to-diameter ratio of the fibers is suitable to permit stress transfer from fiber to fiber. Thus there is now a basis for utilizing the strong fibers free from the dislocation effects, which were previously discussed. Aluminum oxide whiskers, 4 to 20 microns in diameter, have strengths as high as 1.5×10^6 lb/in.^{2} Experimental composites containing aluminum oxide embedded in nickel are significantly stronger than the thoria-dispersed nickel or other strong nickel alloys. The door is now open to use the strongest known materials in useful shapes. It is a challenge to the materials engineer to implement the discoveries of the materials scientists.

A new challenge to the materials scientists is now appearing, namely, the age of man-made composites. Composites require the joining of two or more different materials for the purpose of gaining advantageous characteristics from each or of overcoming disadvantageous characteristics of each. The science of the nature and characteristics of the interfaces is little understood. The principles of

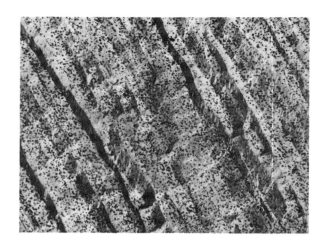

Figure 10   Photomicrograph of TD nickel.

Figure 11   Average tensile strength of Al_2O_3 whiskers at various temperatures.

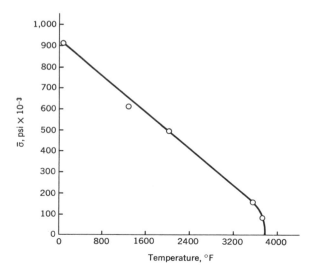

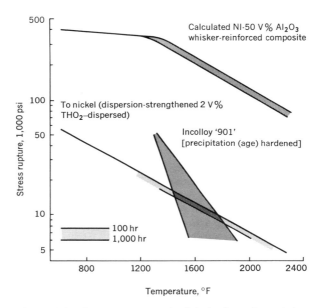

Figure 12 Stress-rupture of nickel strengthened by Al_2O_3 whisker reinforcement, precipitation hardening, and dispersion hardening.

the selection of combinations beyond simple pairs are not understood. Through composites, materials hitherto unknown will be systematized and synthesized with the understanding of the science of materials behavior (properties and processing) and the engineering of materials design, manufacture, and use. The materials scientists will be soundly grounded in physics, chemistry, and mathematics, and will be expert in depth in the behavior of solids, liquids, and gases under diverse forces and environments (in both diagnostic and discovery areas).

The materials engineer will be soundly grounded in all the aspects of materials science, and will be expert in depth in using this science to fulfill the needs of a technological society advancing under the stimulus of challenging economic, political, and sociological change. Other technologies will advance as rapidly as there are suitable materials to build the required devices, components, and systems on a sound economic and sociological basis. The field is new and sparsely populated. The technology is both demanding and rewarding.

4

Resource Engineering

by Rolf Eliassen

Rolf Eliassen is an expert on water resources and sanitary engineering who has divided his time between university life and the practice of engineering with private firms and government agencies. He was born in Brooklyn, and received degrees of B.S., M.S., and Sc.D. from the Massachusetts Institute of Technology. He then worked with J. N. Chester Engineers in Pittsburgh and with the Dorr Company, Engineers, in Chicago and Los Angeles. During World War II he was with the Corps of Engineers of the United States Army. He has taught at the Illinois Institute of Technology, New York University, and the Massachusetts Institute of Technology, and is currently Professor of Civil Engineering at Stanford University and partner in the firm of Metcalf and Eddy, Engineers.

Dr. Eliassen is author of a hundred technical articles and chapters in books on the treatment of water, sewage, and industrial and radioactive wastes. He is consultant for more than a dozen municipal, Federal, and international agencies. He is a member of many professional societies and is a Fellow of the American Society of Civil Engineers and the American Academy of Sanitary Engineers.

RESOURCE ENGINEERING involves a broad network of engineering and scientific professions or disciplines, all devoted to the utilization and conservation of natural resources for the benefit of mankind.

This chapter will stress the interdisciplinary approach to solving problems of the management of natural resources. The author will attempt to link modern resource problems to the established professions of engineering. These professions are fundamental to the education of engineering students and to their later practice of engineering, as discussed in the first chapter of this book. It is pertinent to note how the horizons of each engineering profession have expanded and overlapped with other professions—providing new and more complex knowledge and better equipping engineers to meet the needs of the era for utilization and control of the water, air, and land resources of the earth.

WATER RESOURCES

Civil engineering is the key profession in the control of water resources. The American Society of Civil Engineers is the professional society, representing about 50,000 civil engineers, and much of the literature on water resource development appears in publications of the ASCE. Members of the society interested in water resources may belong to various technical divisions devoted to special disciplines. These divisions include Construction, Hydraulics, Irrigation and Drainage, Pipelines, Power, Sanitary Engineering, Soil Mechanics and Foundations, Structures, Surveying and Mapping, and Waterways and Harbors. It is apparent that even within one profession, there are many categories of special engineering skills which must be called upon in the conception, design, construction, and management of water resources.

This field presents one of the greatest challenges to civil engineers in this country and abroad. The reason is obvious: The population explosion is creating unprecedented demands for water on the part of municipalities, industries, and agriculture. In the United States, the problems are made difficult by the hydrological facts facing civil engineers: Rainfall is unevenly distributed across the country, and in many areas it comes during only one or two seasons of the year. Arid lands cover most of the southwestern part of the country. If the 30-in. average rainfall of the entire United States could be evenly distributed in area and in time, there would be no problem. The United States has a land area of 2 billion acres; with 2½ ft of rainfall per year, this amounts to 5 billion acre-ft per year of water falling on the land. A common unit of measure is 1 million gal. This is enough to supply a community of 5,000 to 10,000 people with water for one day. The total rainfall averages 5 million million gal per day. Unfortunately, approximately 70 percent of this water is evaporated or is used by plants and thus is transpired to the atmosphere. The remaining 30 percent is stored as groundwater or will run off in streams.

The Federal government has been paying a great deal of attention to water resources planning for many years, through the activities of its Bureau of Reclamation, the Geological Survey, various agencies of the Department of Agriculture, and the Corps of Engineers of the Army. Reports from Washington indicate that only 25 percent of the water supply which might be available in streams and in the ground is presently being put to use. This amounts to about 400 million acre-ft per year. Half of this is used for agricultural purposes and the other half for municipal and industrial needs. Some 300 million acre-ft is returned to streams and the ground after use, averaging 300,000 million gal per day. The remaining 100 million acre-ft returns to the atmosphere as consumption by plants and industries.

It is not possible to speak in generalities about water resources in the United States because the problems are regional in character. Some parts of the country are faced with excess waters which cause great floods. Other parts are very short of water, or will be by the year 2000. Reports of the United States Senate Select Committee of 1960 point out that the total deficit in dry years may be as high as 100 million acre-ft per year for the country as a whole in the year 2000, with water being particularly short in the following areas: Colorado Great Basin and Southern California, Rio Grande–Pecos, upper Missouri, Upper Arkansas–Red River, Western Gulf, Great Lakes, and the Delaware-Hudson region.

Many parts of the country have developed integrated systems of water resource control for the following purposes: navigation, flood control, water supplies for municipalities, industries, and agriculture, hydroelectric power, and recreation. Some projects may have several purposes and are known as multipurpose projects. Generally, these have as their objective the optimum utilization of the flows in a river to serve the greatest number of people. Great multipurpose works have been constructed on the Columbia River, including the famous Grand Coulee and Bonneville Dams. The Missouri River has recently been subject to control through the Pick-Sloan Plan, under which large multipurpose upstream dams were built to control navigation in the lower reaches of the Missouri and the Mississippi, to hold back flood waters, and to use these waters for irrigation and power generation.

An outstanding example of resource management on a broad scale is the Tennessee Valley Authority. Since 1933, TVA has built or acquired 25 dams in the drainage basin (40,000 sq miles) of the Tennessee River—9 dams on the main river and 16 on tributary streams. The Aluminum Company of America also has 15 dams whose operations are integrated with those of TVA, and achieve optimum realization of the combined objectives of the system.

The principal objectives of water resources control were (*1*) to control flood waters which had a long history of destruction in the Tennessee and Mississippi Rivers; (*2*) to provide a navigable waterway for 650 miles on the Tennessee River with a minimum depth of 9 ft from Knoxville to the Mississippi and with locks at the nine principal dams to lift the vessels over 500 ft; and (*3*) to provide for hydroelectric power to be generated in optimum amount consistent with flood control and navigation objectives. That these have been achieved is a matter of record.

Management of the river system includes provision for 12 million acre-ft of available storage volume at the beginning of each year to hold back excessive stream runoff from the winter and spring rains. Hydrologists have acquired knowledge of the statistical nature of stream flows and have developed mathematical models which can be introduced into the computer to optimize contact of the entire system. This system includes the maintenance of operating levels in each of the reservoirs, particularly the multiple-purpose ones which must control navigation, hydroelectric power, and floods. Thus, flood waters which are stored during the winter and spring can be released during the summer and fall to maintain navigation and to prevent difficulties which arose from droughts. It has been estimated that the savings attributable to flood control averaged $13 million annually to Chattanooga and other cities and lands along the Tennessee, the lower Ohio, and the Mississippi Rivers.

The social values of the availability of cheap power to the farmers, industries, and communities of the Tennessee Valley have been publicized over the world. From an area of economic distress, the area has advanced to one of rich agricultural and industrial status. For instance, in 1960 the average annual residential use of power was 9,000 kwhr, about double the United States average and fifteen times the local average in 1933 when TVA was initiated. The number of residential customers rose from about 200,000 to 1,270,000, and the average use multiplied one hundred times because of the low rate of 1 cent per

Figure 1 (*Left*) The Shippingport atomic power plant built jointly by the U.S. Atomic Energy Commission and Duquesne Power and Light is a pioneer in the conversion of atomic energy into electric energy. (*Right*) Interior of Shippingport power plant showing the reactor. (Philip Gendreau)

kwhr. The growth of power-consuming industries has also been phenomenal. Phosphate plants, aluminum mills, and the operations of the Atomic Energy Commission for the refining of uranium have increased the wealth of the area. Steam-electric power plants had to be built to supplement hydroelectric power. Steam provides a base load and hydroelectric power may be used for peaking loads in an integrated system operated at maximum economy. Including the 15 dams of the Aluminum Company on Tennessee River tributaries and 5 dams of the United States Army Engineers on the Cumberland, all of which are integrated into the TVA System, about 60 billion kwhr were generated in 1960.

Another social value of the TVA System is the recreation afforded by the reservoirs. Facilities for bathing, fishing, hunting, boating, and camping have been provided. It has been estimated that the value of the parks built and operated by other agencies was greater than $100 million by 1960. These recreational opportunities serve to attract people and industries to the area.[1]

[1] The TVA System will be discussed as an example of large systems engineering in Chap 9.

One might well question whether any similar opportunities exist
elsewhere. They certainly do in many parts of the world. Take, for
instance, the Mekong River in Southeast Asia. This river drains ten
times the area of the Tennessee Valley. Even with the exclusion of
the area in China, 307,000 sq miles are drained by this great river;
20 million people live within the confines of its watershed in Cambodia,
Laos, Thailand, and Vietnam, and this number will double in twenty-

five years. To date, not a single bridge crosses the river, communications and transportation facilities in the valley are difficult and even nonexistent, and floods from the monsoon rains and long droughts plague the lands. The opportunity for resource management by sound engineering is almost unbelievable. Civil engineers and professionals from many disciplines and many countries are now leading the planning for development of these water resources.

"Confidence in the central premise of the enterprise—that the long-run social development of the region requires the management and distribution of the lower Mekong waters on a basis that comprehends the lower basin as a whole—has grown stronger as the work has gone forward over the past half decade." This quotation is from an excellent article by G. F. White [2] which should be read by anyone interested in resource engineering and in the challenges of the future.

By constructing dams at strategic locations, it should be possible to have a 1,000-mile navigable waterway to irrigate millions of acres, control devastating floods, and generate vast quantities of electrical energy. The people of these countries need more food, more industries, and greater effectiveness in the utilization of human and natural resources. California and Arizona have fought for years over the rights for a few million acre-ft of water per year. Yet the Mekong had a near-annual uncontrolled flow of more than 100 million acre-ft 1,000 miles from its mouth at the Thailand-Laos border near Vientiane. White states that a dam could be built there to hold back a storage reservoir three times as great as that behind Hoover Dam on the Colorado. Nobody knows how much more water flows past the region near the mouth of the Mekong at Phnom Penh in Cambodia. Just think of the challenges the Mekong presents to resource engineers!

What lies behind the conception and design of large projects such as these, as well as smaller water resource systems? Hydraulic engineering is that segment of civil engineering which deals with the design, construction, and operation of structures and facilities necessary for the control of water. Its fundamental tools are fluid mechanics, solid mechanics, and hydrology. The former consists of mathematical analysis, backed by experimental evidence, on the behavior of fluids under static and dynamic conditions and the application of the principles of mechanics to the design of conduits, aqueducts, canals, pumping machinery, and hydraulic turbines.

Hydrology is the science which studies the properties of water on the earth's surface in connection with the occurrence and distribution

[2] Gilbert F. White, The Mekong River Plan, *Scientific American*, vol. 208, no. 4, pp. 49–59, April, 1963.

of rainfall. As you may well imagine, statistics plays an important part in the study of hydrology, since rainfall and runoff are stochastic phenomena. Rainfall predictions—for floods, droughts, and average conditions—must be made for the design of hydraulic structures in order to provide for the safety of the public, economy of construction, and the functional purposes of the project. Evaporation from water surfaces, transpiration from vegetation, the infiltration of water into the ground and the flow of underground water including stream runoff, are studied in detail, along with related subjects such as meteorology, geology, and oceanography.

On the basis of extensive hydrological studies of rainfall, runoff, and percolation into the ground, it has been disclosed that the southern half of California has 20 percent of the annual rainfall of the entire state and 80 percent of the population. The rate of population growth in the south is greater than in the north, and about 80 percent of the water falling on the state is needed in the southern half. The California Water Plan has been developed by the Department of Water Resources of the state to capture stream runoff from the Sierra Nevada Mountains north of Sacramento on the Trinity, Feather, and Sacramento Rivers, as well as on other tributary streams. Water will be transported through canals and rivers over 500 miles to Southern California. Municipal, industrial, and agricultural users will benefit along the way, particularly in the San Joaquin Valley. The major portion of the flow will be pumped over the Tehachapi Mountains against a total head of about 2,000 ft. This will require the largest pumping plant in the world (probably with a nuclear reactor to furnish power for this pumping plant) as well as aqueducts and tunnels to cross the mountains and to flow into the valley in Los Angeles County and adjacent counties. The Feather River Dam at Oroville will be the highest earth- and rock-filled dam in the country, with a total volume of 77 million cu yd. The cost of the dam plus diversionary structures will be $121 million. This is the largest single construction contract awarded in the United States for a public works project of a civilian nature. Thus, bold planning will provide water for the suburbs of San Francisco, Los Angeles, and San Diego, and for the Central Valley of California. Even at great cost, the taxpayers are willing to assure the continued growth of population, industry, and agriculture in order to serve the needs of man in this great state.

The water will require purification before it is delivered to household and industrial consumers. This is the role of the sanitary engineer —a man with a breadth of scientific and engineering background to be able to cope with the chemical, physical, and biological problems involved in the treatment of water, of sewage, and of industrial wastes. He plans and designs hydraulic structures in which these processes of water and sewage purification take place, and he fits them to the needs of man. He becomes an expert in the destruction of viruses and bacteria in water supplies and in sewage. He must design hydraulic structures to dispose of the sewage in a safe manner which will not lead to stream pollution or the contamination of lakes, tidal estuaries, and ocean beaches which people use.

Water and sewage treatment are basic components of the field of water resources management. By 1980, over 150 million people in this country will receive their water supplies from surface sources. Many of these are on streams which receive sewage from upstream communities. Such rivers as the Delaware, the Potomac, the Ohio, the Missouri-Mississippi, the Columbia, and the Sacramento contain waters which must be used several times in their course of flow from the mountains to the sea. Therefore, waste waters must be collected and treated by physical, chemical, and biological processes, somewhat similar to those used for water treatment, but with greater reliance on biological processes to destroy the organic matter present in sewage. Without such treatment, the river would not be fit for recreation or reuse. Therefore, the management of stream pollution control is an important element in the activities of the sanitary engineer.

The sanitary engineer must be concerned with the pollution of groundwaters as well as of surface waters. In a number of areas the quality of groundwaters has deteriorated because of the percolation of waste waters into the ground, carrying along with them synthetic detergents, chromates, and other contaminants not acceptable in potable water supplies. Deterioration in quality has also taken place with the encroachment of saline waters into water-bearing strata near the coast in the Atlantic, Gulf, and Pacific States. In other areas, groundwaters are being pumped at rates exceeding their replenishment, leading to a lowering of the groundwater table or the encroachment of water from the sea. The area of greatest concern in the United States is in Arizona, particularly near Phoenix and Tucson, where 4 million acre-ft per year are withdrawn from underground supplies. It has been estimated that the rate of replenishment of water into the soil is only 2 million acre-ft per year. The Pacific Southwest Water Plan, as put forth by Secretary Udall of the U.S. Department of the Interior, contemplates taking water from the northwestern part of California almost a thousand miles into Central Arizona. Such is the scope of thinking of the modern manager of water resources!

In the underdeveloped nations, the sanitary engineering problems are more acute. Management of water resources for public health is far behind because of lack of funds and materials, the cultural patterns of villages, and many other factors. The World Health Organization has published this statement on the role of water resources in public health:

Half the world is sick, millions are dying, for lack of water—readily available quantities of safe water such as we take for granted in America. Water to drink; to wash with; to carry away wastes. Where it's in chronic short supply, where it is contaminated—there you'll find wretched hordes of people in the grip of cholera, diarrhea, typhoid. Some sanitation authorities believe that three-quarters of the world's population is in just such a miserable fix. In one African country, fewer than 2½ per cent of the people have access to safe water piped to their houses; fewer than 14 per cent are able to get it through public fountains. In 19 Latin American countries, as late as 1958, 39 per cent of the urban population was living without a piped community water supply; 70 per cent in the smaller cities of 2,000 to 10,000. A village stream in India serves as community laundry, bathing spot, waterhole for cattle—and source of drinking water for the people. In many areas around the globe the water problem is just as bad. And it's steadily getting worse, as improved water supplies are being outpaced by population growth.

Something is being done about this problem. Consulting engineering firms from the United States, as well as from many other countries, are assisting countries and cities in the development of plans for water supplies and distribution systems, together with sewage collection systems and treatment plants, in order to control the outbreak of intestinal diseases. Many other types of water resource projects are also being constructed in the underdeveloped nations with the assistance of other more fortunate nations.

Financing is an important phase of any public works project. The civil engineer must be well versed in economics and in money and banking procedures in order to manage a public works project at lowest cost to his clients. Financial consultants are utilized in setting up bonding programs. Legal assistance must also be sought in obligating the community or other governmental agency to repay the loans through revenue bonds, general obligation bonds, or other means of financing. In the international field, the consulting engineer must be familiar with procedures of the Agency for International Development, which has given large sums of money to developing nations for public works construction to improve water and land resources of the nations. There are many sources of loans for overseas public works projects. The International Bank for Reconstruction and Development (the World Bank), the International Development Association (an affiliate of the World Bank), the Export-Import Bank and the Development Loan Fund of the United States, and the Inter-American Development Bank for the Americas are examples of sources of funds which the engineer must study in order to satisfy the needs of his clients.

Management of water works and sewage systems is a very important element of the problem of resource engineering in any city or country. The United States Agency for International Development has a Community Water Supply Development Program with one of its principal objectives being the training of water-utility personnel for management and operation of the systems which are designed and built in many of the developing nations. These people are in need of good engineering so that treatment plants may be built to provide for removal of contamination and disinfection of water supplies and for the distribution of these in a wholesome state to individual homes or central distribution points for homes within the radius of about 100 or so yards. Not every community is ready for piping to homes. The World Health Organization has engaged in a global water program since 1960. One of its objectives is the engineering of water supply systems to furnish water to all parts of the city under adequate pressure 24 hours per day.

The author was in Rangoon in 1962, and observed a situation which occurs in a number of communities throughout the world where pressure is not available all of the time.

Water in Rangoon is supplied to each of two major distribution areas for a few hours each day. Between the periods of water service the distribution reservoir must be refilled. But when water is available, individual consumers are permitted to pump from the mains to fill water tanks in buildings. This creates a negative pressure in certain areas and even empties the mains. To add to the problem, service connections were made with rigid galvanized-iron pipes to handle a corrosive water. As a result, leakage and breakage of service pipes were prevalent. Sewers were not available in most areas, so septic tanks and drainage systems were utilized, resulting in a highly contaminated ground water at the level of the distribution mains. Thus, the populace must boil the water before drinking in order to prevent the transmittal of diseases.

Fresh water from the ocean at a price the public can afford to pay has been a dream of people in arid countries for years. The author recalls a conversation in Lebanon in 1962 when a Lebanese engineer asked why United States engineers, with all of their research funds and abilities, could not develop a process which would make use of the Middle East's most abundant resources, the sun and the Mediterranean Sea, to provide their most needed resource—fresh water. Much research has been done on solar distillation of sea water in the past decade under the sponsorship of the Office of Saline Water (O.S.W.) of the U.S. Department of the Interior. Working processes have been developed. Unfortunately, so much land is required for the solar evaporators and construction costs become so high that greater economy can be achieved by other processes.

For sea water, thermal distillation has proved to be most economical. Flash and long-tube evaporators have been developed to produce distilled water at a cost for fuel, operation, interest, and debt amortization approaching one dollar per thousand gallons. Certain islands like Arube, Curaçao, and the Virgin Islands in the Caribbean have utilized this type of fresh-water supply for some time because they have no other water available but the sea. Demonstration distillation plants with a capacity of 1 million gal per day have been constructed and operated by the Office of Saline Water on the Gulf of Mexico at Freeport and on the Pacific Ocean at San Diego. Engineering, cost, and operating data are being obtained on these plants. Great progress has been made in the development of processes that will convert brackish water, such as the water underlying much of the west central part of the United States from the Dakotas through Texas and New Mexico, to fresh water. Electric power can be utilized to draw sodium and chloride ions out of the water through semipermeable plastic membranes by the process known as electrodialysis. Fresh water can be produced at costs ranging from 10 to 90 cents per 1,000 gal. For sea water the most economical processes to be developed thus far have involved distillation of various types. Many other processes, such as freezing, reverse osmosis, solar distillation, and solvent extraction are undergoing experimental investigation to develop more economical methods. Much research and development lie ahead in this field to achieve lower costs and greater applicability of these and other processes. These figures are expensive when compared with municipal water costs of 20 to 40 cents per 1,000 gal delivered at the tap in the home. But when water becomes short in certain areas, and where the construction of pipelines to bring fresh water over long distances is too great, saline water conversion presents an attractive picture.

If chemicals could be recovered at low cost from the evaporator concentrates, a saving in water costs would be effected. The mineral resources of the ocean are being tapped as one of the principal sources of magnesium, iodine, and sodium chloride. But the tremendous tonnages of chemicals produced in saline-water demineralization—140 tons for every million gallons of distilled water produced—would saturate markets and render the recovery process uneconomical.

AIR RESOURCES

Air is a great resource for the chemical industry. The principal elements of the atmosphere, nitrogen and oxygen, are used for the production of ammonia, nitric acid, and oxygen. The atmosphere also serves as the source of neon, argon, krypton, xenon, and helium. In 1958, more than 38 billion cu ft of oxygen of high purity were produced to be used for medical, metallurgical, and many other uses. Liquid oxygen is used to a great extent for rocket fuels. One of the greatest benefits to mankind has been nitrogen fixation from the atmosphere and the production of agricultural fertilizers, with consequent increase in the yields of farm crops. Anhydrous ammonia is now being applied directly to the soils with great economy. It has been estimated that the use of commercial fertilizers saves the public about $13 billion a year on its food bills.

Of course, the most important use of the air resource is by man, who must breathe approximately 16,000 qt of air per day. If this air is not of the highest quality, extraneous substances will enter the lungs of man and create health problems. Air pollution affects approximately 10,000 cities in the United States, the most publicized of which is Los Angeles.

During World War II, Los Angeles experienced a great increase of population and industrialization. Conditions in the atmosphere changed, in that a light haze seemed to persist for several days during certain seasons of the year. Visibility was reduced, eyes and noses were bothered, and other symptoms were noted by physicians from the complaints of their patients. Extensive studies were carried out by scientists and engineers in order to determine the cause and to indicate possible remedies. Sulfur dioxide was thought to be the main cause, but after a comprehensive program of reduction of sulfur dioxide emission by industries, oil refineries, and power plants, a reduction in the smog severity did not occur. Further studies, particularly those of the Stanford Research Institute and of Professors Haagen-Smit and Wendt of the California Institute of Technology, and of many other agencies and industries, showed that the principal offenders were the hydrocarbons discharged into the atmosphere from automobiles and the nitrogen dioxide produced as a result of combustion in power plants and automobiles.

With over 5 million gal of gasoline consumed per day in the Los Angeles area, attention was focused on automobile exhausts. It was found that the consumption of 1 million gal of fuel by average automobiles will yield the following compounds: 3 million lb of carbon monoxide, 300,000 lb of complex organic compounds, some of which have been shown to be carcinogenic, or cancer-producing, 50,000 lb of nitrogen oxides, and other organic and inorganic substances. Research showed that the presence of nitrogen dioxide in the atmosphere subjected to intense sunlight can lead to the photochemical production of ozone. This, in turn, reacts with some of the hydrocarbons to produce organic peroxides which have been shown to be irritating to man.

Control of air pollution in Los Angeles must center around the control of automobile exhausts, inasmuch as industrial and other sources are under control. Research has been conducted by various governmental agencies, manufacturers of automobiles, and equipment companies in an attempt to develop afterburners or catalytic converters which will destroy many of the hydrocarbons in exhausts. Basically, the automobile engine is a very inefficient combustion unit, as shown by the figures above on the nature of some of the compounds being discharged. What is needed is an automobile engine which will burn its fuel with an efficiency of approximately 100 percent. Such an engine is far from realization today.

Other means of reducing the discharge of hydrocarbons to the atmosphere are worthy of consideration if the people living in urban areas can become convinced of the urgency of individual action in air pollution control. People can control automobile manufacturers and petroleum companies through the market by their demand for other products which will have less deleterious effects on the atmosphere. For instance, smaller cars, with lean fuel mixtures and low-compression engines, perhaps using simpler fuels such as alcohol or butane, would cut down hydrocarbon discharge—and would still provide adequate transportation. Gas turbines are also being investigated.

The fuel cell [3] offers the brightest prospects for efficiencies in the order of 80 percent. When used to drive an electric automobile, the fuel cell might be four times as high in overall efficiency as the modern gasoline engine, no noxious hydrocarbon exhausts would be involved,

[3] See also Chap. 2.

and the quiet operation might be a boon to urban noise control. The smog-free automobile must be developed if urban civilization is to survive!

One of the principal solutions to the air pollution problem lies in adequate metropolitan transportation facilities. Mass transportation has gone over very heavily to automobiles, trucks, and busses, all of which discharge great quantities of pollutants into the atmosphere daily. Commuter service of a high order of speed and convenience must be furnished to compete with the automobile. This problem will be discussed in a later portion of this chapter.

Other sources of air pollution can be corrected by known mechanical engineering means. Such facilities as cyclones, scrubbers, electrostatic precipitators, and filters have been developed to a high degree of efficiency. The principal problem is cost. The public must be willing to pay for air pollution control in its purchase of the products of industry. The New York State Department of Health has as one of its mottoes: "Public health is purchasable at a price." This is certainly true in the field of air pollution control. The public does not yet know how much it is willing to pay and what pressure it should put on city, county, and state legislatures to adopt stringent air pollution regulations and enforcement practices. The medical profession itself is not positive of the long-term effects of various categories of air pollutants. Disasters such as the London smog of 1952, when 4,000 people died in a week of heavy air pollution, have occurred in various parts of Europe and the United States. These are short-term effects which are dramatic but do not occur very frequently.

Physicians are noting greater increases in the occurrence of bronchitis, emphysema, lung cancer, and cardiovascular diseases in metropolitan areas subjected to heavy air pollution. If the public health effects of air pollution could be more accurately determined, the public would know how to evaluate the need for more stringent controls. In the meantime, with increasing concentrations of population and increasing use of automobiles, as well as increases in other sources of pollution from homes, municipalities, industries, and transportation systems, smog is getting worse all over the country. Smog control is a complex problem involving engineering, public health, and political and social values which have not been assessed to the point at which air pollution is controlled. Much remains to be done before successful management of the air resources of the nation can be achieved.

Utilization of the air resources for transportation may be considered a phase of resource engineering. Air transportation has grown so enormously, both for passengers and freight, that the engineer is called upon to design new and expanded transportation systems each year. Domestic airline passengers have increased from 13 million in 1948 to about 50 million in 1963. The Port of New York Authority alone handled 750,000 plane movements at its airport in 1961, involving 13 million domestic and 3 million overseas passengers. Design of aircraft and airports, with all of the runways, taxiways, passenger and cargo handling facilities, aircraft servicing and fueling, traffic control, and other factors, presents enormous challenges to aeronautical, civil, mechanical, and electrical engineers concerned with air transportation systems.

LAND RESOURCES

Resources of the land include all phases of human life and activities. All types of engineers are involved in the control and utilization of this resource, even the aeronautical engineer, who must design his aircraft to take off and land at airports specifically designed for whatever type of vehicle may be used. This chapter cannot go into all phases of land resources with which the engineer may be concerned. Rather, a few highlights such as urban problems, transportation, mineral resources, and agriculture will be discussed. The reader can undoubtedly think of many others. This is what makes resource engineering so challenging—the problems are almost infinite in scope and close to the needs of all human beings.

Urban land use in the 50 largest cities of the United States averages about 33 percent for single-family residences, 6 percent for other dwelling units, 33 percent for streets and other transportation systems, 16 percent for public and semipublic use, 6 percent for industrial uses, and 3 percent for commercial properties. Excessive densities exist near the centers of cities, and suburban sprawl yields very low densities. For instance, in New York City there are about 25,000 persons per square mile; in Manhattan there are 88,000 per square mile. In the suburbs, the values drop as low as a few thousand per square mile. The advantages of urban living in many cities have been offset by congestion, high costs of living, and many discomforts; these have driven people out to the suburbs and have created many problems. Slum areas cover large sections of cities, some as high as 20 percent of the residential areas. Unfortunately, figures show that, on the average, slum areas may contain as much as one-third of the urban population in the largest cities. These areas take almost half of the cost of municipal government, but contribute only a few percent of tax revenues. This has created the need for urban renewal which, in turn, has become one of the largest problems for engineers in the postwar era.

The planning of urban renewal areas calls for engineering of a high order of imagination and competence. Low-cost facilities with adequate public health measures such as light, heat, sanitation, and air space are involved. Architects, mechanical, electrical, and civil engineers, city and regional planners, and other professions associated with engineering are making great contributions in helping the Federal, state, county, and city governments to accomplish effective urban renewal programs. Everyone has seen these in cities near his home; there is no need to discuss the magnitude of the task.

Transportation becomes the critical factor in urban living. This is in a state of crisis all over the country. More than 100 million people are living in cities and suburbs in the United States, and urban areas are expanding at a rate approximating 1 million acres per year. Such a concentration of people and the establishments where they work and by which they are serviced is made possible by human mobility and the logistics of supply. The growth of cities has strangled the transportation systems on which they are founded. One of the greatest difficulties has arisen in the shift from public to private transportation, creating heavy burdens on highways and streets and on the parking facilities for automobiles and trucks. With over 60 million motor vehicles on the road today, and with urban traffic arteries designed for conditions which existed half a century ago, the problem of utilization of the land in urban areas becomes almost insuperable.

The Brookings Institution has studied this problem and published a report.[4] The following quotation highlights the problem:

Highway standards and expenditures are generally in inverse relation to the need of traffic. The modern highways in open rural areas often degenerate at the city limits to an obsolete right-of-way, crowded on both sides with commercial activities strung out in unsightly array to create what has been aptly called America's longest slums. In the city, the concentration of traffic on narrow streets with their numerous crossings means that the speed and service potentials of the motor vehicle cannot be realized. The accident toll is outrageous. Since the turn of the century, one-third of a million people have been killed in motor vehicle accidents on city streets. City traffic accidents during the past two decades have injured 14 million people, most of them pedestrians. . . .

---

[4] Wilfred Owen, "The Metropolitan Transportation Problem," The Brookings Institution, Washington, D.C., 1956.

City governments burdened by the heavy outlays required to accommodate ever-growing volumes of city traffic frequently find that attempts to relieve congestion serve only to move the critical point somewhere else. Expressways or parking facilities established to meet the demand attract further use and magnify the need. Moreover, new facilities mean not only heavy outlay, but the loss of large areas of land from the tax rolls, reducing receipts at the same time added revenues are being sought.

The crisis in public transportation is being studied at all levels of government and by many engineers and planners seeking to achieve an optimum use of land resources to satisfy the needs of the people. Public transportation must be the answer to many of the urban problems, but this takes service for which the public must be willing to pay. The U.S. Department of Commerce has a large group studying this under the Assistant Secretary of Commerce for Transportation. Railroad commuter transportation, rapid transit lines, and streetcar and bus facilities are all losing money, principally because of the tremendous demands placed on their systems during peak hours and the relatively low rate of use at other times. No answer is offered here because the extent of the studies is too voluminous and the magnitude of the problem is too great to find a ready answer. But the challenge is there, and so is the need for young engineers equipped with a sound education in mathematics and in the physical, engineering, life, social, and political sciences. Universities all over the country have established centers for the study of transportation problems in the belief that solutions can and must be found if urban life is to survive.

City and regional planning is the key to the urban problem, and is a profession to which many civil engineers belong. Their affiliations are with the American Institute of Planners and with the City Planning Division of the American Society of Civil Engineers. This profession strives for a unified development of cities and their suburban environment to achieve optimization of land use. Perhaps the best way to describe the activities of city planners is to outline the community planning and renewal services which Metcalf & Eddy, the consulting engineering firm of which the author is a partner, offers its clients. The services provided by professional city planners include:

1   Investigation, evaluation, and determination of community problems and needs
2   Preparation and design of comprehensive or master plans for towns, boroughs, cities, counties, regions, and states
3   Selection, replanning, and performance of technical phases of

urban renewal projects employing the techniques of clearance, rehabilitation, and redevelopment

4 Carrying out land-use inventories and preparing urban, rural, and airport zoning ordinances

5 Layout and design of subdivisions including development of land subdivision regulations

6 Consultation and expert testimony on planning, zoning, and renewal problems

7 Technical assistance with the writing, adoption, and enforcement of all types of community codes covering construction and physical environment

8 Survey, analysis, and design for traffic and parking, plus central business-district, school, recreation, industrial-park, shopping-center, and plan financing, implementation, and administration

9 Public relations assistance to obtain citizen understanding and support for all plans and programs

Breadth of concept on the part of engineers in this profession is obvious. The need for their services is as great as in any phase of resource engineering.

Although a portion of land resources, minerals are important enough to receive special consideration. The management of mineral resources is in the hands of mining or minerals engineers and geologists who work with men in many other fields of engineering and science in the discovery, mining, processing, and utilization of minerals. Feiss, in a survey of the mineral situation of the world, stated: [5]

The total estimated value of the world's mineral production in 1960 was approximately $50 billion, of which fuels represented about $37 billion. The value of all other minerals, including construction materials such as sand and gravel, came to only $13 billion. Of this sum, U.S. production for its own consumption and U.S. imports from other countries added up to approximately $7 billion, leaving only about $6 billion worth of non-fuel minerals to be consumed by the rest of the world. This translates into a world consumption, outside the U.S., of only about $2 a head. In comparison, U.S. consumption in 1960 was roughly $40 a head. If allowance is made for a consumption of perhaps $10 to $30 a head in other well-developed countries, the per capita mineral consumption in the under-developed regions of the world is reduced to well below $1.

[5] Julian W. Feiss, Minerals, *Scientific American,* vol. 209, no. 3, pp. 129–136, September, 1963.

Many of the under-developed nations, of course, count on exports of indigenous minerals to provide the foreign exchange needed for industrial development. Such countries can look forward to a steadily rising demand for ores and minerals from the U.S., and other well-developed countries of the world. The U.S., for example, imports all its tin; more than 90 per cent of its manganese, antimony, beryllium, and chromium ores; more than 85 per cent of its nickel; about 75 per cent of its bauxite, and about 55 per cent of its zinc and lead. Across the board the U.S. consumes roughly 25 per cent of the world's total production of metals.

In spite of the accelerating drain on the world's mineral resources, it is now becoming recognized that they will never really be exhausted. Just as advances in technology have made it possible to exploit today ores so lean that they would have been considered worthless only fifty years ago, new advances will make it possible to extract metals from still leaner ores in the future. In effect, technology keeps creating new resources. Meanwhile new geophysical and geochemical tools have uncovered a remarkable number of unexpectedly rich mineral deposits, which the world, if it is wise, can use as capital assets to advance the well-being of all.

Mining engineering is an old and highly respected profession devoted to the discovery of ore bodies which can be mined economically, the removal of ores from the earth, and the processing of these ores to the point at which the metallurgist can extract the valuable metals or minerals. The most famous mining engineer of the century was Herbert Hoover, the thirtieth President of the United States.

During the period following his graduation from Stanford University in 1895 to the outbreak of World War I in 1914, Mr. Hoover enjoyed an enviable reputation as a mining engineer in the United States, Asia, Australia, Africa, Central and South America, and Russia. Minerals from coal to gold were discovered by him and his colleagues and extracted from the earth by companies that were established by his consulting engineering firm for their clients. His investments in mining properties were shrewd and he amassed a personal fortune early in life; thus, for the past fifty years he has been able to devote his time, money, and skills to public service.

The discovery of mineral resources has been greatly facilitated by developments which have taken place in the past two decades, particularly with the advent of airborne instruments. The aerial camera has been used for years, and refinements made through photogrammetry by civil engineers have been employed by mining engineers. This permits large-scale aerial mapping at minimum cost and in areas where most of the land is inaccessible. The airborne magnetometer is used

Figure 2   Geiger counter used for prospecting uranium and other radioactive ores. This instrument is sensitive to products of radioactive decomposition and measures the emission strength. (Philip Gendreau)

to detect irregularities in the magnetic flux of the earth. Many times these may be attributed to mineral deposits beneath the area being surveyed, and huge deposits in Canada, Venezuela, and Liberia have been located by this instrument. Prospecting for oil is facilitated by an airborne scintillometer. This instrument can detect variations in radioactivity over the earth's surface. It has been found that this radioactivity has been given off more from areas under which oil pools are found than from the normal earth. Electromagnetic surveying, using principles similar to those of the mine detector developed for the Armed Forces during the war, has led to the discovery of huge copper and nickel deposits in Canada. Thus, the management of land resources for mineral exploitation has been greatly facilitated through modern instrumentation techniques. The activities of mining engineering are closely related to and depend upon the cooperation of the professions of civil, mechanical, electrical, chemical, and metallurgical engineering.

Mineral engineering is a special phase of mining engineering. It deals with the art and science of extracting valuable minerals from the ores by such processes as grinding and comminution, followed by classification by means of size, density, and magnetic, electrostatic, and surface-active properties to separate valuable minerals from the parent rocks in which they are trapped by nature. It utilizes metallic ores containing gold, silver, copper, lead, zinc, aluminum, and iron, as well as many ceramic materials including cement, abrasives, and glass.

Petroleum engineering might be considered a special phase of mining engineering. The petroleum engineer is concerned with oil and gas resources and their exploration by means previously described, as well as by other geological and geophysical methods. Drilling for oil and gas, extraction of these fuels from beneath the earth's surface, and their

Figure 3   A mobile self-elevating petroleum drilling barge on location in Alaska's Cook Inlet. The barge is operating in 22 ft of water and is drilling toward a target depth of 9,000 ft on the Middle Ground Shoal structure. (Pan American Petroleum Corporation)

Figure 4   Offshore oil drilling barge viewed from the superstructure. (H. Armstrong Roberts)

transportation and storage are all within the realm of responsibility and competency of the petroleum engineer. Over 125,000 miles of pipelines have been installed in the United States; oil is transported over 1,000 miles from Texas to the Northeast and natural gas about 1,400 miles from Canada to California.

Mining engineering, mineral engineering, and petroleum engineering are so closely related to geology and geophysics that they become interdisciplinary fields of study. At Stanford University and at other universities, all of these fields are presented in the School of Earth Sciences, where the students obtain common backgrounds in mathematics, physics, chemistry, geology, and the specialties of their particular professions. Science and engineering are unalterably wedded together in such an academic environment to produce engineers who are equipped to handle the most exacting demands of the future for a greater utilization of the mineral resources of the earth.

The production and refining of metals from concentrated ores is the province of the metallurgical engineer. Mechanical, electrical, thermal, and chemical processes may be utilized. The familiar blast furnaces of the ferrous metallurgist depend upon chemical reduction of the iron oxide in the ore in the presence of carbon monoxide, which is oxidized to carbon dioxide at temperatures up to 1500°C. Further refinement of iron to steel takes place usually in the open hearth furnace. Other furnaces are used to melt and mix iron with specific elements such as chromium and nickel to produce stainless steel and high-strength steels for bridges, buildings, jet engines, and thousands of other uses. Electrometallurgical processes refine copper and produce aluminum. Gaseous and chemical separation processes are used to recover uranium from pitchblende ore.

Fundamental studies are carried out by the metallurgist on the crystalline structure of metals and on all of the processes which might conceivably be applicable to metallurgical practice. The metallurgist is vitally concerned with the properties of metals and their alloys in order to adapt mineral resources to the needs of man. These may include metals which are resistant to corrosion, to high or low temperatures, or to radiation; metals which are light or massive or which have unusually high strength; or metals which have special magnetic or electrical properties. Research has found answers to many of these problems, but engineers from other professions, particularly those dealing with supersonic aircraft, missiles, and space vehicles, are placing increasing demands on metallurgical engineers to produce even more exotic substances, including ceramics, to withstand ever more rigid environmental conditions. The challenges to research and production workers in this field of resource engineering are never-ending, as was explained in detail in Chap. 3.

If one were to trace the path of metals from the metallurgist's mill to the consumer's automobile or kitchen, one would have to trace many steps of design, manufacturing, marketing, and distribution. Mechanical engineering plays a large part in the fabrication of consumer products, and also of devices which are used to process natural resources. (The latter may include furnace and boilers, which are covered under the subject of energy in this book and need not be repeated here.) Many aspects of mechanical engineering are closely related to resource engineering. This is also true of industrial engineering, which integrates the human factors in production with the economic and engineering factors. Biotechnology, as discussed in Chap. 6, is very closely related to the activities of industrial engineers. Sophisticated mathematical techniques, such as operations analysis, have greatly facilitated studies in this field to arrive at a greater economy in the use of men, machinery, and materials in order to achieve an optimum production system.

Chemical engineering is also a phase of resource engineering in that it seeks to apply the principles and theories of chemistry, physics, and the engineering sciences in the production of chemical products from raw materials which are derived mainly from natural resources. For instance, the heavy-chemical, petrochemical, and petroleum industries utilize such resources as petroleum, natural gas, coal, salts, sulfur, nitrogen, limestone, and many other materials to produce literally hundreds of thousands of chemical products. Among these are fuels, synthetic fibers, plastics, drugs, synthetic detergents, paints and finishes, synthetic rubber, insecticides, fertilizers, and many other products that are used by industrial and domestic consumers. To a considerable extent, the comforts of living today are attributable to the advances made by chemical engineers in converting natural resources to products beneficial to man.

Figure 5   Oil refinery at work in converting crude petroleum into commercial products. (H. Armstrong Roberts)

Chemical engineers are employed mainly by industries. In a survey of about 13,000 chemical engineers conducted in 1961 among the members of the American Institute of Chemical Engineers, it was shown that two-thirds of them were employed in chemical manufacturing industries, 7 percent in consulting engineering firms, and about 5 percent each in governmental service and education. The remaining 15 percent were spread in various categories. Chemists and other scientists and engineers are continually searching for more useful materials to satisfy the needs of man. Therefore, many chemical engineers are engaged in research and development work on new processes and operations that will assure the economical conversion of natural resources to useful products.

Agricultural resources are subjected to engineering control by the profession of agricultural engineering. This field endeavors to apply scientific and engineering principles to the control of the land, power, buildings, and machinery used in agriculture and in the processing of agricultural products. Agricultural engineering has done wonders in the United States and in the more advanced countries of the world by helping to create an extremely high level of agricultural production. In some cases this level has led to an overabundance, a situation that exists particularly in the United States and in the Common Market countries of Europe.

However, consideration must be given to the underdeveloped countries of the world, which include so much of Asia, Africa, and parts of Latin America. Close to 2 billion people live in these areas; of these, about 1.5 billion either are undernourished or suffer from totally unbalanced diets. Social and economic developments are hindered by low productivity of agriculture and low purchasing power for food. It is difficult to develop other spheres of national economies as long as so much of capital and labor must be devoted to food production. The agricultural engineer is much in demand to work with the organizations affiliated with the United Nations, in particular the Food and Agricultural Organization. F.A.O. has estimated that the production of food throughout the world will have to be doubled by 1980 and tripled by 2000 in order to keep up with population growth and to provide a more acceptable level of nutrition for the developing industrial areas of the world. Agricultural engineering has helped to find part of the answer to this dilemma. In the United States the productivity of farm workers has tripled since 1940. For instance, the production of cereal grains has increased by 50 percent, even though there has been a 7 percent reduction in the total acreage under cultivation. In the case of corn, the difference is even greater. Fertilization and mechanization, as well as the development of better seeds and agricultural practices, have led to this great increase. This development must be translated to other areas of the world.

The agricultural engineer is part of an interdisciplinary team of scientists and engineers well acquainted with the earth sciences, the social sciences, economics, and the engineering sciences. Many of his courses are taken with civil engineers and geologists in order to prepare for such work as irrigation, drainage, and land development. Much work must be taken with the agricultural scientists who are specialists in chemistry, biology, and agronomy. Mechanical engineering and electrical engineering are also phases of his responsibility in the development of farm mechanization and farm power plants, as well as rural electrification systems. Food technology is an important field which he must understand, inasmuch as he will work with the technologists in the development of food-processing equipment and in the preparation of foods for processing by machinery.

Agricultural machinery has greatly facilitated the construction of irrigation systems to distribute water from pond or canal sources furnished by the Bureau of Reclamation or the many irrigation districts throughout the West. Irrigation has opened millions of acres to cultivation in the United States. It is an old art which was practiced in the arid zones of India and the Middle East many centuries ago, but practiced poorly. One of the major problems with irrigation is the drainage of the soils, particularly in flood plains of large rivers such as the Nile in Egypt, the Indus in Pakistan, and the Tigris-Euphrates in Iraq. If drainage systems are not installed, the underground water level will come close to the surface and may drown the roots of many crops. When water is close to the surface it rises through the soil by capillary action. In arid climates evaporation takes place at a high rate, leaving a high concentration of salts in the top layers of the soil, since most underground waters have considerable concentrations of salt within them. The resulting soil salinity and high water table can ruin good irrigation lands.

Take the case in the Indus Valley in West Pakistan. Revelle [6] described the activities of an interdisciplinary mission of scientists and engineers from the United States in helping to solve the agricultural problems in the Punjab and Sind regions of West Pakistan. There the waters of the Indus are used to irrigate approximately 23 million acres of land, the largest single irrigated region in the world. And still the

[6] Roger Revelle, Water, *Scientific American,* vol. 209, no. 3, pp. 93–108, September, 1963.

people of the country go hungry! The mission found that approximately 5 million acres of land were damaged by waterlogging and salinity. In other areas, land management and poor agricultural practices led to very low productivity. Revelle stated:

In West Pakistan we have the wasteful paradox of a great and modern irrigation system pouring its water onto lands cultivated as they were in the Middle Ages. Plowing is done by a wooden plow of ancient design, pulled by under nourished bullocks. Unselected seeds are sown broadcast. Pakistan uses only a hundredth as much fertilizer per acre as Egypt. Careful investigation shows that in most of the Punjab, the problems of water-logging and salinity could be cured, and at the same time adequate water could be supplied to the crops, by sinking fields of large wells to pump the underground water and spread it on the cultivated lands. Part of the pumped water would be carried off by evaporation and transpiration, and part would percolate back into the ground, in the process washing the salt out of the soil.

Removal of salt and provision of additional water are necessary, but by no means sufficient, measures to raise agriculture in West Pakistan from its desperate poverty. Equally essential are chemical fertilizers, higher yielding seeds, pest control, credit and marketing facilities, and above all incentives and knowledge to adopt better farming practices. The project cannot be done all at once; it is necessary to concentrate on project areas of manageable size. Initial capital costs for a million-acre project in the Punjab would be of the order of $55 million, including costs of wells and electrification, nitrogen-fertilizer plants, pest-control facilities and filling of administrative, educational and research pipelines. After a few years the minimum net increase in crop value in each million-acre project in the Punjab would be $55–$60 million a year, equal to the capital cost and twice the present gross production, excluding livestock.

This is the type of resource management problem that the agricultural engineer and the civil engineer of the future must face in order that the exploding population of the world may not lead to catastrophe. Since the United States has taken the leadership in the management of agricultural resources on a large scale, we are obligated to share our knowledge and experiences with the developing nations of the world.

5

Computers, Communication, and Control

by J. R. Pierce

John R. Pierce is Executive Director, Research, Communications Principles Division, and Executive Director, Research, Communications Systems Division, of the Bell Telephone Laboratories. His individual contributions to engineering research have ranged from the microscopic to the cosmic. The "Pierce gun" is the key element in focusing charged beams for electron microscopes and microwave tubes and in ion propulsion of spacecraft. His definitive work on the traveling-wave tube led to its perfection as a key element in radar, microwave relay links, and space satellites. He was one of the first to conceive of satellites for practical long-distance communication, and deserves credit for pushing this dream to the stage of the successful Telstar systems. His professional contributions have also included work in the psychology of communications.

Dr. Pierce was born in Iowa and received B.S., M.S., and Ph.D. degrees from the California Institute of Technology. He is a member of the National Academy of Sciences, a Fellow of the American Academy of Arts and Sciences, and a fellow of many scientific and professional societies. He was Editor of the Proceedings of the Institute of Radio Engineers and received the Morris Liebmann Prize of that institute, the Edison

Medal of the successor Institute of Electrical and Electronics Engineers, and many other honors. Art and music are included among Dr. Pierce's varied interests. (He composes both for computer and more conventional instruments.) He writes popular books on communication principles and science fiction under a variety of pseudonyms. He is a member of the British Interplanetary Society.

IT IS HARD FOR ANYONE who has not been closely associated with engineering research and development to realize how deeply society can be affected by a few simple and powerful inventions and discoveries. Ignorant people sometimes believe that a leader can "order up" progress and buy any amount of it with billions of dollars. This is not so. Profound changes in our industrial and social structure follow important discoveries and inventions, and nothing illustrates this more clearly than the technology which has given us electronic computers, communication, and control.

Today electronics is so highly developed and so diverse in its applications that it is hard to know where to start in telling a comprehensible story.

For instance, the telephone system, which enables us to dial to all parts of the country and to talk to all parts of the world, must transmit the human voice distinctly. This has led to a whole science of acoustics in which experimental psychologists and physiologists, as well as engineers, have studied speech and hearing. Surely this is fundamental to communication. Should this be our starting point?

Then again, transistors were invented through the study of solid-state physics, and many other devices such as magnetic cores, masers, and lasers involve important physical principles. Should we discuss modern physics as a starting point?

Or, in an overall way, in order to understand some of the problems of communication and to enable us to make deepsighted comparisons of various communication systems, a branch of mathematics called *communication theory* or *information theory* has been invented. Since this has something to say about communication, should we start with it?

Or, in order to design telephone switching systems, a branch of mathematical logic called Boolean algebra has been applied. In order to understand the theoretical limitations and possibilities of digital computers, some mathematician-engineers study recursive function theory. If these subjects have something very fundamental to say, perhaps we should start with them.

Any such approach would be missing the point. What the foregoing paragraphs tell us is that all sorts of knowledge enter into the field of computers, communication, and control. An engineer working in a part of this broad field may specialize in a particular area or may merely have to take advantage of what some specialist has found. Fundamentally, however, engineering advances partly through improved devices or tools (e.g., transistors as well as or in place of vacuum tubes) and partly through using existing devices to do new jobs which lie in their capability.

Figure 1   Echo ground station. This is an example of engineering research. It includes the first steerable horn-reflector antenna, the first use of a maser amplifier in communication, the first automatic tracking of a satellite by predicted position, and other new features. About twelve engineers were involved directly, about forty altogether, in its design and construction over a period of about a year.

There was a steady development of telephony after Alexander Graham Bell showed the way. The invention of the vacuum tube by De Forest gave us both radiotelephone and telephony over unlimited distances. The application of the vacuum tube in a new field gave us the first electronic digital computers. The transistor is working further miracles.

Charles Babbage tried to build a complicated digital computer in the nineteenth century, using mechanical instead of electrical devices. He did not succeed; the tools just were not up to the job.

Probably the best way to begin is with the tools and processes that go into computers, communication, and control, and to describe the sort of things which have been accomplished and the sort of work that was necessary to accomplish them. If we do this, everything else will fall into a reasonable place.

The oldest and most extensive of the three C's is communication. Today we see it typified in a telephone system of bewildering complexity, but all of this grew up around Alexander Graham Bell's invention.

Bell's telephone consisted of an iron diaphragm close to a magnet with a coil on it. When the sound wave made the diaphragm vibrate, it produced an electric current in the coil, and this current faithfully represented the sound wave. When the current flowed through another coil near another iron diaphragm, an audible replica of the first sound was reproduced.

Bell had made the first successful *transducer,* a device which would produce an electric current corresponding to a sound wave. Today transducers are an important and absolutely essential part of the electronic art. If you become an engineer, you may work on telephone transmitters or receivers that are more effective or less expensive—there is still room for improvement. But there are other sorts of transducers: high-fidelity speakers to produce powerful and faithful sounds, strain gauges to measure tiny elongations of mechanical structures, accelerometers to measure accelerations in guidance systems, and ultrasonic transducers to produce in liquids or solids sounds having frequencies far above the range of audibility—sometimes almost a thousand times as high as we can hear. Work just on this problem of transducers occupies the time of a good number of talented engineers and physicists.

It was not until electronic *amplification* had been achieved that man's voice could span the continent. The original amplifier was De Forest's audion, or vacuum tube. This was certainly the most im-

Figure 2   TL microwave repeater. This small unit is a complete commercial microwave repeater, with its own standby power in case of power failure. Years of research and development were required to produce so simple and compact a device. (Bell Telephone Laboratories, Inc.)

portant single invention in electronics, and it was one of the very greatest inventions of all times. In the audion, electrons boiled off a hot filament flow to a positive plate. A grid of wires is interposed between the filament and the plate, held a little negative with respect to the filament. A weak signal applied to the grid produces a much more powerful signal in a circuit connected to the plate.

Amplification is essential in talking over long distances, but it is

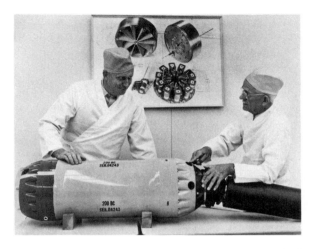

Figure 3   Submarine cable repeater. Decades of work on reliable components, corrosion, and laying techniques went into the design and manufacture of this repeater, which itself must operate for decades, lying on the floor of the ocean, powered by current supplied through the communication cable itself. (Western Electric Company, Inc.)

revolutionary in other ways. Through amplification, one part of an electronic machine can control others. Through amplification, weak radio signals can guide powerful missiles. Amplification is the utterly essential ingredient in the electronic art, and the audion was the first practical amplifier.

Engineers are still working on better amplifiers. The vacuum tubes (very similar to De Forest's original audion) that lie on the ocean floor in transatlantic telephone cables last decades without failing. Klystrons and traveling-wave tubes are amplifiers which use beams of electrons, but are otherwise very unlike audions: they amplify at frequencies as high as 60 billion cycles per second, and at lower frequencies they can produce pulses of energy with powers of tens of megawatts which are used in radar. Transistor amplifiers use electrons and absences of electrons (or *holes*) in a solid instead of in a vacuum. Maser amplifiers, which are based on quantum-mechanical principles, add very little noise to the signals they amplify, and are useful in receiving faint signals from satellites such as those from the Echo and

Telstar communications satellites. Optical maser, or laser, amplifiers can actually amplify beams of light (like radio waves, light is an electromagnetic wave).

There is plenty of work to be done on amplifiers. The author spent ten years of his life working largely on one type of amplifier, the traveling-wave tube, in order to devise a theory of its operation and to invent or devise ways of overcoming its shortcomings. The amount of hard work and thought that it takes to make something new work well is amazing—and it takes even more work to turn it into a practical, usable device.

The end of work on amplifiers is not in sight. The transistor, for example, takes less power than a vacuum tube and can be made to have a longer life. This makes extremely complex systems possible, including electronic telephone exchanges and very large and fast digital computers. The effect of the transistor is revolutionary. Improving and exploiting it will keep engineers busy for years. And who knows what will come next?

With the microphone, the amplifier, and the receiver, it became possible to talk across the country. But the amplifier made many other things possible as well. For instance, prior to the existence of amplifiers, one needed pairs of wires strung on poles to send messages over long distances. Amplifiers made it possible to send messages long distances over twisted pairs of wires grouped together in cables, which have a higher loss than wires on poles.

But amplification led to something more profound. In telephony, we transmit frequencies from about 200 to about 3,600 cycles per second. But wires can carry much higher frequencies. We can generate such frequencies by means of an *oscillator*. We can make an oscillator connecting the output of an amplifier to its input through a *tuned circuit* which passes the frequency desired. Then, by means of a device called a modulator, we can, in effect, add this frequency to the frequencies we desire to transmit. Thus, through modulation, we can send a telephone conversation using frequencies from 10,200 to 13,600 cycles per second, or from 100,200 to 103,600 cycles per second—or as far up as we want to go.

This makes it possible to send two dozen telephone signals over a twisted pair of wires, or more than 2,000 signals by means of a wire in a ⅜-inch copper tube, called a *coaxial cable*. This process of sending many messages over the same wire by using different frequencies is called *carrier telephony*, and today it is universally used in long-distance transmission.

Carrier telephony has brought two highly developed arts into electronics. A requirement in carrier telephony is that one be able to design a combination of inductors (coils), capacitors, and resistors which will filter a narrow range of frequencies carrying a particular telephone signal from the whole signal, which includes many other frequencies. This has led to the development of a branch of electrical engineering called *network theory*, which provides an analytical basis for specifying the electric elements and interconnections needed to accomplish these goals.

Network theory is a highly developed mathematical art. But it is far from exhausted and its range is continually increasing, for it has come to include new elements. The mechanical vibrations of quartz crystals, coupled to electric circuits by the *piezoelectric effect*, have been used for many years. (This is the effect used in record-player pickups, whereby a mechanical stress on certain crystals produces an electrical signal.) More recently, waves on quartz or aluminum strips have been used. And at microwave frequencies of thousands of millions of cycles per second, almost-closed cavities take the place of coils or capacitors. Finally, the inclusion of amplifiers such as transistors in "active" networks poses new problems for network designers.

Carrier telephony has also brought another class of problems into prominence—those associated with *nonlinearity*. In a nonlinear device, the current is not simply proportional to the voltage, as it is in a resistor. A modulator functions by making use of nonlinear devices in order to change a signal from one frequency to another. But amplifiers are not perfectly linear, and this factor tends to cause crosstalk in carrier telephony—the mixing up of signals which initially have different, completely separated frequencies. The analysis of nonlinear effects keeps many astute mathematicians and engineers busy, and the goals have not yet been reached.

Nonlinearity would have prevented the effective use of carrier telephony if it had not been for the invention of the *negative feedback amplifier* by H. S. Black. In an oscillator, the output is connected to the input in such a way that the signal produced by that input adds to the output. If this feedback is made small, the amplifier will not oscillate but the feedback will increase its gain. If we reverse the connection between the input and output (negative feedback), the gain will be decreased. The reason for doing this seemingly mad thing is that the gain can be made to depend almost entirely on the connection between the input and output, which can be very precise, linear, and constant, and not on the tubes or transistors which supply the gain and which are somewhat nonlinear and variable.

If it were not for negative feedback amplifiers, long-distance wire communications and transatlantic telephone cables would not be feasible. But the principles and theory of negative feedback, which were developed in connection with amplifiers for carrier telephony, have a wide application in the field of control in servomechanisms: for gun pointing, missile guidance, and a host of other possibilities.

The use of electric signals of high frequency in carrier telephony reminds us of radio. A current of high frequency radiates electromagnetic waves, which travel though space without wires. Frequencies of 500,000 to 1,500,000 cycles per second are used for broadcast. Frequencies from 5 million to 30 million cycles per second are used in transatlantic telephony. Waves of such frequencies can go around the world because they are reflected by the charged ionosphere which solar radiation creates in the upper atmosphere.

But, unless they are deflected, radio waves travel in straight lines. Waves of high-enough frequencies pass right through the ionosphere, and so they can travel only comparatively short distances between points on the earth. This is true of television (around 100 million cycles per second), very-high-frequency television (up to 1,000 million cycles per second), and microwaves (about 1,000 million cycles per second).

Radio forms a powerful adjunct to wire communication. Until the first transoceanic telephone cable was laid in 1956, it provided the only linkage among the telephone systems of the world. Microwave systems, which send beams of microwave radio waves from one hilltop tower to another perhaps 30 miles away, and thence hop by hop across the continent, carry thousands of telephone conversations as well as television signals to all parts of the country.

To reach points beyond the horizon we can send out signals so powerful that the small amount of power scattered by irregularities in the atmosphere is sufficient for a receiver which may be more than a hundred miles away. Such *tropospheric scatter* has been used for military communication in the Arctic, and also for telephony between the United States, Cuba, and the Bahamas.

Though tropospheric scatter can reach only a few hundred miles at most, radio, and specifically microwave radio, can span oceans by using communication satellites such as Echo, Telstar, or Relay to pick up signals from one side of the ocean and transmit them to the other. This method requires highly reliable and rugged equipment on the satellites and large, steerable transmitting and receiving antennas on the ground, such as those built at Andover, Maine, by the American Telephone and Telegraph Company, or those at Goonhilly Downs in England and Pleumeur Bodou in France.

Figure 4   The Telstar II satellite. The Telstar experiment included the construction of satellites and of a ground station at Andover, Maine, as well as the launching of two satellites. At the peak of activity, 500 men worked on the project.

We can see that an amazing diversity of devices, arts, and methods are available to the designer of a communication system. Somehow, he must make use of the services, past or present, of men who know about vacuum tubes, transistors, modulators, network theory, and nonlinear effects, and of designers of antennas who understand electromagnetic waves. And there are many things not yet mentioned—power supplies, the mechanical support of equipment, cooling, and corrosion of things located in the open or in the ocean.

Somehow, talents and devices must produce results which meet certain specifications of signal level, noise, and crosstalk. And a new communication system, or part of one, must serve some useful purpose economically.

In the course of the evolution of communication, *systems engineer-*

ing has come into being. This art is essential to the planning of a new system and permeates its development.

Ideally, systems engineering is the art of the possible. It evolves, from existing devices and techniques (or devices or techniques that are near enough to existing art so that they can be produced without danger or failure), one or more ways in which an overall objective can be met economically, taking into account the imperfections of all devices and the interactions among them.

Like all human arts, systems engineering sometimes fails. If there is a lack of systems engineering, an impressive group of component parts may fail to function as a whole: transmission may be too noisy in a communication system or the system may be too expensive; a computer system may be inoperable or its operation slowed by some subsystem; an antimissile system may fail to track a missile or to shoot it down. Engineers sometimes count on devices that cannot be made or that cannot be made soon or inexpensively enough. The result can be no system at all, or a system so long delayed that it is obsolete by the time it is completed or so costly that even the national government cannot afford it.

So far, we have discussed the transmission part of communication—getting the human voice (or a television, teletypewriter, or data signal) from one point on the face of the earth to another, or, for that matter, out into space. There are other sides to communication, however. There is a *control* side. In communication systems, *pilot tones* are transmitted in order to regulate the gain of amplifiers properly. Provisions must be made for detection of interruptions of transmission and for switching to alternative standby transmission means. But, there is another problem—that of interconnecting two or more people or machines that want to intercommunicate.

One way of doing this is to provide a private line. This is sometimes a good solution, but only in special cases.

The usual solution is to provide means for switching, in order to connect various communication circuits and thus provide a path across a state, a nation, a world.

At first this was done by means of *plug-and-jack* switchboards, but in 1889 Alman B. Strowger invented a step-by-step means of automatic switching which is still in use.

In *step-by-step* switching, the customer is connected to an idle switch which he operates by means of a dialed digit; this connects him to another idle switch which he then operates, and so on, until he is able to reach his party.

In *common-control* switching systems (first used in England in

1914) various pieces of equipment such as *translators* (to convert one number into another), *senders* (to send out the digits of the new number), and *markers* (which locate and select an idle talking path and establish a connection) are used by the customer only while the connection is being set up. A common-control switching system is a sort of electric computer operating switches, usually *crossbar* switches.

In a switching system it would be impractically expensive to provide a guaranteed path between each pair of subscribers. Instead, multistage switching is used. For example, in crossbar, one of around 50 subscribers can be connected to any of 10 wires, each of these to any of another 10 wires, and so on. Multistage switching has led to

Figure 5   ESS101—Electronic switching system control unit. This new switching system, designed to provide PBX (private branch exchange) service, uses a centralized-transistor electronic computer to control talking paths at several distant locations. Switching is done with solid-state devices, not metallic contacts. Though based on engineering research, this is a fully developed system; many different sorts of engineers worked a period of years in designing a sound, manufacturable system. (Bell Telephone Laboratories, Inc.)

mathematical studies of *blocking* (one connection preventing another) in order to minimize this phenomenon.

By the beginning of World War II, the telephone industry had built up a formidable armory of equipment and ideas for doing the on-off-on *digital* operations of telephone switching. As noted earlier, these included the application, by C. E. Shannon, of Boolean algebra to the design of switching circuits.

Modern automatic switching systems choose among available routes to distant parts of the country, provide ringing, busy, and other tones, record the length and charges for calls, and perform other complicated functions.

In the late 1930s, the idea of applying the techniques of telephone switching to computing occurred to G. B. Stibitz at the Bell Telephone Laboratories and to Howard Aiken at Harvard University. Mechanical desk calculators more complicated than adding machines had been available for years. The electrical art provided not merely a means for duplicating the performance of these ingenious devices but also for going far beyond it.

In 1937 Stibitz began his work toward such a machine, and construction of the Complex Computer was completed by October, 1939. The Complex Computer added, subtracted, multiplied, and divided complex numbers. In the early 1940s, Aiken at Harvard built several more powerful relay computers, and several were built at the Bell Laboratories.

These computers received instructions for various calculations from a punched paper tape and then printed out the answers. They were simple compared with large telephone switching systems, but they differed in another way; the computers were *general-purpose* devices capable of solving many problems, whereas a telephone switching system did only what it was designed to do—telephone switching.

Computers became more flexible and powerful through two innovations. In early computers, instructions were written on an input tape, and numbers produced as intermediate steps in a calculation were stored in a "memory" made up of telephone relays.

John von Neumann conceived of and introduced the idea of storing the program in the internal memory of the machine. This innovation greatly increased its flexibility of operation.

Shortly after World War II, Eckert and Mauchly built the Eniac, in which vacuum tubes rather than relays were used. This development greatly increased the speed of computation. It was followed by the building of the Whirlwind, Sage, and TX-0 and TX-2 computers at the Massachusetts Institute of Technology, and these led directly to modern electronic computers. Among the more important advances have been the introduction of magnetic-core memory, in which a binary number (0 or 1) is stored by magnetizing a tiny ferrite toroid in one direction or the other, the use of transistors instead of vacuum tubes, and high-speed input and output tapes.

Today, computers operate remarkably swiftly. During the time a person who uses a motor-driven mechanical desk calculator takes to multiply two 8-digit numbers, an airplane traveling at a speed of 600 knots will go 1½ miles. During the time a modern digital computer takes to perform the same operation, the airplane would travel about ⅜ of an inch.

Today, we can put data into computers by means of keyboards, punch cards, and magnetic tapes. Experiments have been made with other means, including writing with a "light pencil" on a cathode-ray tube. Computers can produce diagrams or drawings as well as printed letters and numbers, and they can be used to control a variety of other machines.

Computer engineers are seeking better ways of communicating with computers, including input and output devices other than key punches and printers. They seek ways for many users to gain quick access to a computer. And they seek new and faster circuits, faster and cheaper memory elements, and means of storing more information, including the use of magnetic drums and disks. Some favor building computers of superconducting or cryogenic elements, which have to be held at the temperature of liquid helium. There are even hydraulic computer elements which operate by the controlled flow of liquid or gas.

Certainly, one can see no end to the possibilities of devices for digital computers. And yet all of these devices deal with just two electric conditions of operation—on and off—which can correspond to the 0 and 1 of binary notation.

In nearly all computers, the internal operations are carried out in this binary form, and sequences of letters or numerals are translated into sequences of zeroes and ones before the computer operates on them. Yet we have said that a computer is a general-purpose machine. How general is it in its capabilities?

A. M. Turing, an English mathematical logician, has shown that a simple computer can match the performance of the most elaborate computer.

Turing made a mathematical study of the capabilities of a simple computer called a *Turing machine*. This hypothetical computer employs an infinitely long tape which the machine can move back or forth one step at a time. At each step, the machine can read the symbol written on that particular spot on the tape, erase the symbol, and write a new one.

Turing proved that a machine of this type, which is called a *universal Turing machine*, could "compute any computable number." (A number can designate a letter, word, or anything else.) "Computing any computable number" should be understood as "arriving at any answer if we can specify clearly and exactly a procedure, however, complicated, for arriving at that answer."

Even if it were built, a universal Turing machine would be too slow for any practical use, and it would be very difficult to program. But the result of Turing's theorizing is extremely important, for it shows that the operational limitations of present computers are not mechanical or electronic, though they can, of course, lack sufficient speed or memory. The principal limiting factor of the computer is human direction in the form of a *program*, or set of instructions, which will guide the machine in a given task.

Thus, programming is a great intellectual challenge in the world of computers. Without a program, a computer is a senseless heap of complexity. With a program, a computer may be an accounting machine, a model of a battle, or a checkers-playing machine. A computer can carry out only those operations specified by the programmer. If the programmer knows the sequence of steps which will lead to a desired result, he can direct the computer to reach that result. If he does not, the machine is useless. The "how" must come from the human mind.

Certain procedures can be stored in a computer. Also, by using programs called compilers, a computer can be directed to carry out some of the routine chores of programming. A computer can, for instance, translate one form of symbolism to another. The following table gives an example of part of a program for adding the numbers in two columns, as expressed first in a compiler language called FORTRAN (Formula Translation), then as translated by the computer into a language called FAP (FORTRAN Assembly Program), and finally as a translation made by the computer of the FAP commands into the binary machine language.

This is literally translating one language into another, but the languages are not natural languages; they are artificial languages devised to be completely unambiguous and logical. In the course of this translation the computer makes an orderly assignment of input data to locations in the memory and so relieves the programmer of this chore. But someone has to write the compiler program which directs the computer to do this; the computer does exactly what it is told to do. Because programs are complicated and because each step of a solution depends on the outcome of previous steps, a programmer may

Table 1   SAMPLE COMPUTER PROGRAM

Part of program in FORTRAN	Corresponding part of progam in FAP	
C(I) = A(I) + B(I)	037	CLA A + 1 , 1
SUMA = SUMA + A(I)	040	FAD B + 1 , 1
SUMB = SUMB + B(I)	041	STØ C + 1 , 1
SUMC = SUMC + C(I)	042	CLA SUMA
	043	FAD A + 1 , 1
	044	STØ SUMA
	045	CLA SUMB
	046	FAD B + 1 , 1
	047	STØ SUMB
	050	CLA SUMC
	051	FAD C + 1 , 1
	052	STØ SUMC

Corresponding part of progam in machine language

000 011 111	000 101 000 000 000 000	001 000 000 011 001 100
000 100 000	000 011 000 000 000 000	001 000 000 011 000 010
000 100 001	000 110 000 001 000 000	001 000 000 010 111 000
000 100 010	000 101 000 000 000 000	000 000 000 010 101 100
000 100 011	000 011 000 000 000 000	001 000 000 011 001 100
000 100 100	000 110 000 001 000 000	000 000 000 010 101 100
000 100 101	000 101 000 000 000 000	000 000 000 010 101 011
000 100 110	000 011 000 000 000 000	001 000 000 011 000 010
000 100 111	000 110 000 001 000 000	000 000 000 010 101 011
000 101 000	000 101 000 000 000 000	000 000 000 010 101 010
000 101 001	000 011 000 000 000 000	001 000 000 010 111 000
000 101 010	000 110 000 001 000 000	000 000 000 010 101 010

not be able to predict the outcome of a computation. But he knows that the rules used in the various operations will be carried out, for he specified them. A successful outcome depends on whether he specified correctly.

The advent of sophisticated computers has led speculative men to attempt the programming of particularly challenging and difficult tasks such as language translation, recognition of spoken words, and proving theorems—with curious results.

Although computers can translate one artificial, unambiguous, logical mathematical language into another with ease, efforts to make them translate, say, Russian into English have been somewhat disappointing. Tests indicate that the resulting text conveys somewhat less to a reader than a translation made by a human being does, and that readers just do not like present machine translations. Computers can be equipped with microphones to pick up sounds, or with photocells and other scanning devices that can "see" objects. By using such inputs, computers have been made to recognize a few words spoken by a few people, but not many words spoken by many people. The electronic voice-operated typewriter is still far from a reality. Computers have been made to recognize simple, uniform print, but they cannot read fanciful varieties of type face. Also, they cannot recognize a person in a photograph.

Computers can be programmed to play simple games, such as tick-tacktoe, perfectly. A multimillion-dollar computer has been made to play checkers better than most people, but not as well as an expert. Computer-played chess is poor stuff. Some computer programs can prove some mathematical theorems, but rather slowly. One program proves very simple theorems, such as those in *Principia Mathematica*, very rapidly. None can compete with a good mathematician.

The real strength of computers has lain in other fields. As an example, the speed of computers made it possible to track the Echo and Telstar satellites. During the Echo experiment, data from the Minitrack network were sent to the Goddard Space Flight Center. There the orbit was computed, and pointing data were computed for the JPL Goldstone antennas and the BTL Holmdel antennas for every 4 seconds of each pass of the satellite. These data were received at Goldstone and Holmdel as teletypewriter tape. A digital-analogue converter read the taped data at appropriate times and controlled the servos steering the antennas. A similar system was used in connection with the Telstar satellite. Without the use of a computer, satellite tracking of the sort I have described would be impossible.

This is an example of straightforward numerical computation in which speed is essential. It is much like other work in guidance, either for missiles or for the launching of satellites. But computers are used for many other things as well.

For instance, a programming language for symbolic algebra has made it possible to tackle problems which would ordinarily have involved months of routine manipulation. It has been used, for example, to compute the first nonvanishing term of each of $\frac{3}{5}$-order determinants of power series. Although about 2,000 terms were in storage at the floodcrest of the computation, each of the final answers can be written on a single line. The computing time for all three cases was only 92 seconds.

By measuring the amplitude of a signal at successive instances of time, the signal can be converted into a sequence of numbers. Then a computer can be programmed to produce from these numbers another sequence, corresponding to another signal. By this process the computer can be made to simulate the effect on a signal of some complicated but nonexistent piece of communication equipment, something that would have taken many months of work and hundreds of thousands of dollars to build. This has proved very helpful in a wide variety of research.

We usually think of the output of a computer as a sequence of numbers or letters; indeed, it always is. But these numbers can represent many different things. For instance, they can represent lines and curves. An attachment is available which enables the computer to print graphs and even pictures on microfilm. One ingenious engineer programmed a computer to make a motion picture of a satellite tumbling in orbit, in order to show how a particular attitude control system would eventually point the satellite at the center of the earth. In this case the computer computed the motion of the satellite and turned it directly into a form easily comprehensible to a human being.

One course of work which calls on both the *hardware* experts (who design and build equipment) and the *software* experts (who write programs) is that of making computers accessible and easy to use. Some ingenious engineers at the Massachusetts Institute of Technology have caused a computer to impose certain predetermined constraints on any input data. Thus, they can make a computer square up and fit together as a neat drawing, parts drawn roughly on the screen of a cathode-ray tube by means of a "light pencil."

Other workers have been interested in giving individual workers access to a large computer by means of a typewriter or a small satellite computer. In this case several users must share the computer. Either they must have a means of storing what they type, so that they can use the computer intermittently, or the computer itself must be able to serve many people at once. In general, present-day computers do not do this, although such operation has been achieved experimentally.

One interesting application of a computer is in designing other computers or computer-like devices.

Today, many computers and computer-like devices are built up of small plug-in subassemblies or "logic packages." These are interconnected according to a logic diagram to perform some overall function.

In the past this arrangement involved:

1 A freehand logic diagram, drawn by an engineer
2 A fine drawing, made by a draftsman
3 A choice of packages from a list of available types to realize the various functions called for

4 A physical location of the packages, and production of wire-routing information in the form of lists of connections and drawings, plus specifications for an automatic wiring machine
5 The wiring of the device

This process took a minimum of three months.

In using a system called Blades, which was developed at the Bell Telephone Laboratories, the steps became

1 A freehand logic diagram
2 Conversion of this to logic equations by a clerk
3 Punching of this information into cards by a keypunch operator
4 Production by the computer of
    a A deck of cards to run an automatic wiring machine
    b Essentially the same list of connections as before to allow hand wiring or checking
    c A machine-drawn logic diagram

This can be done in three days. Similar systems have been developed at IBM and elsewhere.

We have returned again into the field of control by saying that the Blades program produces punched cards that operate an automatic wiring machine. Such machines exist, and so do others as well. There are computer-controlled machine tools, which mill out or otherwise fabricate parts to dimensions specified by punched cards.

In a Western Electric plant, there is a resistor-production line in which a computer is programmed to produce various numbers and sizes of resistors. The computer also calculates, from various data on the product and the manufacturing process, what adjustments should be made to produce the desired product—and makes the adjustments. As shown in Fig. 7, the process begins with the deposition of carbon on a tiny ceramic core. Then the core goes successively through inspection, termination, capping, spiraling to value, second inspection, molding of a protective case, marking, leak inspection, final inspection and packing—with the resistor untouched en route by human hands. The computer performs in three areas: (*1*) It programs production control. A month's requirements can be fed into it at random. It completely schedules and programs the work, arranging it according to the four resistor-power sizes and an almost infinite number of possible resistance values. (*2*) Using the methods of statistical quality control, it analyzes control data plotted at three critical points in the

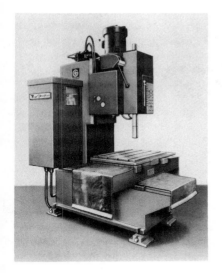

Figure 6   Bendix numerical contouring machine. This is one of a number of commercially available numerically controlled machine tools. It can be operated so that all information that directs tool slide movements comes from punched tape. Work at the Massachusetts Institute of Technology has led to the use of computers to transform English-like descriptions of the parts to be produced into detailed numerical data for the control of such machines.

automated process and applies statistical tests to determine if a trend is developing. (3) It formulates the information to detect any drift away from the accepted manufacturing tolerances. No control action takes place while this analysis indicates normal statistical distribution around a desired nominal. But when a trend away from this condition develops, the computer uses stored data to calculate new setup information for an appropriate station. In addition to feedback control functions, the computer provides an initial setup of wattage size at eight machines and resistance value at six machines.

Other control operations fall within the scope of other chapters. In the Nike missile systems, radars observe the courses of the missile and its target and guide the missile to intercept the target at some favorable point. In the Titan guidance system, used in the successful launching of over 125 missiles and satellites, a ground radar observes the missile and a ground-based computer corrects its course so as to put the satellite into the desired orbit.

But we encountered computer control a long way back in this chapter. As we have already noted, telephone switching has for years been carried out by rather specialized computers. The latest innovation in telephone switching is the use of more general-purpose high-speed electronic digital computers to control the switching operation. In the

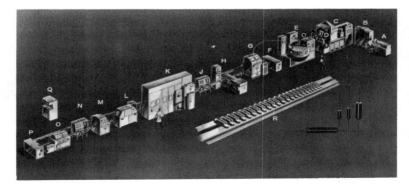

Figure 7   Computer-controlled production line: (A) computer, (B) output-input control station, (C) coating station, (D) first inspection station, (E) terminating station, (F) conveyor control equipment, (G) capping station, (H) helixing station, (J) second inspection station, (K) encapsulating station, (L) leak detector station, (M) marking station, (N) third inspection station, (O) packing station, (P) conveyor control equipment, (Q) cap-lead welding machine, (R) detail of conveyor line. This computer-controlled system makes accurate resistors. Various measurements are fed to the computer, and it makes the adjustments necessary for a uniform product. The line consists of 12 stations—all tied into control by a general-purpose computer. Feedback of process data from three key points along the line permits rapid control of operation by the computer.

past, it has been necessary to modify the common-control portion of automatic switching equipment in order to provide new sorts of telephone service (for instance, transferring your telephone service to another phone when you are temporarily with a friend). With general-purpose electronic control, new services can be provided merely by reprogramming the control equipment.

The reader may wonder why, in writing about computers, communication, and control, we have not said much about some romantic things he has undoubtedly heard of. What about computers playing chess? Retrieving information? Thinking (whatever that is)? This reminds me of the man who designed a computer that was so nearly human it could act without thinking.

We have not said much about these things because we have been writing for people who might be interested in engineering, and, above all, good engineers want to do things which are useful and will work.

Of course engineers are interested in the future. It is chiefly maintenance men who are stuck in the present, and we would not need so many maintenance men if engineering and manufacture were better. But good and wise engineers are interested in bringing an attractive future into being as quickly and painlessly as possible. This they can do in a variety of ways.

Some are natural inventors. The whole course of history has been changed by the telephone; the whole course of electronics has been set by the vacuum tube. And we are not at the end yet—the transistor shows that.

Some engineers, persistent or inventive, like to work on new devices such as transistors and lasers, and to show experimentally that these can be made to do useful things.

Some engineers like to develop new devices so that they can be made uniform and reliable and can be manufactured in quantity.

Some engineers like to study the ways of interconnecting devices to make optimum filters or amplifiers.

Some engineers like to put things together for the first time in order to show that a new idea will really work. The men who worked in our research department on a ground communication terminal for the Echo satellite were men of this sort.

Some engineers like to develop efficient and effective systems of communication, switching, or control that can be manufactured and used in man's interest.

There is a place for all sorts of engineering talent in the field of computers, communication, and control, however narrow or broad one's interests may be, or whether one is highly mathematical or intuitively practical. And what has been done is as nothing to what will be done.

We like to think of a world in which there will be more electrical communication and less travel to and from meetings, and in which computers will ease brain fatigue and avoid mistakes, whether in designing computers, or in shopping, or in packaging and delivery. An advanced form of mechanization has scarcely touched many of our industries, and computers as design tools are not widely known.

But, although we sometimes dream, our dreams are always incoherent and blurred. That is because they are not based on the real future. They cannot be. The real future has no being today; it will be what a new generation of engineers makes it.

6

Bioengineering

by Charles Süsskind

Charles Süsskind is Professor of Electrical Engineering at the University of California at Berkeley and Assistant Dean for Research in the College of Engineering
there. He was born in Czechoslovakia, and after a period
with the United States Air Force in England during World
War II, he came to this country for a B.S. degree at the
California Institute of Technology and for Master of
Engineering and Ph.D. degrees at Yale University. At
Stanford, at the University of California, and in Bay Area
industry, he made many contributions to microwave
tubes and electronic display devices. In recent research, he has studied the effects of microwave radiation on such diverse biological species as mice and
yeast. In the Institute of Engineering Research he is
also concerned with interdisciplinary aspects of bioengineering.

Dr. Süsskind, as brother of the well-known symphony
conductor, enjoys music as a major hobby. He plays only
for family and friends but he shares his reviews of
Bay Area musical events with readers of local papers
and listeners to FM radio. He is author and editor of a
number of important books, including a manual of style
for technical writing.

THE ENGINEER'S INTEREST in the life sciences might be considered very small. After all, when he chose a technical career rather than one in medicine or the literary arts, was not his decision based largely on a conviction that he would not excel in these alternate professions? Yet quite often the decision was not so clear-cut. Many a high school graduate has wavered between, say, engineering and biology. The two fields seemed to have nothing in common—choosing one meant forsaking the other forever.

That is no longer so. In recent years, a new discipline based on precisely these two fields has begun to emerge in universities, research laboratories, and industry. (It is significant that this new cooperative field was born just when biology was changing from a largely descriptive to a much more exact science; today's biology student needs to know much more mathematics than his predecessor of a generation ago.) The new field is sometimes identified as biomedical engineering, biotechnology, or simply *bioengineering*. Often it is not identified at all, and exists simply as a group effort by various professional people trained in the several specialties and working toward common goals.

What are some of these goals? We can do little more than to describe a few examples that typify bioengineering today, and at the same time to warn the reader that the relative importance of the fields they represent is likely to shift as time goes on, since most of them are still young and developing vigorously. As it happens, engineering has always touched on human resources at several points. Such contacts include the work of the hydraulic engineer who develops water resources with due regard for flood control, reclamation, irrigation, and urban planning, the sanitary engineer who designs a sewage disposal plant, the industrial engineer charged with maintaining safety in a factory, and the mechanical engineer concerned with the design of a modern dentist's chair. (Consider the amount of engineering that goes into the chair: the engineer must provide, in a safe and compact package, such diverse devices as a stepped-lens spotlight, high-speed drill, sandblast turbine, sterilizer, air compressor, X-ray generator, water pump, and sump.) The need for engineers engaged in such "traditional" endeavors is as great as ever, especially as it becomes increasingly clear that, in some directions at least, the evils associated with technological advances temporarily appear to outweigh the advantages and must be attacked. This situation is not unique to engineering. For instance, medicine, like engineering, primarily concerned with improving the human condition, also finds that its greatest successes (in reducing infant mortality, improving hygiene, and increasing life expectancy) sometimes turn into Pyrrhic victories, since they lead to overpopulation and all its horrific consequences. Technological triumphs also may have a dark side. Dislocation of the existing labor force, pollution of water and air, and traffic congestion are some of the problems that must be tackled with the help of engineers who are aware of the broad consequences of their actions on mankind.

In the meantime, the need for engineers trained to deal with the purely technical functions is on the increase. In the United States, for instance, the Veterans Administration has come to realize that *artificial limbs for amputees* can be best designed by engineers capable of precisely analyzing motion and force requirements and evaluating the relative merits of various methods of control according to sound engineering principles. The Veterans Administration has sponsored a number of research projects, notably at engineering and medical laboratories such as those of the University of California, where prostheses are designed, tested, and evaluated by methods that combine the techniques of engineering analysis with an appreciation of the physiological and psychological problems of human locomotion.

In the past, artificial limbs were powered by mechanical energy provided by the amputee himself; the muscles in the stump or (in more advanced systems) elsewhere in the body did all the work. With the development of techniques for designing very small electric and pneumatic motors and hydraulic devices—one of the by-products of space technology—an entirely new approach has become feasible: the externally powered prosthesis. An artificial arm may be operated by motors that derive their power from batteries or from bottles of high-pressure gas and that are controlled by electric signals present in the body, suitably amplified and modified. At least three types of electric signals are available: in the brain (electroencephalograms, or EEG), in the nerves (electroneurograms, or ENG), and in the muscles themselves (electromyograms, or EMG).

At present, EMG signals appear to be the most promising for prosthesis control since they are easily detected and well defined; research workers in Britain, the Soviet Union, and the United States are all concentrating on the EMG mode of control. The change in potential (between two surface electrodes attached to the skin outside a muscle) is amplified and used to actuate an electric motor or pneumatic valve that powers some part of the artificial limb. Current research is centered on improving reliability in the face of mechanical imperfections or false signals from nearby electrical equipment, as well as from internal sources such as the potentials associated with heartbeat, breathing, shivering, and other involuntary motions; on achieving smooth and continuous (rather than mere on-off) control; and on designing

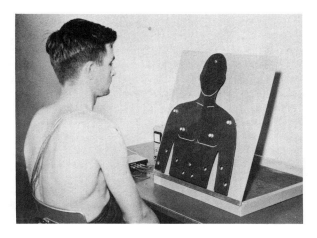

Figure 1   Use of EMG signals for training muscle control. Trainee learns to move specific muscles by observing signal lights in corresponding locations on a dummy. (From UCLA Biotechnology Laboratory.)

specialized equipment to take advantage of the latest developments in the theory of electrical circuits.

If artificial limbs of the future owe anything to space research, the debt is likely to be repaid in another aspect of sensory motor control. In space flights, certain maneuvers (such as reentry into the atmosphere) subject the astronaut to heavy acceleration forces that increase the effective weight of his arms to many times the normal value precisely at the time when manual control of the vehicle might be most desirable. A method has been devised by which EMG muscle signals (the same as those now being used in artificial limbs) are utilized in connection with the astronaut's arms. A special arm brace is operated by an electromechanical control system (servomechanism) that is in turn commanded by electrical signals from selected arm and hand muscles. The brace is thus capable of carrying out specific movements actuated by the astronaut's arm, with full force and more, uninhibited by the apparent increase in weight.

Another problem that is being solved with the help of engineers is *control of the human environment* in manned space vehicles or moon bases. Among the approaches being investigated is a method of utilizing aerobic bacteria; in this method the physiological wastes of the

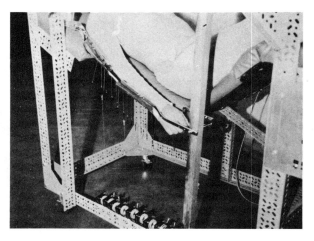

Figure 2   Hand brace comprising a nylon sleeve and
restraining cables is used in amplifying muscle signals. (From UCLA Biotechnology Laboratory.)

occupants are decomposed and then combined with the carbon dioxide
produced by breathing, plus additional nitrogen, to grow a culture of
algae, which provide fresh food and oxygen for breathing. Condensate
from the atmosphere provides drinking water. The entire cycle must be
carefully balanced in regard to waste treatment, gas exchange, food
growth, and water production—just the sort of problem that has concerned sanitary engineers for years, in connection with such prosaic
tasks as the design of septic tanks!

The new field of *human factors engineering* is another area of growing activity for professionally trained engineers. Here the aim is to
combine the capabilities of a human operator and the performance
characteristics of a machine component into a man-machine *system*
that utilizes both for most efficient overall performance. Such work
goes back to the pioneering time-motion studies of F. W. Taylor and
of F. B. Gilbreth (the father in "Cheaper by the Dozen"), who were
mainly concerned with selecting and training personnel to operate
existing machines. Gradually, as machines became more complex and
numerous, making the employment of large numbers of specially
trained operators necessary, psychologists were asked to help through
their knowledge of human behavior and human reactions to special
environments. At first the main objective was to improve the machines

at their point of contact with the operator. Much effort went into designing better handles, knobs, meters, and control panels. Here again, the need for engineers capable of such design work has continued to grow. As an example, the instrument panel of the present-day supersonic aircraft is far from satisfactory in view of the tremendous amount of information that must be received and acted upon (under rapidly changing conditions) in the pilot's mind if he is to avoid disaster; some form of an integrated display system is clearly desirable.

But an even greater task awaits the engineer who can go a step further to design such procedures into the machine from the start in order to ensure that the best man-machine system results. Here the problem is not so much to decide which of the two (man or machine) is to fulfill a certain function, but rather what combination of the two will result in best performance, what information (and in what form) is to be displayed to the operator, and how he is to go about interacting with the machine. The human factors engineer must be willing to cooperate with the psychologist and even be prepared to assume some of his functions at times.

Operations research is another branch of modern technology that is beginning to play an increasingly important part in bioengineering. Operations research is a scientific approach to providing decision makers with numerical data on which decisions may be based. The technique received its first big test in Britain during the war of 1939 to 1945, when civilians with technical training were asked to determine how the newly developed tool of radar should be best employed to make military operations involving its use most effective (e.g., density of installations, frequency and strength of air attacks, bombing accuracy required to disable various objectives, etc.). The method has since been widely employed in such nonmilitary fields as control of business inventories and organization of large-scale construction projects (see Chap. 9). But it is in fields touching on bioengineering that operations research finds some of its most interesting applications.

As an example, consider the management problems facing the administrators of private hospitals in the United States. During the 1950s, the amount of labor hours per patient-day in short-term voluntary hospitals increased by 50 percent. Over the same period, labor per unit of output in American industry decreased by 20 percent. Actually, the disparity is not as great as it seems to be. Many hospital functions cannot be automated as readily as industrial operations; moreover, most medical men would argue that the value of services received per day of hospitalization has increased, as evidenced by shorter hospital stays and convalescence periods (i.e., less time away from gainful employ-

Figure 3   Integrated display (*top*) showing "highway in the sky" and other moving elements, all presented on a picture tube that would replace conventional aircraft instrument panel (*bottom*) in blind flying. (From Kaiser Aerospace and Electronic Corporation.)

ment). But there is no doubt that a case can be made for increased participation of engineers in solving the problems of hospital administration and particularly in reducing costs through the application of such modern engineering tools as statistical analysis (with the help of computers), industrial management, and operations research—to say nothing of the conventional engineering skills involved in designing hospitals and evolving building codes.

The acceptance of the engineers' recommendations by medical men may present a problem. In the past, administrators of health services have been slow to grasp just what it is that the engineer has to offer in the way of skills such as operations research and industrial engineering. The attitudes of engineers may be in turn partly responsible for this lack of understanding. This gap may not be wholly bridged until a new type of engineer—the engineer of tomorrow—becomes available. That such a bridge can be built is evident from the acceptance that the sanitary engineer has earned among his colleagues in the life sciences in the past, and from the increasing respect elicited by the work of another type of engineer—the designer of medical instruments.

Applications of engineering tools to medicine have a distinguished history that extends from the simple surgical tools of antiquity to the manometer used for measuring blood pressure, as well as other mechanical diagnostic devices. The development of electrical techniques (X-ray diagnosis, electrocardiography, short-wave therapy, recording of EEG "brain waves") has likewise had a significant influence on medicine. This field has acquired even greater importance as a result of the many advances made relatively recently in electronics, which have led to the creation of an entire new branch of engineering.

This branch of bioengineering, most generally designated *biomedical electronics,* has come to number thousands of engineers among its practitioners. In the United States alone, at least three journals are currently devoted to the field (*IEEE Transactions on Biomedical Electronics, The American Journal of Medical Electronics,* and the international *Medical Electronics & Biological Engineering*), with distinguished counterparts being published in Britain, Germany, Japan, the U.S.S.R., and other countries. The field is by no means restricted to medical instrumentation, as we shall see, but let us consider that part of it first.

Keeping track of physiological functions has been made easier and more reliable as a result of advances in electronics. Amplification of weak signals, their display in readily accessible form, and their recording all benefit considerably from electronic techniques. But clinical applications of electronics go far beyond monitoring. Such engineering methods have found their way into therapeutics, diagnostics, and the replacement or stimulation of physiological processes. Instrument design for medical purposes is a vast and rewarding new field whose possibilities have been scarcely tapped. A few examples will serve to illustrate the potentials of this exciting branch of engineering.

In the field of *therapy*, high-frequency electronic oscillators can bring heat to deep-seated tissues, since the radiation produced by such oscillators penetrates well below the skin to bring relief to painful joints and other tissues. The physician in effect employs a miniature radar transmitter that is small enough to be installed in his consulting room and which, when directed toward the affected portion of the patient's body, produces heat in adjacent tissue in easily calibrated doses. (The same technique has come to be used in rapid and penetrating heating of food—the "radar" range or oven—which promises to give rise to an entire industry based on this new branch of food technology.)

Among *diagnostic* electronic aids, image intensifiers have attracted much attention in recent years. Much has been written about the dangers of prolonged exposure to X rays. If the length or intensity of irradiation necessary for a thorough examination could be decreased, the patient would benefit; if a more detailed picture could be obtained from a given exposure, the diagnosis could be based on more information. Both goals can be partially accomplished by an electronic image intensifier, a device similar to a television picture tube but capable of amplifying the intensity of an image to the point of turning a barely distinguishable picture into one that is clearly visible and shows good contrast.

Another diagnostic technique that depends on electronics uses acoustic waves at ultrasonic frequencies (above the audible range) for mapping irregularities in soft tissues. This method is derived in part from sonar, the acoustic counterpart of radar that is used to locate submerged objects (such as submarines). The portion of the body to be explored is submerged in a water tank or placed in contact with a thin membrane that serves as one wall of the tank. A device for changing electrical oscillations at ultrasonic frequencies into pressure variations (a transducer) is also submerged and caused to move in a systematic pattern about the region under investigation. As the transducer moves about, the reflections are gradually mapped out on the face of a picture tube from which a two-dimensional permanent record can be made by photographic time exposure. The ultrasonic waves penetrate into tissue and yield information that could not be obtained

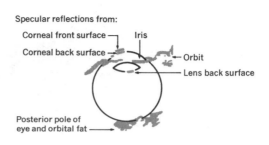

Specular reflections from:

Corneal front surface ─┐   Iris

Corneal back surface ─

Orbit

Lens back surface

Posterior pole of
eye and orbital fat ──→

Figure 4   Ultrasonic image of living human eye (*left*) compared with schematic representation (*right*). Cornea is less than 1 millimeter thick. (From Dr. R. S. Mackay, University of California, Berkeley.)

by X rays, which show contrasts only between bone and soft tissue but not between various types of tissue. Ultrasonics provides a means of differentiating healthy tissue from tumors and other irregularities and, moreover, pinpointing them with an accuracy that serves to make this branch of electronics an important diagnostic tool.

Our final example of electronic devices used for diagnostic purposes is a sensitive pressure-measuring instrument used in detecting glaucoma. This disease, which is responsible for a substantial portion of cases leading to blindness, manifests itself principally through a gradual and otherwise imperceptible increase in pressure of the eyeball liquid. Even small deviations from the norm can be detected electronically by a tiny pressure transducer placed briefly and painlessly against the eyeball, making early diagnosis much more feasible and thus considerably improving the chances of arresting the disease before irreversible blindness occurs.

As an example of *enhancing physiological response* by electronic means, consider the hearing aid. In its evolution from the ear trumpet, through relatively bulky microphonic devices operated by vacuum tubes powered by unwieldy batteries, to the modern miniature unit depending on tiny transistors, the hearing aid has closely followed the corresponding engineering developments. It was the first device to make full use of the newly invented transistor to replace the much less convenient vacuum tube—long before such "transistorization" took place in the fields of radio, instrumentation, or electronic computers. Perhaps the economic factors were particularly favorable; perhaps the manufacturers of hearing aids seized upon the advantages offered by

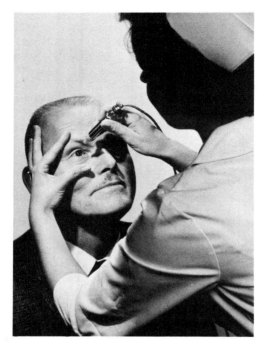

Figure 5   Marg-Mackay tonometer used in diagnosing glaucoma. The same principle has been used for measuring abdominal and blood pressures. (From University of California Optometry Department.)

a new engineering development in a particularly imaginative manner. Whatever the reason, the fact remains that the design of hearing aids small enough so that microphone, amplifier, battery, and volume control—the entire set except for the earpiece—can fit into the stem of eyeglasses is a splendid engineering achievement. One can hope to see it duplicated in as yet unexplored branches of biomedical electronics.

Vast as are the possibilities of clinical applications of engineering, they are no greater than those of *research applications*. To many engineers, notably to those in university and other research laboratories, this is certainly the most exciting branch of bioengineering.

We noted above that the systematic cooperation of the physical and life sciences is, by and large, relatively recent. Biochemistry is well established as a science in its own right today, yet the active cooperation of biology and chemistry that led to the emergence of biochemistry as a separate discipline came about comparatively recently. The establishment of another "boundary" field, biophysics, is an even more recent process, one that is in a sense still under way. Bioengineering is the youngest of them all, scarcely as yet out of its swaddling clothes. In each of these disciplines, the most telling contributions that the physical sciences have made and are making do not fall into the category of "gadgets," although we have seen how important new instruments and measurement techniques can be to fields such as medicine. Much more important in the long run are the new insights that the physical sciences provide in leading to a greater understanding of the fundamental problems of the life sciences.

The tremendous advantage to be gained from doing away with rigid barriers between the several fields involved are very well illustrated by a branch of science called molecular biology—the application of the physicist's and chemist's methods to biology on a molecular level. Most research workers in this field would agree that the rapid advances that have characterized it during the past decade were made possible precisely by removing all interdisciplinary barriers. And if this approach has proved to be so fruitful in molecular biology, a field concerned with the study of biological components, what might not be accomplished in this way in the broader subjects of biology, and also in related fields such as physiology, clinical medicine, agriculture, ecology, psychology and other behavioral sciences, and even the social sciences!

The engineering profession is fully conscious of its responsibilities in this regard. The research committee of the Engineers Joint Council has thoroughly studied the subject. In a 1962 report, "Engineering in Medicine," the investigating subcommittee headed by Allen Latham stated:

These broader subjects involve complex biological systems and are perhaps even more in need of the contribution of the physical sciences. . . . It is erroneous to assume that engineering's total contribution to the biomedical sciences will be instrumentation and that nothing more is either needed or available. Certainly instrumentation is of vital importance and the most obvious needs of the moment are in this area. But much of engineering's future contribution will be through the application of its ways of thinking as well as its instrumentation. Systems analysis, servomechanism theory, and simulation are several of the recently developed techniques of great potential in biomedical research. At this level the engineer may assume a dominant role in research provided he also has appropriate biomedical competence.

This theme, that engineering has much more than instrumentation to offer to the life sciences, is echoed by John S. Gray, Northwestern University physiologist. In a two-part article in *Science* [1] he says, "The physiologist can learn from engineering an enormous amount of pure physiology that he cannot learn from any other source."

What Professor Gray has in mind is the fact that the step which takes the investigator from understanding the characteristics of components to understanding how a system made up of those components functions—one of the principal goals of physiology—is being studied in a field traditionally unrelated to physiology, namely engineering. The analysis and synthesis of systems, that is, organized arrangements of interacting components, have been carried further in engineering than in any other endeavor. In that growing body of knowledge known as system theory, engineers are assembling information on the principles of designing and interconnecting devices that respond to input signals, adapt themselves to new conditions, and generally exhibit a type of controlled behavior that has been associated until now only with living systems. "The accompanying theory and methodology," concludes Gray, "are precisely those that physiologists have long been seeking as guidelines to the synthetic phase of their own science."

An interesting corollary is the possibility that a student trained in engineering may rather easily shift altogether to one of the life sciences, say, physiology, in his advanced training. In physics, mathematics, and system science he would be much better prepared than his fellow physiologists; his principal deficiencies would be in biology and organic chemistry. At some universities, engineering undergraduates are already permitted to take these subjects as additional electives so that they are fully prepared for graduate work in biomedicine—the only approach, Gray thinks, to the study of living systems.

The possibility of contributing to discoveries in the life sciences that might not have been made in any other way is one of the most exciting aspects of biomedical engineering. As an example, Dr. H. P. Schwan at the Moore School of Electrical Engineering of the University of Pennsylvania has been able to deduce new information about the structure of cells, bacteria, and subcellular structures purely

---

[1] Richard W. Jones and John S. Gray, System Theory and Physiological Processes, *Science*, vol. 140, pp. 461–466, May, 1963.

from electrical measurements by means of reasoning familiar to the electrical engineer. He measured properties such as dielectric constant and conductivity as functions of frequency over many octaves, for water, electrolytes, proteins, and cell suspensions. From these measurements he was able to synthesize additional data such as electric polarization at interfaces, the effect of inhomogeneous structure on charge distribution, and the orientation of polar molecules. Finally, by analogy with simple electric networks, he was able to deduce (from the frequency dependence of suspensions of red blood cells, bacteria, and other small organisms) the dielectric constants and conductivities of the cell interior and cell exterior, as well as the capacitance of the cell membrane. This was basic biological information of considerable importance, since the cell membrane serves not only to contain the cell interior but also to control the exchange of matter between interior and exterior. Moreover, Schwan and his associates were able to show that the electrical conductivity of whole blood is (over a considerable range) simply related to the red-cell count, a relationship that has led to the development of a simplified, portable instrument for establishing the blood count by measuring conductivity. In this instance a simple, well-established engineering technique, the measurement of electric properties, has led not only to new biological data of a fundamental nature but also to an unexpected "dividend" in the form of an instrument directly applicable in the laboratory and in clinical medicine.

Such practical benefits of research concerned with fundamentals are more common than one may suppose and are not always fortuitous, but may be deliberately sought. For instance, visual information perceived by the eye reaches the brain and evokes small potentials in a part of the brain called the cortex. These potentials can be measured by means of fine wires attached to the cortex. It is not inconceivable that someone may discover a method of reversing the procedure, of introducing potentials in the cortex so ordered that a visual pattern may be evoked in the brain of a blind person. Science fiction? Perhaps so today, but who is to say that future advances in the design of microelectrodes, in that branch of information theory concerned with pattern recognition, and in our understanding of the functioning of the brain might not combine tomorrow to bring about the ultimate solution to the problem of electronic aids to the blind?

The method of representing biological functions by analogues taken from the physical sciences, such as the representation of the bulk electrical properties of blood by an equivalent electrical circuit in the case described above, is called modeling, or more often *mathematical modeling*, since it is often unnecessary to construct an actual model (such as an analogue computer); knowledge of the mathematical properties of the model is sometimes sufficient for solving the problem. To be effective, a mathematical model must be capable of more than simply matching the experimental results obtained with the actual system—so-called "curve fitting." In addition, the functional relationships among the quantities observed experimentally should be reproduced by the equations connecting the mathematical functions and variables that make up the model. In an ideal model, every experimental function would have an exact mathematical counterpart whose functional behavior would also reproduce that of the prototype. The difficulties of approaching this ideal state are formidable. Even greater are the problems of trying to construct the model physically. At present, we have not even established which engineering components correspond in properties and behavior to which physiological functions. Indeed, we may sometimes have to postulate certain characteristics and then try to invent a technological device that possesses them before an actual model can be constructed. Even after much more is known about such correspondence in component functions, we must still tackle the problems of just which variables should be considered (those that are most easily measured? or those that are most reliably modeled?) and how they might be best combined in a network or system. The application of system analysis to biological processes promises to become one of the most challenging and rewarding fields of engineering.

The flow of information from engineering to the life sciences need not be by any means in one direction only. Nature is a very good designer, with the evolutionary process ensuring survival of the best design. When studying the structure of human bones in connection with helping to develop improved surgical procedures, for instance, engineers were surprised to find that the cross section of certain bones represented the optimum design for the materials and functional requirements under consideration—a finding that has already come to influence structural engineering.

Once again, the greatest advances in this direction have been made in electronics. The method of applying knowledge obtained by investigators in the life sciences to electronics has been christened *bionics*. This field has successfully weathered its early difficulties, largely founded on such naïve assumptions as the comparison of the brain to a telephone exchange or a digital computer—"probably as misleading an analogy as can be imagined," says Professor Jones in the article cited previously.[2] The signals are transmitted in discrete bits, as

---

[2] *Ibid.*

in a computer, but he considers 'it highly probable that the information processing of these pulsed signals within the terminal elements (neurons) is of a continuous nature; it is unlikely that neurons can be described simply as relays or switch-type elements. But might not the very way in which the physiological system differs from the admittedly primitive system devised by technology lead to new ideas for the technologist? By imitating nature, the engineer of the future may be able to design computers on principles as radically different from present-day computers as the latter differ from the abacus.

We have tried to indicate only some of the ways in which bioengineering may lead to improved devices in medicine and the allied fields, to the exploitation of novel techniques, concepts, and attitudes in fundamental investigations in all life sciences, and to a reversal of the flow of information—now from the life sciences toward engineering. We have given concrete examples of the sort of contributions that bioengineering has made and may be expected to make in the future—but they have been no more than examples. As we stated at the outset, we cannot even enumerate all the facets of bioengineering that exist already, to say nothing of the more speculative branches of the subject. (For instance, we have not even mentioned the tremendous impact that the high-speed digital computer described in Chap. 5 is likely to have on the collection, storage, and retrieval of medical data, and possibly on medical diagnosis by near-automatic means.) But we hope that we have said enough to outline the huge potentialities of the field and to have shown that a young person entering it can very well resolve the problem of serving two masters—engineering and the life sciences.

7

The Engineering of Large Structures

by Leonardo Zeevaert

Leonardo Zeevaert was born in Veracruz, Mexico, and received his degree of Civil Engineer from the Universidad Nacional de Mexico in 1939. He then received the M.S. degree from the Massachusetts Institute of Technology and the Ph.D. degree in Civil Engineering from the University of Illinois. At Illinois he was appointed Visiting Research Associate in Structural Engineering, Lecturer, and Special Research Fellow in Civil Engineering.

Dr. Zeevaert has been Professor of Soil Mechanics and Foundation Engineering at the Universidad Nacional Autonoma de Mexico since 1941. He has written about fifty papers on soil mechanics, foundation engineering, and structures, and has given lectures on these subjects throughout the world. In applying his knowledge, he has worked as consulting engineer for the government of Mexico and for many private firms. His investigations on harbors, airport runways, and dams, and the designs of many buildings, including the important 44-story Torre Latino Americana, are characterized by their combination of theory, practical knowledge, ingenuity, and architectural esthetics. Golf and photography are among his recreational activities, but his favorite hobby is model construction.

INTRODUCTION

The structural engineer plays a major role in the design and construction of large, land-based structures such as office buildings, theaters, hospitals, bridges, dams, harbor works, tunnels, and similar projects. Typically, he was educated as a civil engineer, and in his professional practice he has specialized in the design of structures.

In other chapters of this volume the reader will find a discussion of the successive stages in the realization of an engineering project. It is pointed out that delineation of the objectives of engineering works is influenced by many considerations other than strictly engineering principles; social, political, financial, and other factors come into play. This situation is particularly true of structural engineering, which characteristically deals with projects that serve people either directly or through a public service. In the planning and design of structures which serve people directly—for example, buildings, theaters, hospitals —the structural engineer usually collaborates with an architect; he must design the structural framework to be compatible with the functional and aesthetic concept which the architect has created. In other structural projects, the functional objectives of the design are usually formulated in collaboration with other engineering specialists; for example, in the design of a dam, the height, spillway capacity, penstock size and location, and other operational specifications will be developed through collaboration between the structural engineer and the specialists in power, irrigation, flood control, or whatever use the dam will serve. In the background of these studies of functional objectives, there are always questions of cost and financing which the structural engineer must resolve with the sponsors of the project before his work can proceed.

The structural engineer has much to learn from nature, specifically the observation that "for a well-formed and beautiful body, there must be a well-formed skeleton." Just as the skeleton is the basis for a well-formed body, so the underlying structure is the essential basis for an exceptional architectural project. One may carry the analogy even further to the processes of nature which have equipped each living being with the means of defending itself against the elements and the environment it lives in.

The flight of birds taught men how to construct and shape structures with which to fly, and without this concept of structure in form and strength, aeronautics could not have progressed. Physics, applied in its full scope and supported by the powerful tool of mathematics, provided solutions to the difficult problems of flight and led, in the short span of two generations, to the modern airplane. This objective, manned flight, was difficult to the point of being barely possible, and the consequences were a matter of life and death; skillful application of the laws of nature produced a result which is both effective and a thing of beauty. By contrast, structures on the surface of the earth do not pose such severe problems of safety and economy as does the airplane and they have not, in general, been studied as thoroughly, with the result that they contain many faults of economy, function, and sometimes strength. Frequently, architectural design and structural engineering have become merely the art of applying handbook procedures and outdated building regulations. Handbooks, specifications, and "rules of thumb" have their place in routine work, but such work is properly left to technicians. The professional structural engineer should be concerned with the effective and economical design of a structure which is compatible with the environment, the functional requirements, and the architectural concept.

Just as the mature design of the airplane is a thing of beauty and external simplicity, resembling the natural form of birds, so also architectural designs, which are both simple and effective, have an innate beauty. How simple were the old Spanish colonial architecture and structural design, and how much they are still appreciated in our time! Arches, vaults, and buttresses may be seen and understood by students who are not yet fully acquainted with statics because they can visualize the line of action of the forces involved. Even laymen, without technical knowledge but with common sense, see in such structures explicitly the natural action of gravity, and it is this appreciation which makes the design seem beautiful. Modern designs of thin shells, made possible by newer materials and by the more complete awareness of the forces involved, demonstrate again that simplicity is the best tool of design. However, there are also structures which conceal the action of gravity forces by employing hidden members to gain strength and stability, and this disguise seems untruthful to the expert and inexplicable to the layman.

There have been many instances in which the architectural design has been completely divorced from consideration of the supporting structure. Furthermore, each structure exists in a specific environment which must be considered in the design, but this circumstance is sometimes ignored; for example, a type of structure found suitable for cold-weather regions may be designed for the tropics; the same structural solution may be applied in earthquake areas as in regions where high winds are the dominant environmental factor; the same practical rules for foundation may be applied to many locations around the globe regardless of subsoil conditions. Intuitively, it seems evident that the structure, from its foundation to its roof, should look different if it is located on firm foundations in a region of mild winds and weather than if it is in a region of soft foundations subject to earthquakes or to extremes of weather. Despite this obvious fact, structural types compatible with the environment of one region are sometimes applied in totally different environments.

The structural engineer must develop the ingenuity and skill to choose the type of structure best suited to both the functional requirements and the architectural concept and to meet, concurrently, the requirements both of lowest possible cost and of resistance to the environment of weather, wind, earthquakes, and foundation conditions. Another consideration is that the functions which structures serve imply a useful life. Some are built to endure for centuries; others have a limited useful probable life determined by economic and social factors. The architect and the engineer must predict the useful life and potential value of the structure, and these considerations must be reflected in their designs.

Materials—steel, concrete, stone, timber, aluminum, and plastics—are the media in which the structural engineer embodies his design. Cost, quality, and availability are different in different countries, and even in different parts of the same country, and the structural engineer must be well acquainted with the technology of the materials available to him if he is to obtain the best solution at the lowest cost. The properties related directly to strength and deformation are those primarily involved, but other properties may prove to be limiting in the final selection of a design: the effects of aging, internal damping, vibration, heat release in large concrete structures, and so forth. One cannot emphasize too strongly the importance to structural engineers of a sound knowledge of the technology and the economy of materials.

Specialization within the professions is a consequence both of the expansion of knowledge and of the wide range of applications to which this knowledge may be applied. Within structural engineering one finds further specialization such as steel structural engineering, concrete structural engineering, and even timber structural engineering with each area specializing in the application of its respective materials. It is true that the combination of cost, availability, and functional requirements emphasizes the use of one material in preference to others in certain localities at certain times, and specialization to this degree may be the consequence of circumstances which the engineer himself cannot control. However, engineers who specialize to this extent tend to apply their specialty to all structural projects and so to deny their client the benefits of a broad analysis of the feasibility and economy of all materials potentially applicable. An analogous situation exists in the practice of medicine, where specialization has proceeded to a point such that the layman frequently does not know which specialist to consult; in an earlier day, the general practitioner met this need for overall diagnosis, but his place is being taken nowadays by the specialist in internal medicine. So also the client, public or private, who desires a structure to meet some functional requirements—bridge, dam, hospital, or other specific use—should have the advice of engineers with the knowledge and experience to diagnose this need and to choose from among many possibilities the type of structure most compatible with the requirements at the lowest cost. Following this major decision, the talents of structural engineering specialist can be applied effectively.

Pursuing the matter of specialization a little farther, almost any structure, however large or complicated, might be built in either steel or concrete, but it is also true that, in a specific location at a certain point in time, one of these materials will prove superior to the others in effectiveness or cost, or both, in meeting specific requirements. The client is not an expert, although he may have a preference, and he must look to the engineer and the architect for sound advice on the choice. Poor subsoil conditions may limit the foundation design to such a degree as to impose severe restrictions on the design of the superstructure, a circumstance which may not be ignored except at the risk of severe settlement or failure of the structure.

These general statements about engineering need clarification. For this purpose, the author will draw upon examples from his own professional practice for which the full history is readily available, from first concept to the structure in place. In these examples, much detail which might be of interest to practicing structural engineers will be omitted in order to present a broad overview of the nature of the functional and structural problem, the basis for selecting the structural type used, the scientific and mathematical aspects of the design analysis, and the comparison of predicted and observed physical characteristics of the structure.

SOIL MECHANICS AND THE FOUNDATIONS OF STRUCTURES

Each major structure is unique because it must be designed to be compatible with an environment peculiar to itself; the major factor in this environment is the foundation upon which it rests. Judgment based on experience with foundations in local geographical areas dominated the art of foundation design until about 1925, when scientific methods began to be applied to foundation materials. This field of study, known as soil mechanics, has in the intervening years yielded methods of analysis and techniques of measurement which have greatly benefited the practice of structural and foundation engineering.

In 1925, Professor Karl Terzaghi published his pioneering work entitled "Erdbaumechanik," ("The Mechanics of Earth Construction") [1] which marked the emergence of this field as an applied science, a new and important branch of civil engineering. In this work, he reported numerous experiments on the technological behavior of earth materials like sand, silt, and clay, and his analysis of these experiments provided a sound basis for the study and comprehension of the hydraulic and mechanical properties of soil materials and of related stability problems. Today, the student of soil mechanics should be well versed in many aspects of mathematics, physics, and geology. Soil mechanics is important in a large percentage of civil engineering works since structures in general must be built on earth, and many of them are built in part of earth materials. In recent years, the basic concepts of soil mechanics have been applied to structural problems of rock and snow.

Soil mechanics deals with the qualitative and quantitative mechanical properties of earth materials including permeability, shearing strength, and compressibility. The knowledge and understanding of these properties enables the civil engineer to solve problems of stability and deformation of structures such as highways, dams, tunnels, and foundations. The field of soil mechanics has become a broad segment of civil engineering. It embraces subdivisions such as the technology of earth and rock materials, the engineering of foundations and underground structures, the stability of slopes, earth dams, and waterfront structures, and the stability of highways and related earth structures.

Professor Terzaghi introduced his theory of consolidation on the basis of a viscoelastic rheological flow model from which he discovered the most important theorem of soil mechanics: *Total pressure is always equal to intergranular pressure plus pore water pressure.* Therefore, to maintain a constant total pressure to support a fixed load, a change in effective or intergranular pressure must be equal and opposite to a change in pore water pressure. Another development was the application of Coulomb's shear equation (1785) to two-phase materials, like clay, which is expressed as

$$S = A + (p - u)B \tag{1}$$

Here A and B are parameters that depend on the physicochemical

[1] Karl Terzaghi, "Erdbaumechanik," Franz Deuticke, Leipzig and Vienna, 1925.

characteristics of the soil, p is the total applied pressure, and u is the pore water pressure. The theory of consolidation and the new concept of shearing strength enabled him to solve satisfactorily many problems of deformation and stability, primarily of the settlement of buildings and structures in clay beds and of the stability of slopes. Once the basic concepts of strength of materials in soils were established, soil mechanics progressed rapidly in all countries; theories were put to rigid tests, and new refinements and methods of analysis were found. However, it appears that the field is inexhaustible because more precision and better understanding of materials and field phenomena are required. This is one of the reasons why the science of soil mechanics must apply basic concepts, theories, and procedures from the allied sciences.

In designing the foundation of structures, it is important to know two mechanical properties: (1) the compressibility and (2) the shearing strength of the foundation materials, one of which may be predominant at certain locations. In a foundation material with low compressibility, i.e., alluvial deposits containing gravel, sand, and silt, the design usually is based on the ultimate shearing strength. However, in high-compressible materials, i.e., lake sediments, clayey silt, and silty clays, the foundation design usually considers settlement of primary importance. The differential settlements between columns of a building must be compatible with the rigidity designed into the foundation structure and the structural frame, or serious damage may be expected. Therefore, in highly compressible materials it is important to investigate the compressibility properties of the soil. Large deformations may be expected even for low shearing stresses.

The construction of foundations usually requires excavations. In some instances, foundations must be at considerable depth below the surface and may require large areas for one or two basement levels; in these cases, serious problems arise, such as stability of the slopes of the excavation, heave of the bottom, and lateral contractions. These problems must be given special consideration. Sensitive clay soils may be altered during construction if preventive measures are not taken; sometimes the construction must be made in steps or by substitution; that is to say, the weight of the soil excavated must be replaced in steps with the same weight of foundation, construction, and superstructure. This procedure is known as a *compensated foundation*. In case of poor soils, piles or piers must be used to transfer the load to deeper and more resistant soil strata and these piles may be designed either as point-bearing or as friction piles. The author has found, in Mexico City's high-compressible soils, that the combination of friction piles and deep compensated foundations for large and heavy buildings gives very satisfactory results. In places, the ground has subsided because water has been pumped from the underlying strata, and buildings resting on point-bearing piles have emerged from the ground surface, creating serious problems for public utilities and adjacent structures (Figs. 1 and 2).

As an example of the type of analysis made by engineers, consider the problems of designing a foundation using friction piles. Compensated foundations with friction piles reduce the long-term settlements due to "creep," or plastic-viscous behavior taking place in the soil under sustained load (Fig. 3). Consider that a clay layer of thickness h and compressibility m_v experiences deformation under pressure p according to the relationship

$$S = m_v p h \qquad (2)$$

Figure 1   Subsidence of ground surface below acqueduct on piles.

Assume that the same layer is pierced with piles equally distributed and the same pressure is applied. The piles will then reduce compression of the soil because the friction between soil and piles, limited by the shearing strength of the soil, will be applied entirely along the pile shaft to a certain depth Z_0, and the pressure applied to the soil will be absorbed in part by the piles. If a is the tributary area to each pile, then

$$pa = c\bar{\omega}sz \tag{3}$$

represents the load taken by one pile. Thus

$$Z_0 = \frac{pa}{c\bar{\omega}s} \tag{4}$$

where $\bar{\omega}$ = perimeter of the pile

s = shearing strength of the soil

c = coefficient, a function of the potential surface of sliding along the pile shaft

Figure 2   Hotel Plaza, heavy steel structure on piles with resulting subsidence of adjacent ground.

Therefore, the load placed on the soil will be transferred to the piles gradually and approximately linearly from the boundary surfaces to a distance Z_0, and the clay layer will compress only in the amount

$$S = m_v pz \tag{5}$$

Therefore, the compression of the clay strata will be reduced to Z_0/h times that of the case without friction piles.

Large earthquakes occur in Mexico City and in other major cities of the world. In Mexico City, strong earthquakes have been measured accurately by means of strong ground-motion seismometers, capable of recording these intense but infrequent disturbances, and the measurements have provided data for comparison with the results of theoretical analysis. The analysis of seismic waves is an example of the application of physics and mathematics to practical engineering problems with results which show good agreement between theory and observation. However, the full mathematical and physical treatment of the problem is beyond the proper scope of this chapter. In the case of Mexico City, the author discovered that the seismic waves having the greatest effect on structures are shear waves traveling from deep-seated compact, rigid sediments and basal rock into the soft-clay lake

Figure 3   Compressibility reduction due to friction on piles.

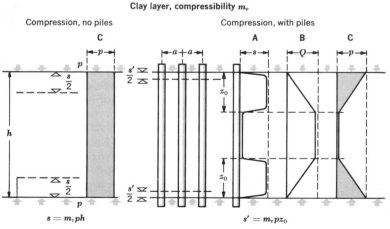

A Ultimate shearing stress along pile shaft, s
B Load on friction pile, Q
C Vertical effective pressure in soil, p

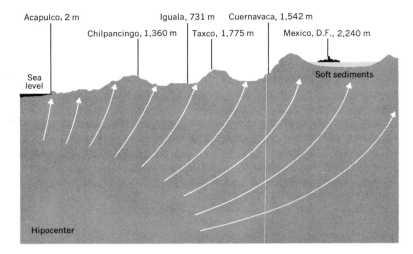

Figure 4   Cross section, Acapulco to Mexico City.

deposits (Fig. 4). The soil response is nearly elastic to this phenomenon. When the soil is saturated with water it may be considered in-
compressible during vibration; therefore the only important waves are
shear waves, as previously mentioned. Assume for simplicity that the
direction of shear displacements u, parallel to the x axis, is normal to the
direction of the earthquake wave propagation, as shown in Fig. 5. The
shear rate $\partial\tau/\partial z$ is equal to the inertia force $\rho\,(\partial^2 u/\partial t^2)$, that is, unit
mass multiplied by acceleration; hence

$$\frac{\partial\tau}{\partial z} = \rho\,\frac{\partial^2 u}{\partial t^2} \tag{6}$$

If μ is the shear modulus of elasticity, the shear distortion is

$$\frac{\partial u}{\partial z} = \frac{\tau}{\mu} \tag{7}$$

Therefore the equation describing the motion of the unit element becomes

$$\mu\,\frac{\partial^2 u}{\partial z^2} = \rho\,\frac{\partial^2 u}{\partial t^2} \tag{8}$$

The boundary conditions are

$u = 0$ at $z = 0$ (bottom of clay layer moves with basic layer, and

$\dfrac{\partial u}{\partial z} = 0$ at $z = h$ (surface, angular distortion zero)

The equation of motion may be integrated; if μ and ρ are assumed constant, the resonance periods of the layer are found to be

$$T_i = \frac{4h}{2i - 1} \sqrt{\frac{\rho}{\mu}} \qquad i = 1, 2, 3, \ldots \tag{9}$$

The resonance periods are in the proportion of $1 : \frac{1}{3} : \frac{1}{5}$, etc., for an elastic isotropic solid. A knowledge of the elastic properties of the clay under these conditions, i.e., the shear modulus of elasticity μ, plays a very important part in the solution of earthquake foundation problems. Knowing this mechanical property, it is possible to compute the resonance periods of the ground. Buildings should be designed in such a way as to introduce into their structures enough rigidity or flexibility to obtain periods which differ from the resonance periods of the ground.

Figure 5   Equation of movement of soil during earthquakes.

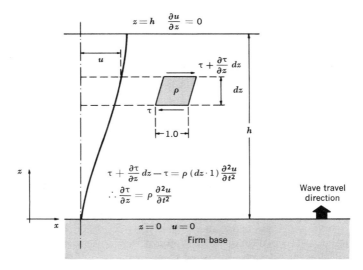

FOUNDATION PROBLEMS IN MEXICO CITY

Twenty-five years ago the behavior of Mexico City subsoil was not understood. Foundations for buildings, houses, and other structures were designed exclusively on allowable bearing values obtained empirically by past experience. The city was growing at a tremendous rate, extending outward to areas where subsoil conditions had not been explored, and heavy, tall buildings were being constructed. Large errors were made because of deviations of the actual conditions from the mean bearing values given for footings and pile foundations by the city code then in use. Many building foundations, which had been designed using this practice, settled as much as three feet, to the surprise of their designers. In most cases, these large settlements damaged adjacent buildings and public utilities beyond repair.

Until recent years, water was pumped for domestic and industrial use from pervious strata underlying the city at rates which reduced the piezometric water levels and also created a ground surface subsidence. This relationship between water extraction and land subsidence was not understood until recently. The largest surface settlement took place during the years 1949 to 1950 and amounted to about 14 in. per year with respect to a firm sand and gravel stratum encountered at a depth of 148 ft. The settlement of the ground surface became critical during those years, when intensive damage occurred to public utilities (Fig. 1) and to buildings mainly adjacent to pile foundations (Fig. 2). The photographs shown give an idea of the intensity of the problems created by this settlement. The city authorities then prohibited water extraction within the city limits, and the rate of subsidence was reduced gradually after the regulation became effective; at present, the settlement in the center of the city is less than about one-third of the maximum observed in 1950.

Mexico City is located about 160 miles from an active seismic area. The epicenters of destructive earthquakes are located south of Mexico City on the Pacific coast of the state of Guerrero. As in the case of foundations, the design of buildings with regard to seismic forces followed a city code based on empirical experience, and the defects of its regulations became apparent as the city expanded into new areas and as the new buildings constructed were of greater height and mass.

The rational structural design of buildings employing a dynamic theory of design began in Mexico City in 1948 to 1949 with the design and construction of the Latin American Tower, a 44-story office building that passed unharmed through the strong earthquake of July,

1957, described later in this chapter. It was not until May, 1962, that records were obtained in Mexico City of the strong ground motions and the behavior of the subsoil during seismic movements. These records permit a more refined understanding of the subsoil behavior under static and dynamic forces, and they will form the basis for future research to provide the structural engineer with the tools to design foundations and structures on a more rational basis than in the past. In summary: In Mexico City, the foundation and structural engineer has to overcome a very special environment of high-compressible subsoil, ground surface settlement, and severe earthquakes. All these problems must be considered concurrently in the design of a structure and its foundation; the omission of one of these phenomena may be fatal to the life behavior of a building. Many well-constructed buildings have failed because of inadequate consideration of these phenomena.

Mexico City is an unusually difficult location in regard to the design of foundations. The city is founded on a lake bed of materials of very high compressibility. The closed basin of the Valley of Mexico was formed by sedimentation of fine and ultrafine materials of volcanic origin that decomposed into clay. The clay containing the mineral montmorillonite has developed a high bond between the grains, permitting water contents as high as 400 percent by weight with respect to that of solid matter; that is to say, in volume proportions, ten volumes of water are held by one volume of dry solids. To anyone not acquainted with this clay, such a material would be considered as a suspension in which the soil grains could only float; however, the strong bonds between the montmorillonite grains make this material a solid, but one with most unusual properties.

The general geological profile under the city (Fig. 6) shows two highly compressible typical volcanic silty clay layers. In the center of the city at a depth of 115 ft and with a thickness of 15 ft, there is a sand stratum in a semicompact state, known as the first hard layer. Most of the buildings are supported on this layer on point-bearing piles. At a depth of 148 ft there is a second sand stratum. Below this depth, the materials are of low compressibility and are not important in foundation problems because the overlying deposits are the ones responsible for the behavior of foundations and for the distortions of the ground surface as a result of water pumping from deeper water-bearing strata.

The seismometers used in Mexico City to register strong motions during earthquakes generate accelerograms such as that shown in Fig. 7, recorded in Mexico City in May, 1962, during a strong earthquake. The accelerogram records instantaneous accelerations. The response of a structure to the earthquake motion depends on the time of duration

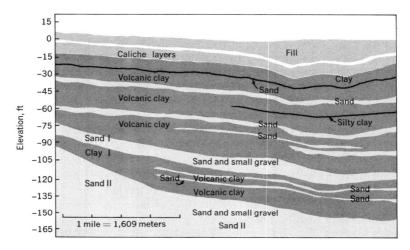

Figure 6   Geological profile beneath Mexico City.

of the earthquake. Therefore, an acceleration-time history such as that
in Fig. 7 does not represent the total response of the structure, except
when its period of vibration is considerably smaller than the dominant
periods of vibration of the ground so that the structure moves with
the ground. The response of a single degree of freedom structure, or

Figure 7   Accelerogram, May, 1962.

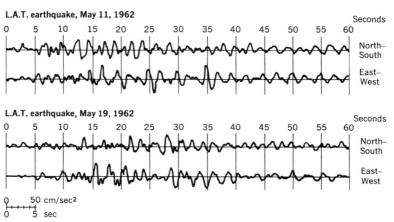

its equivalent, to the earthquake motion may be computed using the response equation

$$R_s = \left[\int_0^t a(\tau) e^{-\lambda \omega_i (t-\tau)} \sin \omega_d (t - \tau) \, d\tau \right]_{max} \quad (10)$$

Here $a(\tau)$ is the acceleration recorded as shown in Fig. 7, at time τ measured from the start of the earthquake; ω_i is the natural frequency of the structure; ω_d is the frequency taking into consideration the damping factor of the structure represented by λ, and t is the integration time at which the response becomes a maximum. In order to integrate the above equation, it is necessary to use a digital computer. Figure 8 shows the response spectrum, also called pseudovelocity spectrum, corresponding to the accelerogram shown in Fig. 7. The integration of Eq. (10) was performed at the seismological laboratory of the California Institute of Technology. If the response or pseudovelocity spectrum R_s is multiplied by the frequency ω, one obtains the acceleration response R_a or pseudoacceleration spectrum shown in Figure 9. The spectrum shown corresponds to the central part of Mexico City. The pseudoacceleration spectrum shows the well-defined resonance periods of the ground for $T = 2.63$ sec for the first resonance period, and .9 sec for the second resonance period. The resonance periods for the first and second modes of vibration of the subsoil are in the proportion three to one, which conforms with the conclusions previously mentioned concerning the behavior of the subsoil under pure shear waves.

Figure 8   Pseudovelocity spectrum, Latin American Tower, May 11, 1962, N 81° W.

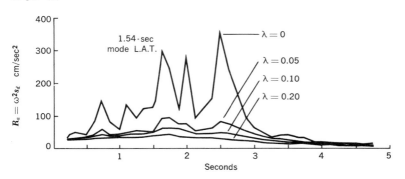

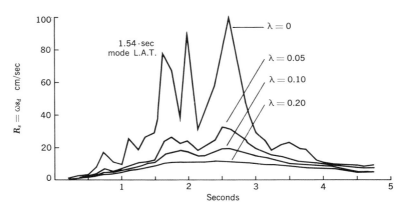

Figure 9   Pseudoacceleration spectrum, Latin American Tower, May 11, 1962 N, 81° W.

The response spectra are of great value in seismic engineering because, if the period of a structure is known, its response may be obtained as a basic value for design; with a knowledge of different modes of vibration of the structure, the response for each one of them may be obtained. With these values, a dynamical analysis of the structure can be made and the structure can be designed for the most probable seismic forces acting at the site in question.

EXAMPLES OF STRUCTURAL DESIGN

To show how structural and foundation engineering practices are related to environmental conditions at certain locations, some examples of structural design have been selected from the author's professional practice in Mexico City. In preceding paragraphs, it was shown that in the central part of Mexico City, the engineer has to overcome the following three principal natural forces: (*1*), very poor subsoil conditions, (*2*) large ground surface subsidence, and (*3*) strong earthquakes. In addition to the above environmental forces, it is necessary for the designing engineer to find the most suitable materials, whether reinforced concrete, steel, or timber, to meet the economic requirements of the project. Foundations design must give special attention to the settlement problem because of the highly compressible subsoil materials. The structural frame must be designed to withstand earthquake forces.

In Mexico City, it is sometimes necessary, for certain building projects, to reduce settlements considerably or to equalize settlements of a very heavy unit with another unit of less weight. In such cases, friction piles can be used to reduce settlement from one unit to the other and to equalize, as much as possible, the rate of settlement. This type of foundation is called a *compensated friction-pile foundation.* It has been used intensively by the author and recently by others in Mexico City. Buildings supported on point-bearing pile foundations, which rest on the first hard stratum, emerge from the ground surface when surface subsidence takes place. Because of this phenomenon, negative friction is applied to the piles, and the foundation design becomes complicated and expensive. Public utilities are damaged if they are not treated specially. Protection must be given also to adjacent buildings in order to permit large differential settlement from taking place between a building on point-bearing piles and an adjacent one on a surface foundation; this requirement increases the cost of the foundation.

In Mexico City, concrete and steel structures are competitive, and careful comparisons must be made to select the material best suited to a particular design; in general, concrete construction is less expensive than steel construction, and there is a preference for the use of concrete as the primary material. A new type of inexpensive concrete

Figure 10　Inverted dome.

Figure 11   Reinforcing steel in inverted dome.

structure was conceived to fulfill an architectural requirement that a certain building be designed without columns in its interior; furthermore, there was a requirement for economy in the design of the permanent roof to cover this area. (Figure 10 shows the solution conceived.) The structural solution for this roof was to hang an inverted dome, with the idea that forms would not be necessary for pouring concrete, thus reducing considerably the cost. A concrete ring was placed and supported by V-shaped light columns that would withstand effectively the torsion induced in the roof during earthquakes. From this outside ring the shell was freely supported (Fig. 11). The construction was made by placing cables and adjusting them at the outside ring by means of specially designed adjustment screws. Once all the cables were placed, the configuration of the steel net was adjusted and the shell was poured with lightweight concrete, using a fine wire mesh suspended on the steel net to hold the fresh concrete in place.

Next is a very typical example of structural design meeting specific architectural demands. In this particular building, steel and rein-

Figure 12   Shafts, hanging building.

Figure 13   Steel structure of hanging building.

forced concrete were used as the principal materials forming the
structure. The architectural concept of this building called for a completely free space on the ground floor; that is, no columns at the front
were allowed, and the only possible solution was to hang the floors
from the top of the building. After analyzing several designs for
economy, it was decided to construct a gigantic reinforced-concrete
frame with two shafts as columns (Fig. 12). The elevator, ducts, stair-
ways, and other services were placed in these shafts. The upper part,
as shown in Fig. 13, has two large reinforced-concrete beams, like
those in the foundation, on which the steel trusses are supported.
At the edge of the steel trusses, steel tension members are hung to
support the curtain walls of the building; the steel joists rest at one
side on the hangers and at the opposite side on the concrete shaft or
steel structures supported on the two main shafts (Fig. 14).

This structure is very light. The floors are rigidly fixed to the shaft
in the horizontal direction; therefore, during earthquakes the large

Figure 14   Steel joists of hanging building.

frame will vibrate with only one degree of freedom and the floors will move following the same movements as that of the enormous bent. The period of vibration is on the order of 1 sec. At the upper part of the building as shown in Fig. 15, inverted frames have been used. They are supported at its narrow central part between shafts in order to reduce the bending moments at the support of the frames, giving these frames a daring and unusual proportion. The building was finished and the total weight was in place before the earthquakes of May, 1962. Inspection after the earthquakes showed the building had behaved satisfactorily.

The next and most interesting example demonstrating the action of the environmental forces to be considered in structural design in Mexico City is the Latin American Tower, a 44-story office building located in the center of Mexico City, presenting a most interesting problem of design because of poor subsoil conditions, ground surface subsidence, and severe earthquakes. The Latin American Life Insurance Company, owners of the building, wished to erect a monumental structure on this site, which had been its headquarters for many years. Several designs of proposed structures up to 26 stories in height had been studied when the author was commissioned in 1949 to design the tallest structure that the foundation conditions and the

Figure 15   Upper part, inverted frames of hanging building.

Figure 16   Finished building.

earthquake forces would permit. The magnitude and novel character of the Latin American project required thorough investigation of all aspects of the design and particularly of the limitations imposed by the foundation conditions at the site and its vicinity. A knowledge of the basic causes of ground surface subsidence in the city, the precise stratigraphy at the site, and the mechanical strength and compressibility of these underlying deposits was essential; to explore the general features of the problem, sets of bench marks and piezometers (water-pressure gauges) were installed at a depth of 160 ft, resting on the second sand deposit, at 110 ft on the first hard stratum, and at 6.5 ft over a considerable area. (See the preceding sections regarding the general foundation conditions in Mexico City.) It was found that, relative to the bench mark at the 160-ft level, the surface of the ground was settling at the rate of 10.8 in. per year and the first hard stratum at the rate of 6.2 in. per year. Furthermore, it was found that the bench marks at that level were settling at the rate of 12 in. per year relative to firm ground at the edges of the valley. The relative velocity of the first and second sand stratum was 3.5 in. per year. The piezometric measurements showed that the water pressure was decreasing rapidly below the 92-ft level. Pumping from these strata, prohibited subsequently, was believed to be the cause of the pressure reduction and of the subsidence.

Detailed investigations were made at the proposed site of the Latin American Tower. Undisturbed samples were obtained between 8.2 ft and 230 ft below surface, 5-in.-diameter samples were obtained in the lacustrine clays, and 3-in.-diameter samples in the clayey sand and silt. Figure 17 shows a representative compressibility analysis of these samples, comparing them with clays from other locations. Piezometers were installed in the most pervious strata at depths of 6.5, 26, 40, 53, 69, 125, and 156 ft. The curve marked B in Fig. 18 shows the effective overburden pressure for downward water flow, computed with the piezometric pressures encountered; the curve marked A shows what the effective pressures would be in hydrostatic conditions (with all piezometers reaching the same level). Analysis of these data provided the basis for designing the foundation of the building and for the planning and design of the deep excavations.

The conclusion reached from the subsoil investigations was that the first hard stratum, at a depth of 110 ft, could support point-bearing piles satisfactorily with an allowable average load on the stratum of 1.2 tons/sq ft, taking into account the reduction of pressure because of the excavation, the rigidity of the foundation, and the distributing effect of the supporting sand layer itself. At a depth of 42.6 ft, sufficient

154   *Leonardo Zeevaert*

to accommodate two basement levels and the foundation structure, the uplift water pressure would be 1 ton/sq ft. The decision was reached to design the building for a total weight of 2.1 tons/sq ft, with 55 percent of the load to be carried on piles bearing on the first sand stratum at a 110-ft depth and the remaining 45 percent of the load to be balanced by the uplift water pressure on the foundation slab. To reduce differential settlement and torsional vibration during earthquakes, the building would be symmetrical about the vertical axis. A primary objective was maximum building height and, for this purpose, the structural design consisted of a steel frame, thin concrete floor slabs, and a very light aluminum curtain wall.

The deep excavations for the Latin American Tower presented a severe construction problem because the site, one of the busiest intersections in Mexico City, is surrounded by major buildings, some of which date back several centuries. There was apprehension on the part of the owners of the adjacent property. It was known that excavations to a depth of only 12 ft had shown "heave" of 10 to 12 in. if

Figure 17   (A) Clay compressibility curves; (B) unconfined compression curves.

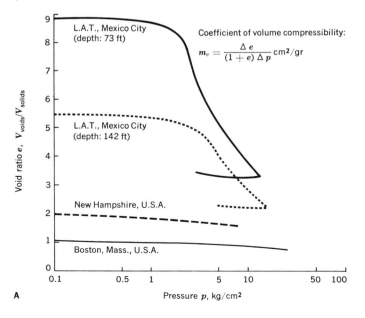

A

no special precautions were taken during excavation; the banks of the excavation might slide and damage adjacent buildings and utilities; pumping to dewater the excavation might cause subsidence of adjacent property, as had occurred at excavations to the mentioned depth. The design objective was to avoid both heave of the bottom of the excavation and subsidence of the surrounding area; the principle followed in the design was to avoid large changes in the effective stresses in the clay mass during excavation and construction.

The area to be excavated, approximately 11,000 sq ft, was surrounded by Wakefield timber sheet-piling to the sand stratum at a depth of 52.5 ft. As the excavation proceeded, this piling was supported by horizontal timber shoring extending across the excavation in both directions. Upon saturation, the timber piling swelled to form an almost impervious membrane that both prevented inflow of water

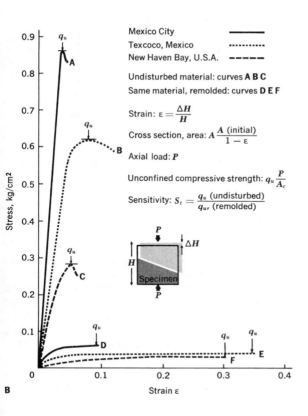

Mexico City ————
Texcoco, Mexico ··············
New Haven Bay, U.S.A. — — — —

Undisturbed material: curves **A B C**
Same material, remolded: curves **D E F**

Strain: $\varepsilon = \dfrac{\Delta H}{H}$

Cross section, area: $A \dfrac{A \text{ (initial)}}{1 - \varepsilon}$

Axial load: P

Unconfined compressive strength: $q_u \dfrac{P}{A_c}$

Sensitivity: $S_t = \dfrac{q_u \text{ (undisturbed)}}{q_{ur} \text{ (remolded)}}$

Stress, kg/cm^2

Strain ε

B

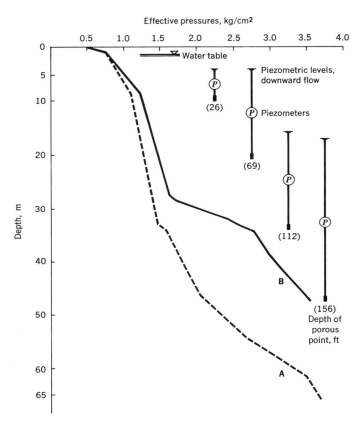

Figure 18   Effective pressures.

and avoided drawdown of the water table outside as the excavation
was dewatered. Pressure was maintained in the sand layers by inject-
ing clean water under pressure into the subsoil by the system of eight
wells shown in Fig. 19; these injection wells were perforated at depths
of 39, 52, 69, and 92 ft to feed water into the sand lenses at these
levels. The water table in the upper pervious deposits was maintained
by a ditch which fed absorption wells extending downward 26 ft. This
system maintained the water table outside the excavation at the same
level as had prevailed before excavation started; the observed settlement was small and not detrimental to buildings and utilities. Heave

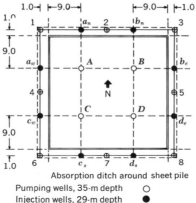

Absorption ditch around sheet pile
Pumping wells, 35-m depth ○
Injection wells, 29-m depth ●
Absorption wells, to 8-m depth ⊕

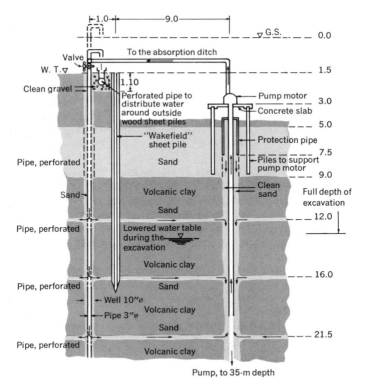

Figure 19   System of eight deep wells.

within the excavated area was avoided by reducing the uplift hydraulic pressure by means of pumping from wells drilled to a depth of 115 ft (located as shown in Fig. 19). The upper clay deposit was under an increased load during this period amounting to 0.4 ton/sq ft. The water pumped from these wells was injected into the injection wells outside the excavation. This hydraulic system was operated while the area was excavated from 8.2 to 42.5 ft in depth, and it fully met its objective of limiting the settlement outside, and of preventing heave inside, the excavated area. It is believed to be the first application of this system. These pumping and injection wells were later sealed with cement, and initial hydraulic conditions were reestablished.

The volcanic clay deposits underlying the foundation are non-homogeneous in compressibility, and differential settlement might cause the building to tilt. To correct this action if it occurred, injection wells, which could be used to apply a differential uplift pressure, as well as a restoring movement to overcome tilting, were installed at the four corners of the foundation. The building has been completed for ten years, and this injection system has not been used except for testing purposes during construction.

The cross section of the foundation is shown in Fig. 20. There are 361 piles, each carrying a building load of 36 tons. Piles were tested, and showed the elastic-limit working conditions to be 100 tons per pile and the force necessary to penetrate the sand layer to be 132 tons. Subsidence of the material surrounding these piles would exert a downward force on the piles (negative friction) which analysis showed to be 21 tons for piles in the central area, 28 tons for piles along the edges, and 30 tons for piles at the corners. Earthquake forces would increase the load at the edges of the foundation approximately 7 tons per pile. Summation of these loads showed a coefficient of safety of approximately 2 against penetration of the sand layer and 1.5 against elastic failure of the piles; these factors were judged satisfactory.

Excavation of the foundation area was completed to a depth of 26 ft. Below this level a rectangular grid of reinforced concrete foundation beams was constructed in trenches excavated down to 42.5 ft. The panels between the beams were then cleared one after another, and the foundation slab was constructed under the concrete beams and resting on the piles. After this work was completed in each panel, it was filled with sand and gravel to load the foundation to 1.25 tons/sq ft, equivalent to approximately one-half of the ultimate building load. Following completion of this foundation structure, the water table was permitted to rise and the uplift pressure on the foundation slab to increase, in order to balance progressively the additional load of the

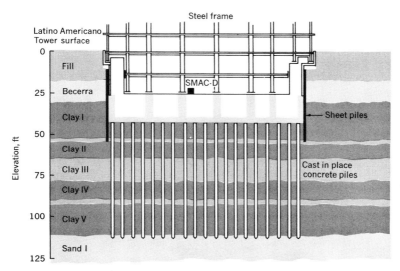

Figure 20 Cross section of foundation of the Latin American Tower.

building as erection of the steel structure proceeded. This procedure was followed until the entire load of the building was in place, and under this condition the groundwater table was restored to its original elevation. Observations of subsidence and of the piezometric water levels were made continuously during construction of the foundation and thereafter.

The third major environmental factor in the design of the Latin American Tower (LAT) was the effect of earthquakes. Earlier in this chapter, the response to earthquakes on the Mexico City subsoil was discussed in the light of our present knowledge, but at the time the tower was designed, the data available were incomplete. Records of earthquakes at Mexico City between 1900 and 1956 showed 3 earthquakes with maximum accelerations of 10 in./sec^2, 12 with accelerations of 8 in./sec^2, and 24 with accelerations of 2 in./sec^2. The author concluded that, during the next century, 3 or 4 more accelerations of 10 in./sec^2 might occur, and that one of the order of 20 in./sec^2 could be expected. From records at the Seismological Station at Tacubaya on firm ground within the valley and from other records, the author concluded that the period of the ground motion at the LAT site during strong earthquakes would be of the order of 2 sec and that the maximum velocity of ground motion would be 6.3 in./sec^2. The building code required that the structural design assume a horizontal force equal to 2.5 percent of the building weight, but the author concluded that this factor should be increased to 5 percent.

An earthquake applies a horizontal force to the foundation of a building. The building must be designed to withstand this force and, in particular, to be strong enough at every level to resist without damage (1) the horizontal shearing forces and (2) all the other forces which develop as the elastic structure vibrates. If the fundamental period of the building or of its lower harmonics coincides with the period of the applied forces, the displacements and the stresses in the structure may become very great. The permissible load on the foundations had been established from studies of the subsoil conditions, and preliminary design of the structure led to a height of 460 ft from ground level to roof, containing 44 floors, plus a 132-ft television tower, as shown in Fig. 21. The design concept was a steel frame, reinforced concrete floors, and aluminum curtain walls supported independently on each floor. Analysis of the first design showed that the periods of vibration of the structural frame alone were high and that the second mode of vibration had a period very close to the estimated period of the ground motion. The rigidity of the building was increased, and the period of oscillation decreased, by adding shear connectors, causing the steel beams of the frame and the reinforced concrete floor slabs to act as composite sections (Fig. 22). The 3.5-in. concrete floor slabs were cast monolithically with diagonal reinforcement to resist diagonal tension in the plane of the slabs. These changes resulted in calculated periods of vibration of 3.66, 1.54, 0.98, and 0.71 sec for the first four modes. The analysis of periods and of the mode shapes utilized a numerical procedure devised by Professor Newmark of the University of Illinois which took into account shear stiffness and rotation of the column ends at each story. Another phase of the analysis was the calculation of the shearing forces which depend upon both the accelerations applied at the base and the distribution of rigidity and mass with height. A very rigid building will show a greater initial response to earthquakes than a more flexible building. One might conclude that the most flexible buildings will better survive an earthquake; however, this is not the case, as very flexible structures show large accelerations, and correspondingly large displacements in response to seismic motions and "whip" action in the upper stories may damage the structure itself, the partition walls, the building services, or the curtain walls. In order to estimate the shear, the building was assumed to have a constant stiffness. A constant veloc-

Figure 21   The Latin American Tower during
construction.

162 *Leonardo Zeevaert*

Figure 22   Shear connectors.

ity, horizontal pulse was applied at the base; the shear in the first story was computed approximately using the equation

$$V_{\text{base}} = \sqrt{mk}\,\dot{x} \approx 450 \text{ tons } (1 \text{ ton} = 2,000 \text{ lb})$$

where V = base shear
m = mass of first floor
k = spring constant of first floor
$\dot{x}$ = maximum ground velocity

This value is approximate because the actual ground motion does not agree with that assumed and because this force will be modified by the manner in which the shock pulses travel through the building; however, with this figure as an approximation of the total response of the building at the base, a complete dynamic analysis was made of the first four modes of oscillation, yielding the results shown in Fig. 23A. In Fig. 23B, Curve A shows the results obtained using the combination of the modes of vibration of the building; for comparison, Curve B shows the shear for a base force of 450 tons and a constant acceleration distribution.

The writer was much concerned about the possibility of whip action at the top of the building and, in order to make certain that it would not occur, the rigidity of the structure from floor 32 to the top was increased so that this section would move with an almost vertical tangent during an earthquake. Analysis had not indicated this phenomenon as probable, but the uncertainties underlying the assumptions of the analysis were such that precaution seemed desirable.

The reader will recognize that this brief account of the design of LAT omits many steps which the designer must take before the final drawings and specifications can be prepared. The design did not proceed in as simple and straightforward a manner as may have been implied. In reality, a series of approximations is necessary: starting from the basic concept, analyzing this concept approximately, using these approximations as the basis for designing successive levels of detail, and finally analyzing the completed design for compatibility both with environment and with the objectives of the project.

All aspects of the construction of the foundations and the superstructure were closely controlled through detailed inspection to assure that the actual building conformed to the design as closely as was physically possible.

The steel structure was made up of prefabricated, milled sections with only the major joints riveted at the site. The quality of the concrete and the positioning of the reinforcing steel were subjected to the detailed scrutiny of inspectors representing the designer.

The Latin American Tower was completed in 1955. It has been subjected to several earthquakes including the severe shocks of July, 1957, and May, 1962, without even minor damage and without breaking a panel of glass in the curtain wall. Some instruments were installed during construction and more have been added during the intervening years so that LAT is today a field laboratory, well-equipped for the study of earthquake motions, structural dynamics, and soil mechanics in the environment of Mexico City. A few of the records obtained may be of interest as an indication of the degree of correspondence between the design and the reality.

The relative displacements of the floors was measured by meters such as those shown in Fig. 24, and these measurements were analyzed to obtain the shear forces. During the earthquake of July 28, 1957, deformation of the first floor indicated a shear of 550 tons, equal to about 3.2 percent of the total weight. The recorded acceleration was 20 in./sec^2, corresponding to degree 7 on the Mercalli Intensity Scale. These figures on shear and acceleration show that the flexibility of the building greatly reduced the shear, because this acceleration would have produced a shear of 870 tons if the building were rigid. The building movement corresponded to the second mode of vibration, as recorded by the shear displacement meter of the 39th floor (Fig. 25).

In 1960, a Japanese strong-motion accelerograph (SMAC) was installed in the basement of the LAT building and in May, 1962, records were obtained, for the first time in Mexico City, of earthquakes of intensity 7 on the Mercalli Scale. These accelerograms, like the example shown in Fig. 7, were analyzed at the California Institute of Technology to obtain the pseudoacceleration spectrum shown in Fig. 9 with damping equal to zero, 5 to 10, and 20 percent of critical. The peak at 2.5 sec represents the resonance period of the ground (2 sec assumed in the LAT design); another peak at 1.60 sec is the period of the second mode of the building; the peak at 0.9 sec is the second mode of vibration of the ground. Knowing the periods of vibration and the coefficients of participation of the different modes, it was possible to compute a more accurate value of the base shear for the earthquake

Figure 23   (A) Dynamic shears, first four modes of vibration. (B) Configuration of shear forces.

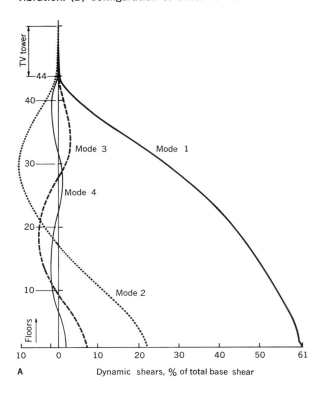

of May, 1962; the value computed in this manner on the assumption of 5 percent of critical damping was 430 tons—surprisingly close to the value of 385 tons measured at the first floor during the same earthquake.

The Latin American Tower has been a considerable source of satisfaction to the author; to his brother Adolfo Zeevaert, who acted as Chief of the Construction Department for the LAT; and to all the engineers associated with him in its design and construction because, in ten years, it has passed through three major earthquakes without even minor damage; the actual behavior of the foundation has been very closed to the predicted behavior; the building and the instruments installed in it have yielded data and design methods applicable

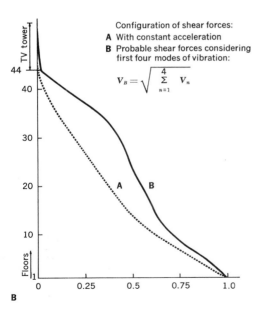

Configuration of shear forces:

A With constant acceleration

B Probable shear forces considering first four modes of vibration:

$$V_B = \sqrt{\sum_{n=1}^{4} V_n}$$

B

Figure 24   Displacement meter, first floor, (*top*) and record, July 28, 1957 (*bottom*).

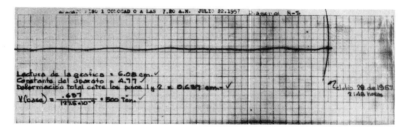

in two areas of engineering practice, namely, the design of foundations for tall and heavy buildings and the design of structures against seismic forces.

BIBLIOGRAPHY

The bibliography of soil mechanics is extensive. Only a brief account of the most important books and proceedings of international conferences is given here. Some papers by the author, in connection with this chapter, are also included, and others appear in the proceedings of the conferences listed.

Figure 25 Graphical-displacement meter, thirty-ninth floor (*top*) and earthquake record, May 11, 1962 (*bottom*).

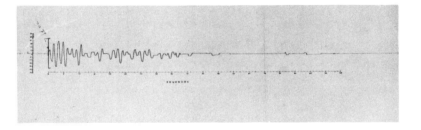

BAVER, L. D.: "Soil Physics," John Wiley & Sons, Inc., New York, 1940.

KRYNINE, D. P.: "Soil Mechanics," McGraw-Hill Book Company, New York, 1941.

PECK, R. B., and W. E. HANSON: "Foundation Engineering," John Wiley & Sons, Inc., New York, 1953.

Proceedings of the International Conference on Soil Mechanics and Foundation Engineering, Bureau of Engineering Research and Department of Civil Engineering, University of Texas, vols. I–III, 1936.

Proceedings of the Purdue Conference on Soil Mechanics and Its Application, Society for the Promotion of Engineering Education, Purdue University, 1940.

Proceedings of the Second International Conference on Soil Mechanics and Foundation Engineering, Rotterdam, Holland, vols., I–VI, 1948.

Proceedings of the Third International Conference on Soil Mechanics and Foundation Engineering. Switzerland, vols. I–III, 1953.

Proceedings of the Fourth International Conference on Soil Mechanics and Foundation Engineering, Scientific Publications, Butterworth & Co. (Publishers), Ltd., London, 1957.

Proceedings of the Fifth International Conference on Soil Mechanics and Foundation Engineering, Dunod, Paris, France, 1961.

Proceedings of the Seventh Texas Conference on Soil Mechanics and Foundation Engineering, Bureau of Engineering Research and Department of Civil Engineering, University of Texas, 1947.

Proceedings of the World Conference on Earthquake Engineering, Earthquake Engineering Research Institute and Department of Engineering, University Extension, University of California, Berkeley, Calif., 1956.

Proceedings of the Second World Conference on Earthquake Engineering, Science Council of Japan, Tokyo-Kyoto, Japan, vols. I–III, 1960.

TAYLOR, D. W.: "Soil Mechanics," John Wiley & Sons, Inc., New York, 1948.

TERZAGHI, KARL: "Erdbaumechanik," Franz Deuticke, Leipzig and Vienna, 1925.

——— and R. B. PECK: "Soil Mechanics in Engineering Practice," John Wiley & Sons, Inc., New York, 1948.

TSCHEBOTARIOFF, G. P.: "Soil Mechanics, Foundations, and Earth Structures," Civil Engineering Series, McGraw-Hill Book Company, New York, 1951.

ZEEVAERT, LEONARDO: Application of Soil Mechanics in Designing Building Foundations, *Transactions of the American Society for Civil Engineers,* vol. 109, 1944.

———: Compensated Foundations, *First Panamerican Conference on Soil Mechanics and Foundation Engineering Proceedings,* Mexico, D. F., vol. III.

———: Consolidation of Mexico City Volcanic Clay, *Proceedings Joint Meeting of A.S.T.M and S.M.M.S.,* December, 1957.

———: Dynamic Design and Behavior of Friction Piles and Compensated Foundations, reprint from *De Ingenieur* no. 25, 1962.

———: Foundation Problems Related to Ground Surface Subsidence in Mexico City, *Fourth Pacific Area National Meeting of the American Society for Testing Materials,* Los Angeles, Calif., 1962.

————: "Heavy and Tall Building Problems in Mexico City," Paper 917, *Proceedings of the American Society of Civil Engineers,* March, 1956.

————: Reduction of Point Bearing Capacity of Piles Because of Negative Friction, *First Panamerican Conference on Soil Mechanics and Foundation Engineering Proceedings,* vol. III, reprint, pp. 1145–1152.

————: "Strong Ground Motions Recorded during Earthquakes on May 11th and 19th, 1962, in Mexico City," Seismological Society of America.

———— and N. M. NEWMARK: Aseismic Design of Tower Latino Americana in Mexico City, *Proceedings of the World Conference on Earthquake Engineering,* Earthquake Engineering Research Institute and Department of Engineering, University Extension, University of California, Berkeley, Calif., 1956.

ACKNOWLEDGMENT

The author wishes to extend his appreciation and thanks to Dr. Morrough P. O'Brien for his excellent suggestions and valuable help in reading and correcting the manuscript of this chapter.

8

Space Engineering

by Charles T. Morrow

Charles T. Morrow, Manager of Technical Relations at
the Aerospace Corporation, has a B.A. in physics from
Harvard College, and an S.M. in communication engineering and an Sc.D. in acoustics from Harvard Engineering School. He directed development of vibratory
gyroscopes at the Sperry Gyroscope Company. At the
Hughes Aircraft Company his responsibilities were initially in the development of electromechanical devices
for the Falcon missile and later in shock and vibration
engineering and reliability. These last responsibilities
were expanded at the Ramo-Wooldridge Corporation's
Guided Missile Research Division, which carried out
technical direction of the Air Force ballistic missile
program.

Dr. Morrow conducts a yearly Symposium on Ballistic
Missile and Space Technology for the Ballistic Systems
Division and the Space Systems Division of the Air
Force Systems Command. He also has staff cognizance
over educational matters, but has continued to write
fundamental papers on shock and vibration engineering
and is the author of a reference book on the subject.

INTRODUCTION

The objectives of space engineering involve the lifting of suitable payloads through the earth's gravitational field into orbit or into the gravitational field of the moon or another planet, the accomplishment of landing and takeoff if necessary, the measurement of data necessary for the understanding and utilization of space, the performance of missions essential to defense, and the accomplishment of tasks contributing to other beneficial operations such as long-distance communication and weather forecasting. With objectives of cosmic proportion, it should not be surprising that both the scope of science and technology finding application and the range of careers available should be unusually broad. Almost all branches of mathematics, science, and engineering have application. (The types of engineering to be discussed in other chapters are included to some degree.) Both systems engineering on a large scale and detailed engineering are involved. This does not mean that each space engineer must know everything and be capable of everything. Rather, people with a wide variety of knowledge and capability contribute to the effort.

EDUCATIONAL REQUIREMENTS

For brevity, we will indicate the general flavor of the operation, rather than try to be comprehensive. A major breakdown of space engineering would include such fields as systems engineering, propulsion, structure, attitude control, guidance and astrodynamics, telemetry and communication, payload instrumentation, reentry, bioastronautics, ground support, reliability, and environment. For comparison, consider some more traditional scientific and engineering disciplines taught at universities and institutes of technology, such as physics (atomic physics, nuclear physics, optics, thermodynamics, mechanics, acoustics, etc.), astronomy, chemistry, and the several branches of engineering discussed in Chap. 1. There is no clear correspondence. The educational institutions have deep roots in traditional sources of knowledge. Engineering in an industry, as opposed to advance research, is and should be almost obsessed with the requirements of immediate and future end products.

Does this mean that engineering education must be uprooted and reworked to supply the needs of space engineering? No, that would be too drastic. Some change, not too uniform, will be beneficial and is being carried out. Some educational programs are being designed specifically for space engineering. Such programs have the virtue of being directed toward the practical objectives that are within view and that help to produce a coordinated effort in the industry. The more traditional disciplines have the virtue of versatility of application. They tend to be more useful "across the board." Not being subject to the same constraints, they provide ensurance that new problems, not yet encountered or understood, will be solved. Some educational programs should be specifically for space engineering, but most programs should follow a traditional pattern of classical disciplines.

What are the relative roles of scientific and engineering education in preparing students for space engineering? Some subjects, such as physical optics and the quantum theory, are taught primarily in schools of science. Some subjects, such as stress analysis and metallurgy, are taught primarily in schools of engineering. Other subjects, such as acoustics and phenomena of plasmas (low-density ionized gases), may be taught in both, perhaps with a slightly different choice of topics for emphasis. It is possible for a student in either (or even in a department of pure mathematics) to become a space engineer. Both share a fund of applied-science or scientific knowledge that can be used. The scientific school places somewhat more emphasis on the discovery and assimilation of knowledge. The school of engineering places somewhat more emphasis on the application of scientific knowledge and on design. Yet it is good for the scientist on occasion to have a practical attitude. Conversely, engineers frequently carry out original research as challenging and significant as that of the most distinguished scientists.

The space engineer is not a stereotype. Space engineering is necessarily accomplished by teams of varied specialists and generalists as well. The latter are usually engineers or scientists who have specialized, who understand what can be accomplished by specialization, and who have some understanding of the point of view and dedication of the specialist. But they have attained a broader perspective and general understanding of matters outside their own specialty.

Let us consider at greater length several of the space engineering fields and their interlocking with classical disciplines.

ROCKET PROPULSION

The most obvious requirement for accomplishment in space is a capability to lift suitable masses against the earth's gravity to extreme altitudes and hypersonic terminal speeds. Although other propulsion systems may contribute to this accomplishment, it has been made possible by the development of the rocket.

All propulsion systems except those that operate by mechanical contact with the solid matter of the earth (as, for example, by a wheel) operate on a principle of reaction. They accelerate mass, whether solid, liquid, or gaseous, in a direction opposite to the motion desired. This generates a *thrust*. In accordance with Newton's second law, except for second-order effects, this thrust is proportional to the mass accelerated in unit time and the change of velocity with respect to the vehicle. An airplane propeller accelerates air outside the engine to which it is coupled. The jet and the rocket expel mass from inside. The unique feature of the rocket is that it is not dependent on oxygen in the air. It carries along oxygen or any other material necessary for the process that provides the available energy. The rocket can therefore be used to generate extremely large thrust or to produce thrust while outside the atmosphere. The material that is carried to be ejected after acceleration by combustion or other means is called a *propellant*.

In order to derive some quantitative relationships concerning the thrust of a rocket, let us imagine ourselves traveling in the same direction at constant velocity. At the instant the rocket velocity equals ours we make some observations. We find that the motion of the rocket is governed by two inertial reactions to which Newton's second law

$$\text{Force} = \text{rate of change of momentum} = \frac{d}{dt}\,mv \tag{1}$$

is applicable.

First, there is a reaction of the mass of rocket exhaust gases. Their velocity may be taken as essentially constant, but the mass is increasing by the amount of propellant consumed. An approximate expression for the thrust may be obtained as

$$\text{Thrust} = \frac{d}{dt}\,(mv_e) = v_e\,\frac{dm}{dt} \tag{2}$$

$$= (\text{exhaust velocity}) \times (\text{rate of change of mass})$$

In addition, there is a reaction of the rocket as a whole to the generated thrust. The net force acting immediately after a vertical launch is the thrust minus the gravitational force

$$m\,\frac{dv}{dt} = \text{thrust} - mg \tag{3}$$

Clearly the thrust of the rocket at launch must be greater than the gravitational force in order to lift the rocket and provide any initial acceleration. Thus thrust is a first important figure of merit for the rocket.

A second useful figure of merit is the specific impulse, which is a measure of the thrust produced for a given rate of propellant consumption. Although most commonly applied to rockets, it can be a useful figure of merit for other propulsion systems such as jets. It is given by

$$I_{sp} = \frac{\text{thrust}}{\text{mass flow rate}} = \frac{\text{lb (force)}}{\text{lb (mass)/sec}} = \frac{\text{lb-sec}}{\text{lb}} \tag{4}$$

Since specific impulse is commonly defined in terms of pound thrust per pound weight of fuel burned per second, the acceleration of gravity (g) must be inserted in the converting force to poundals for Eq. (3). As weight flow rate is taken in terms of standard weight at launch, the value of g used is that at the earth's surface, g_0. Substitution of Eq. (4) in Eq. (3) then gives

$$m \frac{dv}{dt} = - I_{sp}g_0 \frac{dm}{dt} - mg \tag{5}$$

The negative sign of the first term is introduced since an accelerating force is given by a decrease in weight of the rocket corresponding to propellant consumed. Eq. (5) may be rewritten

$$dv = - I_{sp}g_0 \frac{dm}{m} - mgdt \tag{6}$$

Each term may now be integrated from the initial condition (denoted 0) to the final or burnt-out condition (denoted b)

$$\int_0^{v_b} dv = - I_{sp}g_0 \int_{m_0}^{m_b} \frac{dm}{m} - mg \int_0^{t_b} dt \tag{7}$$

or

$$v_b = I_{sp}g_0 \log_e \left(\frac{m_0}{m_b}\right) - mgt_b \tag{8}$$

This is the basic equation giving final velocity in terms of specific impulse, ratio of initial to final mass, and time of burning. For most practical cases of high-thrust rockets, the last term is small, meaning that the gravitational force is negligible in comparison with the thrust of the propellant over the boost phase. The basic equation then simplifies to

$$v_b \approx I_{sp}g_0 \log_e \left(\frac{m_0}{m_b}\right) \tag{9}$$

This simplified form will be used in the following discussion.

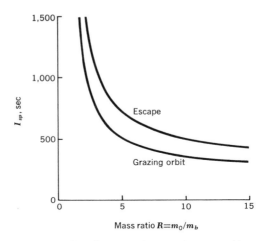

Figure 1   Specific impulses and mass ratios necessary for grazing orbit or escape accomplished by a single stage.

Figure 1 shows values of I_{sp} and $R = m_0/m_b$ obtained by Eq. (9) for the earth's escape velocity (36,900 ft/sec) and for a grazing orbit in the absence of atmosphere. Table 1 shows approximate ranges of I_{sp} obtained with several types of rocket engines. It is difficult to design a reliable structure for R greater than 10. It is apparent from Fig. 1 that no space mission can be accomplished by a single chemical rocket. In fact, an intercontinental ballistic missile of such design would be difficult if not impossible.

During the powered portions of a space trajectory, it is advantageous not to carry along any excess mass longer than necessary. This is avoided by discarding engines or complete propulsion systems along the trajectory as the propellant is consumed. The jettisoned propulsion systems are called *stages*, and the payload with its last propulsion system is called the *final stage*. The process of discarding a propulsion system is called *staging*. The thrust of the first stage must be tremendous, for at launch it must lift the entire vehicle complete with propellant. To save weight and keep stresses within reason the remaining stages are designed for successively less thrust. The velocity increments attained by each stage may be estimated from Eq. (8) or (9) with I_{sp}, m_0, m_b, and t_b, given values according to the stage considered and with g_0 replaced as necessary by a value typical of the

Table 1   APPROXIMATE PERFORMANCE OF SEVERAL ROCKET SYSTEMS

Energy source	Propellants	Energy converter	I_{sp}, lb-sec/lb	Comments
Chemical	Kerosene Liquid oxygen	Combustion chamber	240–270	Excellent for booster stage.
Chemical	Solid propellant with fuel and oxidizer mixed	Combustion chamber	170–250	Simpler and more reliable than liquid propellant system. Less potential for restart or reuse.
Chemical	Hydrazine Fluorine	Combustion chamber	300	Not desirable for lift-off operation because of corrosive and toxic combustion products.
Nuclear fission	Hydrogen	Heat exchanger	800	Can be used at lift-off but not economically unless booster stage is recoverable. Weight of reactor must be accounted for.
Nuclear fission or solar (cells)	Cesium (ion)	Electric field	5,000–10,000	Low thrust unsuited for lift-off. Weight of fission reactor must be considered. Ion beam must be neutralized by negative particles.
	Hydrogen (plasma)	Magnetic field	1,500–2,000	

altitude where the stage is used. Extension of the analysis given here readily shows the increased performance obtainable and leads to optimum configurations that will lift a given mass for a specified mission at minimum total launch weight or possible minimum cost. The performance increase is not unlimited and levels off rapidly after two or three stages. Unless a mission requires additional impulses for changing orbit or deorbiting, it is unusual to design for more than two liquid-propellant stages or more than three with solid fuels.

Approximate estimates of the velocities required for space missions related to Fig. 1 can be obtained from simple calculations. Consider first the grazing orbit, for which the vehicle is fired horizontally. It is assumed that any energy required to overcome the attraction of gravity during the powered flight is negligible. Although the atmosphere prevents such an orbit, the energy requirements are nearly as great as for an orbit immediately outside the atmosphere. Equate the centrifugal force to the earth's gravitational attraction

$$\frac{m v_b^2}{R} = \frac{GmM}{R^2} \tag{10}$$

or

$$v_b^2 = \frac{GM}{R} \tag{11}$$

where m is the mass in orbit, R is the orbit radius from the center of the earth, and G is the universal gravitational constant. But, if centrifugal force on the earth's surface is neglected

$$\frac{GM}{R_0^2} = g_0 \tag{12}$$

where $R = 3,960$ miles or $3,450$ nautical miles is the radius of the earth and $g_0 = 32.2$ ft/sec is the standard acceleration of gravity. Hence

$$v_b^2 = \frac{g_0 R_0^2}{R} \tag{13}$$

or for a circular grazing orbit

$$v_b^2 = g_0 R_0 \tag{14}$$

from which

$$v_b = \sqrt{(32.2)\,(3,960)\,(5,280)} = 25,900 \text{ ft/sec}$$

Consider the escape maneuver with the vehicle; for simplicity, fire straight vertically with respect to the earth. After thrust cutoff, the mass is constant. By Newton's second law

$$m \frac{dv}{dt} = -G \frac{mM}{R^2} \tag{15}$$

or

$$\frac{dv}{dt} = -G \frac{M}{R^2} \tag{16}$$

or

$$\frac{dr}{dt} dv = -\frac{GM}{R^2} dR \tag{17}$$

but

$$\frac{dr}{dt} = v \tag{18}$$

Therefore

$$v \, dv = -\frac{GM}{R^2} dR \tag{19}$$

Integration yields

$$\frac{v^2}{2} - \frac{v_b^2}{2} = \frac{GM}{R} - \frac{GM}{R_0} \tag{20}$$

or for an escape maneuver such that v approaches zero as R increases beyond limit

$$v_b{}^2 = \frac{2GM}{R_0} \tag{21}$$

or from Eq. (12)

$$v_b{}^2 = 2g_0 R_0 \tag{22}$$

Hence

$$v_b = \sqrt{(2)(32.2)(3,960)(5,280)} = 36,700 \text{ ft/sec}$$

Consider a more complicated maneuver, which puts the payload into a synchronous orbit with the same period as the earth's rotation, a condition of great interest for a communications satellite. Assume for simplicity that the vehicle, after a brief boost, coasts so that its velocity goes to zero at the radius of the synchronous orbit. Then an impulse at a right angle to the radius establishes the required orbital velocity.

The first problem is to compute the orbital radius and velocity. From Eq. (13), the angular velocity

$$\omega = \frac{v}{R} = \frac{g_0^{1/2}R_0}{R^{3/2}} = 2\pi \tag{23}$$

from which $R = 26,300$ miles, or $22,900$ nautical miles, from the center of the earth. Then, from Eq. (13), $v_b = 10,000$ ft/sec.

The second problem is to find the boost velocity necessary to bring the payload out to the radius R. From Eqs. (12) and (20)

$$v_b'^2 = 2g_0 \left(R_0 - \frac{R_0^2}{R} \right) \tag{24}$$

yielding $v_b = 36,300$ ft/sec. The total velocity requirement is $v''_b = v_b + v'_b = 46,300$ ft/sec, or somewhat more than the escape velocity.

In practice, because of limitations in specific impulse and mass ratio, several stages of chemical rocket propulsion are necessary to achieve the orbital radius. They need not be fired all at once. The first stage may merely establish a highly eccentric elliptical trajectory. The second stage may be fired at apogee to establish a second highly eccentric elliptical orbit of greater energy. At the second apogee, with the radial velocity (but not the angular velocity about the earth) close to zero, the third stage may be fired to put the satellite approximately into synchronous orbit. Adjustments by a small rocket carried in the satellite may be necessary from time to time as measurements from the earth indicate that the position is drifting.

The thrust is an indication of the magnitude of the mass that can be lifted against gravity; the specific impulse is more an indication of how far and how fast a standard mass can be lifted. At present, the most prominent limiting factor in the United States space effort is thrust capability; this is increased primarily by developing larger propulsion systems. Several years from now, the limiting factor may be specific impulse. But it does not follow that the rocket with the largest thrust and the highest specific impulse is the best for all applications.

TYPES OF ROCKETS

All rockets now in production are *chemical rockets;* that is, they depend on combustion for energy conversion. In liquid-propellant stages, the propellants are usually carried in two tanks, which are integral with the stage structure or airframes.[1] One carries a *fuel*, such as kerosene, hydrazene, or eventually liquid hydrogen. The other carries a propellant such as liquid oxygen, nitric acid, or fluorine, known as an *oxidizer*. The propellants are carefully weighed at launch, and a propellant utilization system incorporated into the stage ensures that both propellants are exhausted at the same time, so that little excess of either remains as dead weight. The propellants are forced along by pressurization or specially designed turbopumps at the rate necessary for the required thrust. They are sprayed into a combustion chamber, react, attain sonic speed at a constriction or throat, and become supersonic in a flaring nozzle.

In the *solid-propellant rocket,* the combustion chamber is enlarged to enclose the propellant. The latter consists of a synthetic rubber or plastic, mixed with an oxygen-bearing salt and other additives, and is cast as a *grain,* which is bonded to the case. The grain is developed so that it burns slowly or not at all in the absence of a suitably high chamber pressure. This property is necessary for safety and for a means of thrust cutoff when the velocity attained is precisely that required or prescribed by the guidance system. The shape of the thrust-versus-time curve is controlled by the configuration of the air core along the longitudinal axis of the grain.

Improvement in specific impulse can be attained by using a single propellant such as liquid hydrogen and heating it with a lightweight nuclear reactor containing a critical mass of fissionable material.

These chemical and nuclear rockets develop high thrust with specific impulses adequate for operations in the immedite region of the earth and the moon. They operate during brief intervals of powered flight, followed by long parabolic or elliptical coasting trajectories or orbits.

For missions to more distant planets or stars, important gains in range or mission duration can be obtained by large increases in late-stage specific impulses, even at thrusts that are small by comparison with the launch weight of the stage. Such propulsion systems will be left on continuously after higher-thrust boosters have carried a vehicle outside the atmosphere and imparted an adequate initial speed. Systems are under development that accelerate ions by electric fields or plasmas by magnetic fields. Photon rockets have been considered. These systems are dependent, of course, on power from a fission reactor or solar cells that must be carried along in the vehicle.

In the research stage is a thermonuclear rocket utilizing hydrogen isotopes as the thermonuclear material and propellant. The hydrogen

---

[1] For this reason, the propulsion and airframe organizations must work closely together. Neither has complete responsibility for the design of the tanks.

is utilized as a plasma. It is "pinched" or compressed by electromagnetic fields to a thin region along the axis of the rocket, thereby being heated to extreme temperatures and being isolated from the walls. The primary research objective at present is to confine the plasma long enough and to heat it enough by compression that a useful thermonuclear reaction will take place. Thermonuclear sources for other purposes are considered in Chap. 2, "Energy Sources and Energy Conversion."

CONTROL AND GUIDANCE

The word *control* has varied meanings. In some contexts, it refers to control systems and servomechanisms in general. In the phrase "command and control," it refers to the mechanization whereby authorized firings for wartime military objectives may be carried out but unauthorized firings prevented. In the context of the heading, it means attitude control.

The first need for control is a means of keeping a space vehicle pointed generally along the desired trajectory during powered flight and limiting any tendency to roll. Any deviation from the proper orientation and any rate of change of attitude are measured by gyroscopes—two for each axis of rotation. The *displacement gyroscope* generates a signal proportional to angular error. Proportionate correction tends to return the vehicle to the proper orientation. The *rate gyroscope* generates a signal proportional to rate of rotation. Proportionate correction damps the system and prevents hunting after a disturbance. Correction is accomplished by deflecting the thrust so that it is temporarily misaligned with respect to the center of gravity, or by deflecting the thrust of two or more rockets so as to produce a torque about the roll axis. Either liquid-propellant rockets have articulated nozzles or else gas is injected into one side of the nozzle to deflect the exhaust gases.

Control during powered flight may require precision angular references but does not require precision transient response to disturbances. The system must be stable, however, over a wide variety of conditions along the trajectory. Regardless of changes in the properties of the atmosphere or consumption of propellants, or changes due to staging, the system must not arrive at a condition such that it shakes the vehicle apart. This requires the measurement or estimation of the dynamical (resonance) properties of the vehicle and propellants and the design of compensating networks with sufficient accommodation to keep the system stable.

The next requirement may be control of payload attitude during orbital or coasting flight. This varies from crude orientation for re-entry to precise control for purposes of observations and experiments in space. Because of the lack of disturbances, rate gyroscopes are not necessary, but displacement gyroscopes are needed if the payload is not spun. In the most exacting applications, the gyroscopes must have extremely low drift or be "slaved" to a star- or horizon-tracking mechanism.

Although guidance is closely related to control, vehicle attitude is a secondary consideration. The guidance system ensures that a vehicle follow a suitable trajectory with precisely the velocity required. This does, of course, require occasional commands to the control system to change the attitude temporarily from the nominal.

For example, the establishment of a satellite on a predetermined orbit demands that the booster be at approximately the right position at thrust cutoff and that the vector velocity have precisely the correct value. Descent from orbit for recovery requires a precisely timed impulse of precisely the right magnitude in order to modify the vector velocity appropriately. Rendezvous with other vehicles and soft landing on the moon require not only placement on a trajectory proper for the initiation of the maneuver but the gradual adjustment of the closing velocity by retrorocket firing until contact is established without excessive mechanical shock.

The limiting factor in guidance system performance is navigation capability; in other words, guidance can be no more precise than the measurements of position and velocity. In one system, these measurements are performed by ground-based radars, and commands are transmitted to the control and propulsion systems. Position can be measured by a single monopulse radar, which provides an estimate of angle for every pulse emitted and returned. Velocity can be measured by three Doppler radars or, with suitable filtering and correction for delay, by taking the time derivative of the position data. A ground-based computer decides on the commands. In another system, called an inertial guidance system, the velocity is measured by three integrating accelerometers on a gyroscope-stabilized platform, and an airborne computer decides on the commands. When drift of the inertial instrumentation is critical, corrections may be applied by tracking stars. Rendezvous and soft landings may require a radar and a computer in the vehicle. Other variations of these ingredients may be useful.

The design of an inertial guidance system requires negotiation with propulsion engineers for suitable, precise, cutoff characteristics or a throttling capability for the rockets, and with control engineers for suitable insertion of guidance commands in the attitude control system.

Perhaps this is the best place to discuss the concept of *exchange ratio*. This is the ratio of an error or increment in a parameter to the effect it produces, or alternately the reciprocal of this ratio. Mathematically it is, in effect, the first term in a Taylor's series expansion. It is a concept used throughout space engineering and in other examples of systems engineering as a quantitative guide to the engineer, who is always involved in small detailed compromises in order to obtain an optimum overall result.

In particular, the guidance engineer cannot build navigation instrumentation that is perfectly accurate and, for reasons of cost, weight, reliability, etc., would not if he could. He and the space systems engineer need measures of the effect of imperfect instrumentation. One exchange ratio used for such purposes is the *miss coefficient;* especially applicable to ballistic missiles, it is the error magnitude that results in a one-mile miss. For simplicity, consider a short-range ballistic missile accelerated rapidly to thrust cutoff and then coasting to impact. Obviously a horizontal error of one mile in the position of thrust cutoff will result by itself in a one-mile miss. For this type of error, the miss coefficient is unity. An azimuth error $\Delta\theta$ in the direction of the velocity vector at thrust cutoff will, according to Fig. 2, lead to a miss $\Delta y = x\,\Delta\theta$, where x is the remaining distance and $\Delta\theta$ is in radians. The corresponding miss coefficient is therefore

$$\frac{\Delta\theta}{\Delta y} = \frac{1}{x}$$

or x may be multiplied by an appropriate factor to yield $\Delta\theta$ in degrees, minutes, seconds, or whatever units are desired. The error $\Delta\theta$ might in turn be related to drift rate of an azimuth navigational gyroscope to yield a miss coefficient for azimuth gyroscope performance. Similar approaches are used for all the significant errors of ballistic missiles, short- or long-range, and of space vehicles. Usually, it is necessary to calculate a first derivative. The miss coefficients are used in the choice

Figure 2   Miss distance produced by azimuth error.

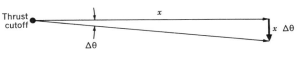

x=remaining horizontal distance to target

of trajectories for specific missions and in the determination of the performance specifications for navigational instrumentation.

PAYLOADS AND REENTRY VEHICLES

Let us consider payloads and vehicles intended for reentry into the earth's atmosphere or for entry into another atmosphere. We shall comment on the roots of this field in traditional scientific and engineering disciplines as we go along. For example, all of it obviously involves mechanical engineering.

The payload carries whatever may be directly necessary for the mission of a firing, as opposed to the boosters used to lift the payload against the earth's gravity. The ballistic missile is marginally a space vehicle. A ballistic-missile payload, if designated for possible wartime use, is designed to contain a thermonuclear bomb. This destructive device is widely recognized to be based on relativity theory and nuclear physics. But for effectiveness and safety, the payload must also contain instrumentation and electronic circuitry to arm the bomb at the proper point along the trajectory so that detonation can occur, and to fuze the bomb so that detonation does occur. Most space payloads, however, are not intended to have catastrophic effects. They may contain instrumentation and equipment to perform observations, measurements, and experiments in space. These contents are similar to the usual apparatus of the university physics laboratory except that they are much more carefully designed and pretested. They must survive the acceleration, vibration, and other unusual environments of the boost period and operate reliably under the conditions of space. They must have no extra weight. The payload may contain a man, equipment to keep him alive, and controls and instruments for him to use. Here we encounter *bioastronautics,* or the biology associated with space flight of man and animals. Medical and psychological tests are an important aspect of the selection and employment of astronauts. Whatever measurements and observations are made in space, unless they are manually recorded by the astronaut, must be transmitted to the ground by electronic and microwave equipment. In the design of payloads, however, the weight is critical, for the launch weight of the completed vehicle is proportionate and may be more than ten times as great.

Design for entry into other atmospheres is made less certain by the fact that we do not entirely understand their composition and properties. Some observations and measurements will have to be made before this question is entirely settled. However, the general character of the problem is the same as for earth reentry. The payload must be decelerated to suitable speed without overheating and without injuring the astronaut if one is carried along. It must approach a predetermined point on the planet or satellite. Eventually, this goal may be accomplished in part through the aerodynamic lift of wing-like structures, which would permit maneuverability and simplify recovery operations. At present, the deceleration is limited in magnitude by control of the reentry angle, since the ratio of weight to drag affects primarily the timing rather than the magnitude of the deceleration. For typical earth reentry, the kinetic energy per pound is more than five times that required to heat a steel reentry vehicle uniformly to the melting point. As much energy as possible is dissipated in the *shock wave*. This wave, which is analogous to the bow wave of a ship, is a phenomenon of supersonic aerodynamics and is strengthened by a blunt shape. In addition, the contents of the reentry vehicle must be protected against heat radiation from the shock wave and the temperature of the boundary layer, in which the effects of viscosity are concentrated. One method of protection is to design an adequate *heat sink* of a material with high heat conductivity and high specific heat, such as copper. It may be necessary to prevent turbulence, which would increase heat transfer, or, in other words, to design for laminar flow. Another method is *ablative* cooling by a solid material that is transformed to a gas at the high temperature. Still another is *transpiration* cooling by a liquid that passes through suitable pores or passageways and evaporates from the surface. The best approach depends on the speed change required and the time interval over which it is to take place. In any case, some of the disciplines fundamental to reentry engineering are subsonic and hypersonic aerodynamics, thermodynamics, heat transfer, chemistry, and materials sciences.

SPACE SYSTEMS ENGINEERING

We have noted several examples of problems that affect more than one engineering group. The size of the booster required is proportional to the weight of the payload. Attitude control requires coordination between the control engineers and the propulsion engineers on the one hand and the airframe engineers on the other. The guidance system involves guidance engineers, control engineers, and propulsion engineers. The specific examples discussed in previous sections are merely some of the more obvious interface problems. For any radically new space system all developments go on in parallel and require constant negotiation between groups. Even if a portion of the system is to utilize already-existing hardware, this equipment will undoubtedly undergo some detailed modification for the new application.

Usually, there is still another engineering group, the systems engineers, involved in these negotiations. These engineers have the responsibility of ensuring that the compromises made by the various groups have an optimum effect on the performance and reliability of the overall system. The engineers of this group are the first to begin work. They establish the requirements (weight, thrust, specific impulse, precision of guidance, etc.) for the others. As development progresses, they keep these general specifications up to date in accordance with further studies they carry out and various detailed changes that other groups find necessary.

What preparation is necessary for becoming a systems engineer? He is even less a stereotype than the engineers in other groups. On the average, he is somewhat more of a generalist. But systems engineering is more of a special emphasis than a new discipline—its technical content is determined by the system under consideration. Some aspects of trajectory analysis are more important to systems engineering than to the work of other groups. There is more concern with the effect of overall parameters of propulsion, guidance, etc., than with the detailed engineering that achieves these parameters. Yet, while some engineers take a broad look at the system, others must be capable of penetrating deeply enough into details to ensure that requirements are not unrealistic. The decisions to be made require good judgment and a realistic evaluation of the engineering state of the art. The space systems engineer is distinguished from other space engineers by his responsibilities and slightly greater breadth of viewpoint, rather than by a specific engineering education. Other aspects of systems engineering will be covered in Chap. 9.

MANAGEMENT

There has been some difference of opinion about whether management should be primarily by technical people assisted by administrators or primarily by administrators assisted by technical people. Many physicists and engineers feel that their group has a privileged right to the management of technical companies. Others feel that management involves many administrative functions that are beneath them or that are a diversion from their true role. We shall not attempt to settle the question here. We shall make only a few observations. In the largest diversified corporations, administrative, financial, and legal aspects often become so varied and important that an engineer is unlikely to have ultimate control. The probabilities are less adverse in smaller technical companies and in space-oriented or technically oriented divisions of diversified corporations. Whether a space engineer should aspire to rise in management depends on his personal capabilities and scale of values. But if he follows such a career, he must recognize that his technical background is to be used in an increasingly different and more subtle manner, and he must find value and satisfaction in certain responsibilities that were once of little concern to him.

Management does not merely mean greater power to make or approve technical decisions. Sometimes technical decisions are guided and even approved by staff engineers who roam across organizational lines but do not take full management responsibility. Some scientists and engineers are peculiarly suited for this sort of operation. Management is fundamentally a matter of people and their relationships. Some of its rudiments are evident as soon as an engineer has another engineer reporting to him. Its character develops more fully as the engineers and other people under him become more varied and numerous and the organization more structured. More and more, the manager becomes concerned with selecting people, maintaining a stimulative environment for creative scientists and engineers, defining responsibilities to the extent that is necessary for people to work together smoothly and avoid overlooking essential tasks, seeing that people carry out their assignments properly, solving personnel problems, assigning priorities to problems, keeping the team on schedule, deferring until the next contract any proposed technical changes that cannot be carried out in the time remaining, and controlling costs. The higher levels of management are also concerned with legal matters, relations with contracting agencies and the government, and relations with universities, schools, communities, and the general public.

Management requires delegation—the process of getting other people to contribute creative ideas in accordance with their ability and judgment, to make their share of decisions, and to exert whatever controls may be appropriate. There are no good, simple rules for delegation. The best approach depends on the project, its status, and the relative talents of the people concerned. A manager is justified in reserving some technical investigations for himself if he has an essential talent for them. But he must not become so absorbed in them that he neglects his *overall responsibilities* or is unavailable to the people that report to him. He must ensure that all known matters critical to the schedule can be taken care of in his absence, so that if an emergency arises, he will have time to troubleshoot or to do whatever is necessary.

Management involves a willingness to tolerate minor errors and risk some incompetence at lower levels. But the risk is not so great as it may seem if the manager is willing to accept his responsibility in all its aspects. He can retain certain approvals. He has the privilege and often the responsibility to modify the organization beneath him and to change assignments. The further he progresses in space engineering management, the more he acquires responsibility for specialists in fields about which he knows relatively little. He cannot do over the work of these specialists for them, but he should not approve their decisions or recommendations without some independent checks on their validity. He may depend in part on selected advisors. But he must develop for himself an ability to determine quickly whether investigations are pertinent to the general objectives of the team, whether assumptions are realistic, whether the most important factors have been considered, and whether conclusions and recommendations are pertinent and not rendered invalid by practical engineering constraints. For such purposes, the beginning and end of a technical report may be more revealing than the detailed arguments and derivations in the middle. Against the risks must be weighed the certainty that the manager has neither the time nor the breadth of talent to do the work of a large team. Thus, as an engineer progresses in management, he must become more of a generalist.

OTHER BRANCHES OF SPACE ENGINEERING

We shall now take a brief look at other branches of engineering that we have not discussed in detail. They are just as essential to the overall programs, and a few comments on them will further illuminate the scope and breadth of space engineering.

First, let us look at some of the efforts necessary for the attainment of reliability. By checking, repeated use, and correction, it is necessary to eliminate any errors from design drawings, and to revise certain tolerances and detailed design features in order to expedite manufacture for the performance and reliability required. It is necessary to have good quality control, in other words, satisfactory measures for rejecting parts and assemblies that deviate in any important way from the drawings and specifications. It is necessary to have exhaustive inspections and tests. There must be laboratory simulation of various environments, such as shock, vibration, temperature, vacuum, dust, fungus, and salt spray, that may be encountered by equipment. Many test flights may also be required to develop reliable systems. It is not enough to observe that a vehicle crashed, and to go back to the drawing board. There must be instrumentation and telemetry to transmit data on environment and on symptoms of failure and malfunction. There must be data reduction to make the data useful for decision makers. There must be systematic collection of data on all failures and malfunctions disclosed anywhere from manufacture to test flight. There must be feedback of these data to engineers who are in a position to analyze and take corrective action. Partly because the effort that can be expended in these various directions is not unlimited, there is always a risk that the program is in some way inadequate. It is necessary to have statistical estimates of the risk.

Most of our discussion has focused on the more obvious distinguishing features of a space system. There are related engineering tasks that must be pursued more or less concurrently, and must not be overlooked in a well-balanced program. There must be test sites for rocket engines in the course of their development. Space vehicles usually cannot take off like airplanes but must be launched from a stand or a silo. Some of these facilities must be designed to protect a vehicle and its launch crew against shocks and against radiation from atomic weapons. There must be ground-support equipment for any storing and handling of propellants, for erecting and positioning the vehicle, with any associated assembly operations, for checking out the systems before launch, and for range safety. If, after launch, a malfunction develops that may be dangerous, a command must be transmitted to bring about the destruction of the vehicle.

RESEARCH, DEVELOPMENT, AND PRODUCTION

We have scanned various branches of space engineering, related them to traditional disciplines, and examined the functions of systems engineering and management. Now, let us look at the matter in another way. Most portions of an engineering program pass through three definite but overlapping phases: research, development, and production. We shall identify these as sharply as possible, and then discuss the blending that is characteristic of missile and space programs.

Research, the first phase, is primarily a matter of investigation by relatively small groups of scientists with a few supporting technicians. It is similar to the work done in the typical university research laboratory, except that we are talking about directed research. The scientist has great freedom of approach but not unlimited free choice of problems. The objective is to develop any theories that may be needed for the application, obtain any necessary scientific data, and perhaps design and construct a prototype. This prototype is machined and assembled from informal sketches with the aid of skilled and versatile technicians and with a minimum of expensive special tooling. It is not intended for manufacture in quantity without further change. Some parts may be hand-fitted without resort to precise dimensions on the sketches. Nonfunctional surfaces may be left crudely finished. The prototype need not have the correct weight or the exact performance for a specific application. But it must demonstrate the feasibility of the design approach, and it should permit identifying as many of the problems as possible.

At this point, we should say something about design. It gains its freest expression in late research or early development. Although many scientists have a talent for it, it is sometimes considered to be the most important feature distinguishing engineering from science. More properly it is an engineering effort and not a scientific one if the immediate objective is something that can be used or adapted for use by other people, rather than solely the attainment of further knowledge. It is, nevertheless, the counterpart of the creative efforts of the theoretical and experimental scientist. It is an artistic endeavor. It is capable of elegance distinguished both by simplicity and proportion in its result and by ease of manufacture to meet exacting requirements. Like its scientific counterparts, it is not systematically taught in university courses. Although it is often a team effort, the most elegant examples are likely to be particularly dependent on the talent and experience of one or two persons.

The second phase is development. Although guided largely by scientific principles and data, it is an engineering effort, and partakes of many industrial practices relatively unexplored by the scientist. It has a counterpart in science—the evaluation of a discovery by the scientist and his peers. The scientist is obligated to report his discovery by submitting a paper to a scientific or technical journal, and to make a presentation that is as logical and defensible as possible, with a realistic appraisal of scope to applicability and any limitations of the results. He often becomes so absorbed in these aspects that the creative character of his research becomes submerged and inconspicuous. Then his peers continue the evaluation, exploring variations of his calculations, testing them in particular applications, or repeating his experiments. The evaluation altogether usually involves much more effort, if less genius, than the discovery. Similarly, development is a large operation by comparison with initial design.

The descendents of the prototype must be made with performance characteristics specified for the particular application—not much greater or less. They must come to be manufacturable and reliable. Manufacture is by repetitive operations in accordance with formal drawings and specifications and followed by inspections and tests for acceptance or rejection. The more versatile technicians employed for this phase are more concerned with tooling and apparatus for inspection and test than with performing the direct operations of manufacture. The items accepted are designated for further tests to detect any deficiencies in the design or manufacturing processes or they are assembled into a vehicle for flight test. Various corrective actions are taken to provide better reliability and performance and to reduce the rejection rate.

One surprising characteristic of development is a tendency toward simplification of design if the performance requirements do not become more exacting. The need for reliability and low rejection rate encourages this but is not the only factor. There are many more possible complicated designs than simple ones. Therefore if design features are picked at random, the design is likely to be complicated. The prototypes for radically new devices are often unnecessarily complicated because there has not been sufficient time to find simple ways of doing things. Development remedies this.

Of course, not all engineering projects involve development. One does not build dozens of bridges and test them before fitting one bridge in place over a river. Development is normally a step toward quantity production. Certain structural items, especially large ones such as launch stands and launch silos not intended for manufacture in quantity, are primarily dependent on initial design. But equipment with elaborate functional requirements cannot be made reliable without development.

How important is creativity in the development engineer? It is essential. However, he is subject to more and more restraint late in the schedule. Development is a process that seldom builds overconfidence in existing designs. The defects are laid bare to the participant. Many were inherent in the original approach and are never entirely eliminated or kept from being troublesome in manufacture. There is always a strong incentive to find radically different principles to serve as a basis for a new design. But there is no development experience on the new design. One may merely be trading a set of difficulties one has learned to live with for a new set as yet unknown. Late in the development phase, a radically different approach can seldom be pursued except as a parallel effort, and it will seldom lead to adoption of a new design until system production is well underway or a contract is let for a new overall program. The more the experience gathered on the first approach, the more the alternate must be tested.

The third stage is production. The trends of manufacture that started in development are carried even further with more dependence on industrial practices. (Not long ago, high-rate production was a uniquely American capability.) Manual operations are further simplified and are designed for repetitive performance by relatively unskilled workers; detailed directions are established for all operations. This procedure increases the output for a given cost, and is more compatible with frequent inspection and testing for control of quality. Interchangeability is an even more important factor in acceptance. There is greater expenditure for special tooling, such as die-casting molds and dies for forming of sheet metal, and for automation. Because of changes in the tooling and processing, there is usually a new set of drawings and specifications that are even more detailed and formal. There is likely to be some initial loss of reliability; the first products of the production line are subject to the extensive evaluation and testing characteristic of development. Where it is reasonable to do so, operational use is deferred until the production models achieve or surpass the reliability of the developmental models.

We have discussed research, development, and production as distinct phases. In practice, in missile and space programs, the three overlap to some degree. There may be three separate organizations, but supporting research continues during development and even during production. Production starts well before development models stop being manufactured. Often further design changes are introduced and tested on late developmental models and adapted to the concurrent production line later. A factor that further confuses the dividing points is that new systems commonly use some existing items of hardware with such further modification or improvement as may be necessary. In other words, the different portions of the system may not start at the same stage of preparation.

Most of the early experimental space firings were performed with modified production ballistic missiles as boosters, coupled to specially constructed payloads. Often there were only two or three vehicles put together with the same configuration and payload. In such efforts, the three phases become quite undistinguishable, except that some of the ingredients for the system come off a production line. With more experience in space, we are able to use more vehicles of a kind and to conform more to established industrial patterns. Except for manned vehicles and ballistic weapons, however, there is little distinction be between a test flight and the intended use of a vehicle. In consideration of the abbreviated development programs, our space shots have had a striking record of successes.

SCHEDULE

It is apparent that all missile and space effort except fundamental research is subject to a schedule. The duration is determined partly by when the system is needed and partly by what is feasible in a given length of time. The schedule affects many engineering decisions. If it is short, there will be the utmost use of existing production items with such modification or scaling up or down as is necessary. If the schedule is less pressing, there may be time to use devices that are in early research.

The schedule often appears to obstruct progress, but it is a necessary feature of any program. It ensures that there will be a usable system in reasonable time rather than the ultimate system by the time the general approach is obsolescent. It ensures that the different portions of a system keep pace with each other. It prevents any obsession with the problems of one portion from obstructing tests of the overall system.

CONCURRENCY

The emergency that gave rise to the long-range ballistic missile program also bred the doctrine of concurrency. This doctrine prescribes not only extreme overlap of research, development, and production, with any parallel approaches that may be advisable, but simultaneous engineering and construction of everything necessary for operational use of the system. It results in some increased confusion and immediate cost, but it is a good doctrine when applied with judgment. It gains time. It gambles the possibility of generating a complete system about an unsatisfactory vehicle against the possibility of having a satisfactory vehicle that cannot be used extensively for several years. At its best, as applied to urgently needed systems with clearly understood applications, it provides much more gain on investment, with negligible slippage of schedule or increase in total cost during the interval from inception to obsolescence.

ENGINEERING ORGANIZATION

The organization of a space-oriented company may follow a variety of patterns. The types of projects to be worked on will affect it somewhat, but there are many ways of organizing for the same projects. Organization is seldom static. Generally it evolves with time—guided by certain principles, but often critically influenced by the capabilities of the particular people available whose responsibilities are to be rearranged.

Especially in the research and development phases, organization tends to be a compromise between project and functional styles. The project style follows a breakdown of the engineering tasks to be accomplished and assigns line responsibilities accordingly from top to bottom. Each department, section, or group is provided with the facilities, designers, draftsmen, technicians, machinists, etc., that are necessary for the task to be performed. This provides the most clear-cut responsibilities and ensures that facilities and services are directly available for each task. However, it encounters difficulty in maintaining equitable and consistent work loads for individuals, and it is difficult to adapt to changing manpower requirements. The functional style groups people by function and operates primarily by temporary assignment of tasks or people horizontally across the organization chart. This tends to equalize work loads, makes it easier to maintain uniform

Figure 3   Space systems management company.

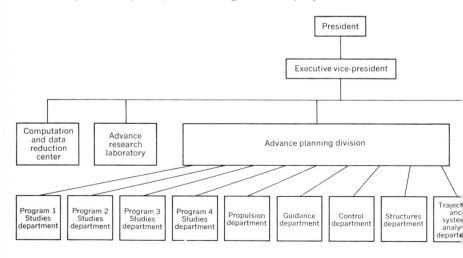

standards, and decreases the chance of generating designs that can be built by only one uniquely skilled technician. It is more adaptable to changing manpower requirements. It maintains versatility of talent through varied experiences. However, there is much less continuous experience on one project. Project loyalty and feelings of responsibility are less intense. The various tasks are necessarily handled according to priority. This makes the functional style less responsive to needs for quick design changes and awkward for exploratory research and development. When functional groups are large and autonomous, management requires large amounts of expensive manpower, and they render inferior service to any small projects that may be dependent on them. Both factors increase the costs. Schedules are often delayed.

A large priority project must have all its own functions rather than compete with other projects for them. Accordingly, in a large, diversified company, the functional style of organization is unlikely to be applied near the top. At the other extreme, the project style of organization may be used for special small projects in order to keep them from becoming entangled too deeply in a complicated priority system.

Let us look at several simplified organization charts. So that we can concentrate on engineering aspects, various functions of administration and support will be omitted. In other respects, the charts are similar to those for existing companies, but probably not identical with any.

The first chart, shown in Fig. 3, is a possible organization for a company concerned with systems management of several space pro-

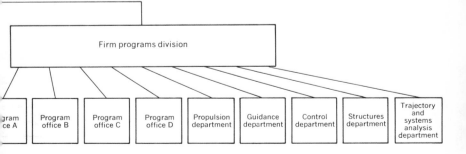

grams, but not with carrying out production or detailed development.

The Computing and Data Reduction Center is a group of mathematicians and programmers who are capable of solving various physical and engineering problems once they are expressed in mathematical terms. When high-accuracy computations are required, the center utilizes a digital computer, which is programmed according to the problem to perform arithmetic operations like a desk calculator. It is of electronic design, capable of handling numerous many-digit numbers at once with extreme rapidity. For less complex problems requiring less accuracy but high speed, the center may use an electronic analogue computer, which computes by performing operations on the magnitudes of voltages as a slide rule operates on distances along the rule.

The organization also includes an Advance Research Laboratory for research on devices not yet ready for incorporation into systems, an Advance Planning Division for planning of systems not yet in a contractual stage, and a Firm Program Division for management of programs for which contracts to associate contractors or subcontractors have been let. The latter two divisions are subdivided into functional departments concerned with engineering disciplines, and also into program offices that have direct responsibility for particular programs, with technical support from the functional departments.

Figure 4 shows a possible organization for a company research and

Figure 4   Project A: Research and Development Division.

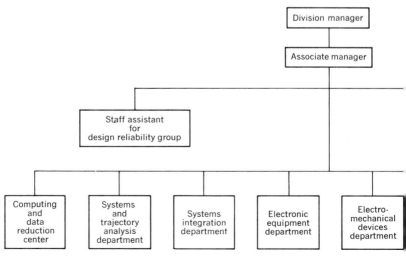

development division concerned with development of a space payload or a late stage of a booster rocket. The actual titles for particular responsibilities would depend somewhat on the company. The manager and associate manager divide the overall responsibilities in accordance with their capabilities and personalities, the associate manager carrying full responsibility for any decisions necessary while the manager is away. There are several staff assistants, who may exert a strong direct influence on the various departments by virtue of the authority of the manager and by virtue of their own experience and personality. There are several departments with responsibility for particular portions of the project. Support is provided by a computing center. Another department ensures that all developmental hardware meets inspection and test requirements according to specification before acceptance for system application. Two other departments provide liaison with the production plant and with associate contractors having other responsibilities toward the overall vehicle.

In Fig. 5, the Electromechanical Devices Department is broken down further into four sections with direct responsibility for certain devices, a design and drafting section, a test section, and a machine shop. Figure 6 shows a possible simplified organization chart for the production corresponding to Fig. 4.

Production and development are not always separated as indicated

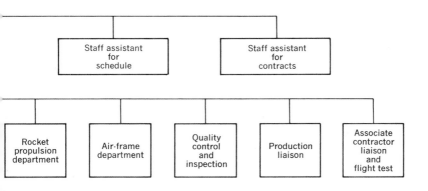

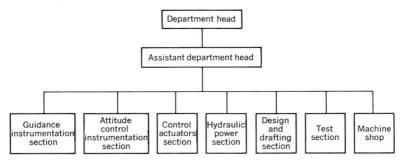

Figure 5   Electromechanical Design Department.

by the charts shown here. Sometimes they are combined into the same organization and intermingled at lower levels. Product engineers are assigned to work alongside development engineers within the same group or section as units of a system reach the stage at which production planning is timely.

There are virtues in some separation of research and development from production, but hazards in complete isolation from it. Research and development, on the average, require more time to contemplate and create. The engineering associated with production is focused more on the minute-to-minute needs of the production line—a matter of

Figure 6   Project A: production.

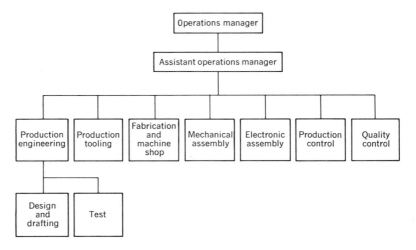

being on immediate call as crises arise. The regulations and working conditions that are optimum for one are not necessarily suitable for the other. Managers with experience primarily in one may lack insight into the other. Mishandling of the matter can lead to chaotic situations or have severely adverse effects on engineering morale. However, extreme isolation does not favor a smooth flow of hardware through development into production. There tend to be too many development designs that are difficult to adapt to production tooling and requirements, and too little attention to detailed functional requirements during redesign for production. Some intermingling is essential.

It should not be presumed that all engineering is done strictly according to the organization chart. Much is accomplished through informal relationships; a chart seldom represents the optimum arrangement of talents for every detailed problem that arises. Often the most significant achievements of an engineer are accomplished by identifying new problems informally and devising solutions when his talent is appropriate if priority work load permits.

Yet, the organization chart and associated responsibility assignments accomplish three necessary things. First, they provide a framework for resolving conflicts of responsibility, should these arise. Second, if management at various levels is effective, they help to ensure that no task is overlooked for a critical period of time. Third, they provide a framework for the administering of salary increases, promotions, and related matters. Such decisions in respect to any particular engineer are influenced also by his reputation among his colleagues, which as a rule spreads widely in a company. Reactions concerning an engineer's ability and personality are readily available for the asking. Usually these are frank evaluations showing a surprising consistency. Any that go to extremes of adulation or maliciousness are immediately suspect. The organization chart, with some built-in checks and balances as, for example, the role of the personnel department in maintaining uniform and equitable standards and controlled total cost, provides the authority for the decisions.

THE MERCURY PROGRAM

The first four orbital manned flights accomplished by the United States were an end result of Project Mercury. A brief review of this space achievement may help to put space engineering in a better perspective.

The boosters for the Mercury orbital flights were modified boosters originally designed for Atlas intercontinental ballistic missiles. The accelerated Atlas project got under way in 1955 as part of the crash program of the United States Air Force to meet the threat of Soviet long-range ballistic missiles. The Atlas was based in part on development work carried on previously by General Dynamics-Astronautics, then known as Convair, but its size was scaled down to take advantage of new lightweight thermonuclear warheads. It was of integral tank and airframe construction—a stainless steel compound balloon kept rigid during launch and flight by pressurization. It was of 1½-stage design, with three liquid-propellant rocket engines in line across the base and operated from the same kerosene and liquid-oxygen tanks. At staging, the two outer engines but no tanks were jettisoned. This rather unconventional design avoided the problem of starting a second-stage rocket engine at altitude.

The Atlas was developed under the overall management of the Air Force Ballistic Missile Division (AFBMD) and procured for the Strategic Air Command (SAC) by the Ballistic Missile Office of the Air Materiel Command. Overall systems engineering and technical direction were carried out by the Guided Missile Research Division of the Ramo-Wooldridge Corporation, now the TRW-Space Technology Labora-

Figure 7   Astronaut in mockup Mercury capsule.

Figure 8   Mercury capsule being serviced on the launch pad.

tories. However, hardware development and production were entirely the responsibility of associate contractors. General Dynamics-Astronautics was responsible for the airframe, attitude control system, overall assembly, overall checkout, and launch. The engines were developed and supplied by Rocketdyne, a division of North American Aviation, Inc. The reentry vehicle, except for the thermonuclear warhead, was the responsibility of the General Electric Co., Missiles and Space Vehicles Division. Two guidance systems were developed. The system having the greater initial priority utilized monopulse and Doppler radars developed by the General Electric Co., Light Military Electronics Department and Heavy Military Electronics Department, with the Burroughs Corporation supplying the ground-based digital computer. The Arma Division of the American Bosch-Arma Corporation had the responsibility for an alternate inertial system consisting of an inertial platform and

Figure 9   Takeoff of Mercury vehicle.

airborne computer. Any misalignment of the platform was sensed by two 2-axis displacement gyroscopes and corrected by three servo systems. The platform carried three integrating accelerometers to measure three components of velocity. The airborne digital computer integrated the accelerometer outputs, to obtain position data as well, and made the decisions necessary to keep the missile on course and to terminate thrust at precisely the instant required.

This brief summary does not by any means include all the contractors involved in the missile, the test program, and the construction of launch facilities, but it should give some idea of the extent of the program needed to develop the Atlas missile. More detail will be provided in Chap. 9, where it is considered as an example of a large system.

Our long-range ballistic missiles were designed entirely as military weapons in response to the construction of similar weapons by the

Soviet Union. Its missiles had a large weight-lifting capability which it proceeded to exploit in various unmanned and manned space missions. Designing for the new small thermonuclear warheads resulted in smaller and better missiles but left the United States with a relative deficiency in weight-lifting capability for space missions that was to persist for several years. We had little difficulty in performing measurements and scientific experiments in unmanned flights because of our skill in miniaturization. For manned flights, the deficiency presented somewhat more of an engineering challenge.

The Mercury program called for replacement of the Atlas reentry vehicle with a spacecraft modification of the Atlas for compatibility with the new flight objectives, the performance of several suborbital flights to "prove out" the vehicle, and the performance of several orbital flights. The McDonnell Aircraft Co., under contract to the National Aeronautics and Space Administration (NASA), developed the spacecraft, which carried an oxygen supply, three rockets for separation, and retrorockets to start the descent into the earth's atmosphere. Modifications of the Atlas to serve as a booster was directed by the Space Systems Division (a descendant of the Ballistic Missile Division and the Ballistic Missile Office) of the Air Force Systems Command. Systems engineering and technical direction for the booster were provided by the Aerospace Corporation, a new nonprofit corporation (or public trust) that took the place of the Space Technology Laboratories for such responsibilities on new programs.

Figure 10   Mercury capsule in the ocean during recovery.

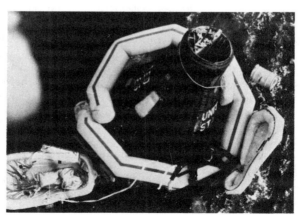

Although improvement in the reliability of the Atlas for the new application was desirable, an extensive test program to demonstrate attainment of the reliability objective was not feasible. Numerous detail changes were made and all systems were prepared and checked out with great care. Some of the changes were made simply for compatibility with the new trajectory and payload. Various space-program radars at stations about the world were used to track and command the spacecraft. Other changes were made in an effort to improve reliability even further. An intensive failure-analysis program was carried out for the Atlas under the direction of Aerospace Corporation with emphasis on all safety considerations. In addition, an abort-sensing and -implementation system was developed. This was intended to sense any major malfunction of the launch vehicle and to trigger the escape mechanism of the capsule before the astronaut was endangered.

Under the direction of NASA, with the effective cooperation of the Air Force, the Navy, and numerous civilian companies and organizations, with all technical problems discussed openly in an atmosphere of mutual trust, Project Mercury achieved a high degree of success. In the full orbital flights, only minor malfunctions, readily compensated for by the astronaut, or of little consequence, were observed. Except that one flight lasted for one orbit less than planned, all objectives including recovering of the spacecraft with its contents were achieved.

In preparation for the orbital flights, there were four suborbital flights using the Redstone rather than the Atlas booster. The last two were manned. The third, the *Freedom 7*, carried Comdr. Allan Shepard on May 5, 1961, to an altitude of 116 miles and a total range of 303 miles. The fourth, the *Liberty Bell 7*, carried Capt. Virgil I. Grissom to 118 miles altitude and 302 miles total range. Comdr. Shepard was the first American astronaut in space.

There were in total six orbital flights using the Atlas booster, with slight changes of configuration from one to another. The first launch was on September 13, 1961. The spacecraft completed one orbit with a simulated crewman. On November 29, 1961, the chimpanzee Enos was carried through two orbits. Three had been planned. On February 20, 1962, the *Friendship 7* carried Lt. Col. John Glenn, Jr., through three orbits. On May 24, 1962, the *Aurora 7* carried Lieut. Comdr. Scott Carpenter through three orbits. On October 3, 1962, the *Sigma 7* completed six orbits with Comdr. Walter Shirra. The sixth and last launch of the Mercury series was on May 15, 1963. The *Faith 7* carried Maj. L. Gordon Cooper through 22 orbits. During the flights the physiological condition of the test animal and the astronauts was care-

Figure 11 Mercury capsule being brought aboard ship.

fully monitored. The astronauts carried out a planned program of measurements and observations in orbit.

EDUCATION FOR THE SEVERAL ASPECTS
OF SPACE ENGINEERING

At the beginning of the chapter, we stressed the fact that engineers and scientists educated in many of the classical disciplines may contribute to space engineering. Now that we have seen some of its aspects, this point may be made more specifically. The propulsion aspect clearly relates to chemistry and chemical engineering. Since chemical and

Figure 12   Air Force control board records progress of all man-made space vehicles. (Philip Gendreau)

fission-hydrogen rockets expel their propellants as a dense gas at hypersonic speeds, aerodynamics is involved. The heating and expansion of the propellants is a thermodynamic and heat-transfer problem. The mechanisms for control of burning involve mechanical and electrical engineering. And the problem of designing the rocket chamber so that it is structurally stable and will not melt requires structural and materials engineering of the highest order.

The control and guidance problem requires instrumentation of both a mechanical and electronic nature, and specialized communication and radar systems. In the guidance problem astronomy and astrodynamics are used in computation of trajectories. Computer specialists and applied mathematicians are especially useful here, as detailed analysis of the problem and processing of the guidance data require both analogue and digital computation.

Industrial engineers will contribute particularly in the manufacturing and reliability phase. Bioengineers will be required in projects on manned vehicles, or in any projects concerned with animals or other living matter. A physicist will find many challenging problems in all phases—even in classical physics. One could go on, but these examples are sufficient to make the point. What about courses and curricula oriented specifically toward space engineering? They are good if basic and sound, but they should avoid overspecialization or overemphasis on the specialist's viewpoint, as each group must work with the other groups and understand their problems, and the manager or systems

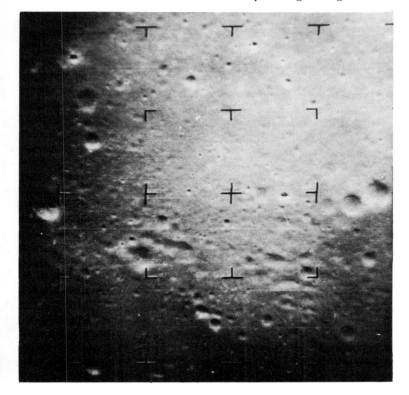

Figure 13   Photograph taken by the spacecraft *Ranger 7* from an altitude of 12 miles above the moon. It shows an area 4 miles square, with craters as small as 45 feet in diameter. (NASA)

engineer must consider all problems impartially. No matter how the curriculum is organized, a good part of the specialized training must take place on the job, as in other very rapidly changing fields of science and engineering.

PARTNERSHIP OF INDUSTRY AND EDUCATION

A space engineering capability is dependent on both educational institutions and industrial competence. Education provides the background disciplines and occasionally some orientation in space engineering. The industry often has motivations for research, because of problems it encounters, that are not found in the university or institute of technology. Sometimes new disciplines are conceived in the industry and expanded in partnership. Control system theory and information theory are examples. The varied problems and the interdisciplinary needs of space engineering will have profound effects on the industry and on scientific and engineering education.

The industry also has many engineering practices developed empirically over the years and not reducible as a whole to a classical pattern. They become evident in the development phase and more dominant in production. They are often improved in detail by application of science or mathematics, for example, the application of statistics to appropriate matters of quality control. In short, space engineering is a decision-making operation with roots both in scientific and engineering disciplines and in available precedent, as well as in education and the industry.

The experience gained in diversified science and engineering and the many interdisciplinary problems of the space effort will enrich both academic knowledge and industrial technology.

The Engineering of Large Systems

---

by M. P. O'Brien

Morrough P. O'Brien graduated in Civil Engineering at
the Massachusetts Institute of Technology. He did graduate work at Purdue University and at the Royal Technical University in Stockholm, the latter on a Freeman
Fellowship. He taught at Purdue University and at the
University of California. He was Chairman of the Department of Mechanical Engineering and Dean of the
College of Engineering at Berkeley. He is currently Dean
Emeritus. He holds honorary degrees from Northwestern and Purdue Universities.

Dr. O'Brien has served as a consultant to industry
and government throughout his academic career. He
was Director, Research and Engineering for the Air Reduction Company from 1947 to 1949 while on leave
from California. Since 1949 he has been a consulting
engineer for the Aerospace divisions of the General
Electric Company; in this capacity he has been involved
in the planning and analysis of large systems.

In 1929, he initiated the program of field and laboratory research of what became the United States Beach
Erosion Board and has been active in coastal engineering since that time. He served as a member of this
Board from 1940 to 1965 and is now a member of its

successor, the Coastal Engineering Research Board.

Dr. O'Brien has served in many capacities as an adviser to government. He has been a member of the Army Scientific Advisory Panel since its formation in 1950 and served as chairman, 1961-65. In 1958 President Eisenhower appointed him a member of the Board of the National Science Foundation.

These consulting and advisory assignments and many others of lesser duration in industry and government are the background for this chapter.

LARGE SYSTEMS ARE SO COMMONPLACE in modern society that the average person has given little thought to the process by which they came into existence or to the mechanisms which keep them in operation —except occasionally when the power fails or traffic jams a highway. We take for granted the smooth functioning of railways, airlines, fuel pipelines, telephone and telegraph networks, radio and television stations, food distribution, weather forecasting, water supplies, sewage disposal, and all the other systems essential to our welfare and safety. These existing civilian systems have evolved gradually around a device or concept which met a social need; the system was not planned as such but grew with the demand for the use of the device. An automobile would be a useless curiosity without the support of a system of highways, fuel supplies, repair and maintenance stations, laws and regulations, insurance schedules, and other adjuncts which grew up around the automobile. Nowadays the magnitude, complexity, and cost of these civilian systems are bringing about the realization that they must be analyzed, planned, and operated as systems, and not piecemeal, if they are to grow and function effectively.

Military operations also require systems of men, equipment, and facilities which must be planned from "scratch" to carry out different missions, and it is this requirement which has stimulated much of the explicit attention to systems as such. During World War II, a technique called *operations research* was applied with great success to the analysis of the operations of combat systems such as underseas warfare, air defense, and bombing attacks; this thinking has carried over to the study of hypothetical future systems to the extent that almost all new military equipment is designed and evaluated as part of a system. The method is also useful to large civilian systems, and this with other tools has brought about the consideration of systems engineering as a separate subject.

The circumstances giving rise to the recent emphasis on systems engineering have been aptly stated by Kershner [1] as follows:

Before the beginning of this century the devices developed by mankind had all been of sufficient simplicity that it was perfectly possible for a single man to fully understand their functioning. Even the first airplane was fully understood by each of the Wright brothers. In this century, and particularly during and since World War II, there have been an increasing number of devices (e.g. gun computers, radar sets, guided missiles, etc.) of sufficient complexity that no one man can understand in intimate detail the entire device. It is further true that these devices exhibit an unprecedented degree of interrelationship of the parts, a dependence of the behaviour of one section on another, that greatly complicates a full understanding of the device. A large thing need not be difficult to understand, from a system standpoint, if it consists of a large number of parts which function essentially independently. It is when the behavior of the parts contributes to an overall intended function and where there is a dynamic behavior that causes complex interrelations between the parts that the characterizing aspect of systems engineering enters the analysis of the situation.

Engineers and engineering play an important role in the planning, design, construction, and operation of large systems, military and civilian. Other specialists and laymen also participate, and there are many aspects other than engineering which are important to the realization of a major system; this chapter, however, will be focused on the engineering phase since engineering is the subject of this book. Chapter 1 discusses the nature of professional engineering in general and describes the series of steps through which an engineering project proceeds from the design concept to its realization in operation. The design of large systems follows the same sequence; the difference between small and large projects lies primarily in the size and complexity of the organization necessary for carrying out these steps.

THE CONCEPT OF A SYSTEM

A *system* is an aggregate of components, sometimes including men and even animals, which act together to perform a desired function. Consider the man-machine system involved in the travel of a motor vehicle

[1] Richard B. Kershner, *Proceedings of the Workshop on Systems Engineering, IRE Transactions on Education*, vol. E-5, no. 2, June, 1962.

along a highway. From a broad viewpoint, the vehicle is a *component* in the system called highway transportation. From another viewpoint, the moving vehicle is a system of two components, a man and a vehicle which act together to achieve the objective of travel along a highway, hopefully without accident. The man controls certain "inputs" to the vehicle—steering, throttle, and brakes—and produces the desired "output"—ordered movement. The man need not understand the mechanism by which these inputs and outputs are related (and generally he does not) so long as he is skilled in their relationship. The vehicle is a "black box" in the slang of systems engineering. Furthermore, the driver is also a black box because the inputs to him—the stimuli of white lines on the roadway, weather conditions, traffic signs, other vehicles, honking horns, and so forth—produce outputs in the form of muscular motions applied to the input mechanisms of the vehicle. The average man knows even less about the mechanisms relating his own inputs and outputs than he does about those of the vehicle he drives—but drive he does, with a relatively high degree of effectiveness, marred occasionally by malfunctions of the system. If we probe deeper, we see that both the man and the motor vehicle are each systems made up of many components. Clearly there is here a semantic problem because *system* and *component* have different meanings depending on the level from which they are viewed. A system becomes a component, or subsystem, of the next higher level of aggregation. This point will be illustrated in later specific examples.

Considering the aggregate of components which act together to perform a desired function, one may analyze the performance of the resulting system by considering only the interactions of the input-output relationships of the components without reference to the internal mechanism of each component. One links together "black boxes" of known input-output characteristics, including in some systems black boxes which measure the output, compare it with a desired value, and send back a command to alter the input. By analysis of the interrelationships between components, one can predict the input-output characteristics of the system as a whole; at least, one can do so in principle if all the pertinent characteristics of the components are accurately known.

Consider the *systems analysis* problems represented in Fig. 1, dealing with a water distribution system consisting of two components, namely, (*1*) a pump (Fig. 1A) which takes water from a source and discharges it into (*2*) the distribution mains (Fig. 1B). What are the system characteristics? The answer to this question requires a knowledge only of the principle governing the interrelationship of these components. It is not necessary, in order to analyze the system, to

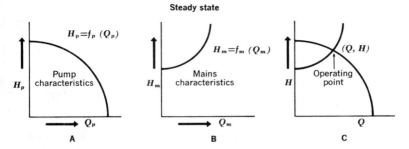

Figure 1   Water distribution system.

understand the factors determining the component characteristics. In this example the physical relationship between the components is

$Q_p = Q_m$ All the water delivered by the pump must pass into the distribution system.

$H_m = H_p$ Flow in the system will increase until the back pressure of the mains equals the pressure developed by the pump.

Applying these conditions graphically (Fig. 1C), we superimpose the two characteristics and find that there is only one steady-state operating point (Q,H). If Q is not the rate of flow desired, the systems analyst may consider the alternatives to achieve the desired result, namely, alteration of the characteristics either of the pump or of the distribution mains until the operating point coincides with the Q desired.

The reader should not conclude from this simple example that systems analysis is a trivial subject. If the system considered were composed of thousands of components, linked together in series or parallel, operating through transient states, with time lags, dead bands, and other complicating factors, the analysis could become very complex indeed; the characteristics may vary because of manufacturing quality, temperature, service wear, or other causes in such an unpredictable fashion that the component characteristics, shown in Fig. 1 as lines, must be represented as zones having a width depending on these uncertainties.

The example of Fig. 1 carries through the systems analysis problem graphically. If the characteristics of the components can be represented algebraically, over the whole range of independent variables or over discrete segments, the solution may be obtained algebraically.

The objective is the same: to discover compatible operating states of all the interrelated components; the method is to relate quantitatively the input-output characteristics of the components in a manner compatible with physical laws determined by the way in which the components are linked together. The key phrase here is "the external characteristics of the components"; the systems *analyst* need not know why these characteristics exist or what must be done to change them.

Systems engineering deals with the creation of systems which do not yet exist; like all engineering, the starting point is a quantitative definition of an objective and the *synthesis* of a concept potentially capable of satisfying that object's requirements. The end point is a working system, ideally one fulfilling the requirements of time and budget as well as technical performance.

To illustrate the preceding generalities, consider the design of a bomber such as the B-52, a component or subsystem of the B-52 weapons system, but a very complex system in its own right. The major subsystems are the airframe, including subsystems for fuel, electric power, etc.; the turbojet engines; the weapons to be delivered on target; the electronic systems for navigation, fire control, communications, and countermeasures; and other smaller subsystems. Examination of these subsystems reveals that in the aggregate they represent applications of the basic sciences of physics and chemistry; of the engineering sciences of structural mechanics, dynamics, metallurgy, ceramics, aerodynamics, heat transfer, combustion, and others; of the professional engineering fields of structural engineering, electrical engineering, aeronautical engineering, mechanical engineering, metallurgical engineering, and other specialties; and of manufacturing techniques ranging from the fabrication of the heavy spars and other main-strength members to the delicate operations required in the manufacture of gyroscopes, vacuum tubes, and semiconductors. As a gauge of the complexity of these major subsystems, the cost of developing a modern aircraft turbine engine through design, development, and test to the point of quantity production, but not including the cost of production, ranges from $50 million to $200 million, depending on the size and the performance specifications. This sum is spent almost entirely on engineering—salaries of engineers, draftsmen, and technicians, test parts, computer time, cell tests, in-flight tests, and so forth. One need not go further with the example to conclude that:

1   No individual can have the knowledge, and much less the time, to review the design of all the individual components involved.

2 Achievement of the overall objective requires tight coordination of the design to assure compatibility of the subsystems and components. Systems engineering is the term used to connote this overall view.

Carrying this example a little farther to illustrate how complex some systems may become, consider the system of which the B-52 airplane is a part. Other major components are the tankers for in-flight refueling; a worldwide system of air bases; ground-support equipment for fuel, maintenance, and spare parts; facilities for storing and controlling the nuclear warheads; early-warning ground-based radar; electronic systems for communication, navigation, and countermeasures; training schools for specialized personnel; a transportation system to move personnel, fuel, weapons, and equipment; and much more. The objective in building the bomber is to perform a mission—delivery of bombs on a target—and the decision to design and manufacture a bomber and introduce it into the military system requires that all these other items be provided to support its operation; the cost of the whole system must be analyzed and considered in making the decision to proceed.

One reason these overall systems characteristics and costs must be considered is that major military systems take an appreciable fraction of the total national income. Another is that there are usually one or more competing systems which may be employed for the same purpose, and the pressure of costs forces a comparison of alternatives in advance of production in order to achieve the desired results at least cost. Furthermore, variations in design characteristics within one type of system—for example, weight and explosive yield of the bomb or speed, altitude, and range of the bomber—will produce different effectiveness and different costs; within the limitation that the ultimate objective must be achieved, the engineer should consider the "trade-offs" between the design variables and the cost in order to achieve the desired results at minimum cost. Moreover, the unique problem of engineering all large systems is that such systems cost too much for a "cut and try" approach. Even though some components may be produced in quantity and may be prototype-tested before being committed to production, the system as a whole is "one of a kind." The time required to bring a system from concept to full operation is too long to try one concept and later another should the first prove unsatisfactory. One must forecast the performance and cost of the *whole* system before it exists and, generally, one cannot make this forecast with sufficient accuracy simply by analogy with existing systems.

TRADE-OFFS IN DESIGN

The aim of engineering is to create new equipment and systems which perform a desired task at minimum cost. The motivation of the sponsors of engineering work, civilian or military, is the expectation of benefits which exceed the costs by a margin sufficient to justify the risk and the effort. In industry, the benefits are normally expressed as money income and profit; for public works projects which do not yield a money return, a term frequently used is the benefit-cost ratio; for military systems, the term used is the cost-effectiveness ratio. However measured or labeled, the objective is to accomplish the desired results at minimum cost and at a cost less than the benefits gained. The systems engineer must consider the effect on cost of many alternatives open to him in all phases of the project between initial design and operation.

The design of an engineering system begins with a quantitative statement of the specifications which the system should meet. If several basically different design concepts appear feasible, they are compared quantitatively but approximately to select the concept which *appears* preferable from the standpoint of both performance and cost. Greater certainty regarding which is the best concept can be achieved only through more detailed analysis with attendant delay and cost; on the other hand, too sketchy an appraisal may lead to selection of an inferior design. Experience counsels thorough analysis before final selection of a design. However, analysis can be carried to extremes; the trade-off between cost and greater assurance that the concept chosen will be validated by final test is a matter of judgment gained from experience.

Within the scope of a single design concept, there is the opportunity to achieve the specified results with different combinations of components and subsystems and with different values of the design parameters. The system engineer must study the trade-offs open to him and select a combination which meets his requirements. Ideally, the optimum combination should be found, but practically, analysis of the possible alternatives seeks first a combination which will "do the job" and then explores variations only so long as the resulting improvements are appreciable. If the system may be "modeled" by a set of equations, by an analogue computer, or by a digital computer program, the process of optimization may be carried out conveniently and extensively.

Kershner [2] gives an example of the type of trade-off which distinguishes the systems engineering approach from the component approach:

At a very late stage in the design of a particular model of the Terrier (air-to-air missile) it was found that the power supply did not have quite enough duration. The normal, old-fashioned, engineering approach to such a problem would have been to say, in effect, "The problem arose because the power supply group failed to meet their specifications. It is up to them to redesign the power supply to meet the requirements." This approach has the virtue of organizational cleanliness and would have been a perfectly possible approach. It would also have been frightfully expensive and would have delayed the program many months. The approach actually used was to consider all the design variations that might result in an acceptable final configuration. And it turned out that the problem could be solved by an appropriate modification of any major subsystem of the missile. Among the approaches that were shown to be possible were the following:

1   Redesign any major electronic package (including the fuse) to reduce the required power to the point that the existing power supply was adequate to meet the reduced requirement.
2   Redesign the propulsion system to increase missile velocity and hence reduce the time of flight to the point that the existing power supply would last for the reduced time required.
3   Redesign the airframe or surfaces to reduce drag and hence increase velocity which again would reduce the time required for power supply operation.
4   Redesign the computer to reduce the amount of maneuver which reduces the induced drag accomplishing the same effect as **3**.

It turned out that the fourth possibility could be accomplished in less than a week and required only the change of a few resistors and capacitors.

Although this example dealt with a design, it illustrates the general approach of the systems engineer in seeking the best balance among component and subsystem characteristics to yield the optimum result.

A second situation requiring the compromise of trade-off may appear early in the design process. Systems analysis may indicate that, although the design concept will permit meeting the performance objectives, the specifications are so severe or so unbalanced in some respect that the system will be too costly, of unacceptable reliability, or otherwise questionable. The specifications should be reviewed with a view to compromise between performance and other system characteristics. It may be that another concept discarded on first screening may prove superior. Rigid, inflexible performance objectives, written without regard to the difficulties, complexities, and cost they impose, can be very expensive and may even cause abandonment of a sound concept; they should be as restrictive as the system really requires, but no more so.

The abilities and limitations of human beings affect the design of engineering systems because these systems must be fabricated, assembled, and tested; they must be operated by human operators at least to the extent of override by an operator in even the most completely automatic systems; and they must be repaired and maintained. The complexity introduced by the designer to achieve superior performance in a system may be nullified by human factors. Major problems of this type in the area of fabrication are usually corrected early because this work is organizationally close to engineering; some systems are found to show less than their potential performance or availability because they are too complex to be operated and maintained at full effectiveness by the technicians available. The designer must consider the alternatives of training better operators, designing a less complex system and accepting lesser performance, or adding features to a complex system to simplify the operation and maintenance. The difficulties encountered in the operation and maintenance of complex military systems by service personnel are forcing systems engineers to give increasing attention to these human limitations.

A few examples of large engineering systems will illustrate some of these points and will provide a basis for further discussion. They are purposely related to the subjects of other chapters, but the use here will be to illustrate the philosophy, the problems, and the tools of systems engineering.

ATLAS INTERCONTINENTAL BALLISTIC MISSILE

Rocket artillery dates back at least to the eleventh century A.D. Thrust is produced by the action of a jet composed of the products of combustion; more precisely, the pressure necessary to exhaust these gases in a backward direction exerts an equal and opposite reaction on the nozzle and exhaust cone. If the thrust developed exceeds the weight, self-launched flight is possible. As the propellant fuel burns, and is exhausted through the nozzle, the mass of the missile decreases and the missile accelerates to a terminal velocity at "burn-out."

The modern development of rockets was pioneered by an American,

Dr. Robert H. Goddard,[3] who developed analytically and experimentally the basic principles of design applied today. (The quantitative relationship between burn-out velocity, impulse, weight of fuel, and weight of missile have been discussed in Chap. 8.) Goddard showed that, in the ideal case, the tankage or container should be shed as soon as the contained fuel has been burned. The practical implementation of this idea is to *stage* the propulsion system and to jettison each stage when its fuel is exhausted A complete missile consists of one or more propulsion stages, a payload, operationally a warhead, and a fire control or guidance system, plus necessary ground equipment to check out and fire the missile. A ballistic missile follows a trajectory determined by its initial velocity and direction, by gravity, and by the aerodynamic resistance. Long-range missiles require a high velocity at burn-out; their trajectory is largely outside of the atmosphere. They reenter the atmosphere and are slowed down by air resistance before impact.

During World War II, German engineers extended the work of Goddard and developed the V-2, an operational missile with a 200-mile range. At the end of the war, both Russia and the United States recruited engineers from the group that had developed the V-2, and both countries initiated missile development programs.

The Atlas Intercontinental Ballistic Missile (ICBM) development was started in 1946 when the Air Force contracted with Convair (now General Dynamics-Astronautics) to study "self-propelled subsonic and supersonic missiles" with ranges from 1,500 to 5,000 miles. The objective was to develop a bombardment weapon with sufficient range and accuracy to attack enemy military targets from launching sites within the continental United States. The military and political advantages accruing to the nation possessing such capability were obvious, but the means of achievement were not available. Major problems included:

1 Rocket engines then available did not have sufficient thrust to accelerate a missile, of the size and warhead weight estimated, to the velocities required for these ranges.
2 The probable error of a missile increases with range. Guidance systems for long-range missiles were in a rudimentary state and could not achieve the desired accuracy. Control of the thrust vector to follow the commands of an accurate guidance system would be necessary.

[3] Robert H. Goddard, "A Method of Reaching Extreme Altitudes," Smithsonian Institution Publication no. 2540, Washington, D.C., 1919.

3 The lethal radius of the *fission* warheads then available was too small in proportion to the probable error of the missile in achieving acceptable effectiveness in attacking military (point) targets.

4 Reentry into the atmosphere of the high-velocity missile at the end of the trajectory would induce extremely high temperatures.

This study by Convair is typical of early, groping efforts to reach a difficult technical goal—one beyond the state of the design art. Problems are uncovered in greater number than solutions, but continued analytical and experimental attack is being made on them. Convair studied both glide and ballistic missiles and in 1949 favored the glide approach because rocket engines of sufficient specific impulse to power ballistic missiles were not available. One advance made during this period was the concept of mounting the rocket motors on gimbals to permit control of the thrust vector. The requirement of extremely lightweight, but structurally stable, tanks to contain the fuel and oxidant clearly presented a major problem, but one for which a solution seemed possible. However, three major problems remained until "breakthroughs" were achieved. North American Aviation had been contracted by the Air Force to study long-range air-breathing missiles which would travel to their targets within the atmosphere. This means of delivery of a warhead lay closer to the state of the design art than did the ballistic missile concept, and development proceeded more rapidly; launching of this missile required large rocket engines to bring the air-breathing ramjet up to self-sustaining velocity. It was the development of these booster rockets which solved one major problem of the Atlas.

Solution of another major problem, and the most difficult, namely, that of the weight and explosive yield of the warhead, was given impetus by the detonation of the first fusion (hydrogen) bomb; however, this first device was excessively heavy to serve as the warhead of a missile. Small hydrogen warheads of large yield were made possible by work in university laboratories during 1952 and 1953. At this juncture, a committee of scientists and engineers under the chairmanship of the late John von Neumann reviewed the technical status of the Atlas program and in 1954 reported that the thermonuclear breakthrough of the year before, which made possible the small fusion bomb of vastly increased explosive yield, "justified a major investment in the strategic-range ballistic missile." This committee concluded that an "operational prototype" could be in hand by 1960. Shortly thereafter, the project was put on a "crash" basis. The other major problem, that of protecting the reentry vehicle carrying the warhead against the extremely high but sharply transient temperatures induced by the reentry velocities, was solved through an intensive program of theoretical and experimental studies by both contractors and governmental agencies, and led first to the metallic "heat sink" design and later to the ablating shield.

A development program passes through many stages of design and test, with successive component tests and reanalyses yielding refinements to be incorporated in later versions. The design and development programs of the major components must proceed in parallel, each subprogram proceeding on the assumption that all others will meet their performance objectives on schedule. (The Atlas program required performance far beyond what had been achieved previously, particularly in regard to the reduction of warhead weight, the rocket thrust, and the weight of the fuel tanks.) Failure to achieve target performance of any component requires changes in other phases of the program. Furthermore, improvements are made in the production versions, making a compact description difficult to compile.

When Atlas ICBM (Air Force Weapons System WS 107A-1) was declared operational in March, 1961, the missile and related ground-support equipment had these characteristics:

Prime contractor	General Dynamics-Astronautics
Airframe	Length, 82.5 ft; body diameter, 10 ft; propulsion section housing diameter, 16 ft; launching weight, 260,000 lb
Power plant	Liquid fuels. 2 NAA Rocketdyne MA-3 booster engines, thrust 150,000 lb each; 1 Rocketdyne E-model sustainer engine, thrust 60,000 lb
Tanks	Length, 60 ft; diameter, 10 ft; thickness, less than 0.040 in.; no internal bracing; shape maintained by internal pressure
Nose cones	AVCO; General Electric
Guidance	GE-Burroughs; Arma. Initially, all inertial guidance; operational versions, radio-inertial; accuracy, 2 nautical miles average at 5,000 range
Performance	Maximum velocity, Mach 20; maximum range, 9,000 miles; Powered flight for 5 min from launch to altitude 100 miles; ballistic trajectory to target. Velocity approaching impact, approx. 15,000 mph; maximum reentry temperature, 10,000°F
Estimated cost in production (1958), excluding development, $2 million per missile	
Approximate number airframe parts, 40,000	

Development work which seeks to achieve performance at the limits of what is physically possible, a goal characteristic of much new military equipment, requires extensive testing, and many tests, which appear to be failures to the uninitiated, are really successful in their engineering objectives. The flight test of a missile requires that it be fired—and expended. Such tests are costly, but they must be made, no matter how much component and full-missile static testing has been done. The Atlas program, which was the pioneering effort in long-range ballistic missiles, had its share of testing troubles. The first firing occurred in 1956 and the first flight test in 1957. Up to July, 1959, 25 Atlas missiles were fired, and of these, 10 firings were rated successful, 6 partially successful, 9 unsuccessful. Unfortunately, among the unsuccessful firings mentioned were the last 5 prior to July, 1959, and among these 5 were all 3 tests made with a new D version of the design. An indication of the troubles and uncertainty surrounding such development work is found in this quotation: [4]

The last three shots have been D models, which is the operational configuration. Cause of failure in the first D-shot was one of two hold-down arms on the launcher, used to retain the missile until booster engine thrust builds up sufficiently for lift-off. They push against the missile with a pressure of 8000 psi which decays to 4000 psi in approximately half a second at the proper time, allowing the missile to pull free. In the abortive firing of the first D, one arm hung too long and damaged the glass fiber shirt around the booster portion of the missile.

The next two D shots failed because of a malfunction, still not precisely located, somewhere in the propellant flow system. Although pressure decayed too rapidly in the liquid oxygen tank, causing the bulkhead between them to reverse, pressurization of tanks has been absolved of blame and the trouble is believed to be farther along in the flow process.

The Atlas program was successful, so much so that the Atlas boosters have been used for the major space launchings. Up to October, 1961, 97 Atlas missiles had been flown; 64 flights were completely successful, 21 partially successful, and 12 failures. These incidents are mentioned here to illustrate the fact that the development engineer inevitably faces a series of crises before his job is done.

The organization brought together to develop and produce the Atlas ICBM and the plan followed are of considerable interest. The importance of this weapon to national security, the resources required to

[4] *Aviation Week,* July 6, 1959, p. 27.

develop and produce it and to introduce it into the military inventory, and its potential impact on other weapons systems led to the establishment of a special program office at Inglewood, California, called the Ballistic Missile Division, which was given an almost autonomous status within the Air Force. A parallel agency of the Air Materiel Command, with similar status, was established at the same location. The Ramo-Wooldridge Company was employed as technical adviser; it was also employed to provide the fundamental systems engineering for the Atlas missile and for two other Air Force missiles, the Thor and the Titan. This organization was responsible for all aspects of the project up to the point of operational use. The prime contractor, General Dynamics-Astronautics, was responsible for system design, design and fabrication of the airframe and related components, coordination of the design of the components supplied by subcontractors and associate contractors, assembly and test of the prototype missiles, production of the operational missiles, and supervision of installation of ground equipment and systems of the Atlas operational missile sites. Many major engineering organizations were involved; the number of individual vendors was approximately 5,000, and the total force required for production and activation involved roughly 2 million people. Following the decision to develop the Atlas missile, two other ballistic missiles, the long-range Titan (ICBM) and the intermediate-range Thor (IRBM), were also assigned to the Ballistic Missile Division. The magnitude of this task is indicated by expenditures on these three missiles in the years when all three were in development, as follows:

FY 1956	$250 million
FY 1957	750 million
FY 1958	1,000 million
FY 1959	1,300 million

These expenditures represented people to be employed, material to be purchased, facilities to be designed and built, designs to be developed and coordinated, tests to be planned, and all the other phases of a development program on an enormous scale.

An unusual aspect of the plan followed was the telescoping of the prototype development, service (military) test, production, and site activation in order to bring the missile as quickly as possible into the Air Force inventory. This principle of development work is termed *concurrency*. The development procedure usually followed is a sequential program in which the weapon is carried through a successful prototype test by the design organization; it is then redesigned to incorporate improvements indicated by the prototype test, and a number are produced for service tests by military personnel; finally the weapon is produced in quantity. This normal sequence is time-consuming, but it avoids early commitments for manufacturing facilities, long-lead time components, training facilities, and other major items of cost, leaving these decisions until the feasibility and exact configuration are defined. The Atlas missile was regarded as justifying the considerable gamble involved in proceeding with development, service test, and production as nearly concurrently as possible. How much time was gained, and at how much extra cost, is not a question which can be answered with finality, but the short span of five years between placement of the program on a crash basis and the first operational missiles was much less than could have been achieved through the normal sequential program.

Publicity regarding the Atlas missile has generally featured the "bird" itself and the exciting events attending its launching and flight —and admittedly these are the glamorous and newsworthy phases of the project. Not so well known is the extent of the engineering design and construction of the equipment and facilities on the ground; this work represents the major share of the effort and the cost. The Atlas launch sites are of three types: (1) The Atlas-D missiles are launched from "soft" sites above ground which are vulnerable to enemy attack but could be built quickly; (2) the E missiles are deployed at semi-hard sites which provide a reinforced-concrete container at ground level to provide some protection; and (3) the F missiles are located in hardened silo sites which extend 174 ft below ground level. Figures 2 and 3 show these types of sites and a schematic diagram of the F-missile launcher. In all, 129 missile-launch sites of the types shown were constructed at 11 widely dispersed locations in the United States. Each launch site includes electrical, electronic, hydraulic, pneumatic, and mechanical systems to load the propellants, raise the missile to launch position, check out all the operating systems, insert the target instructions, fire the missile, and guide it into its prescribed trajectory. The missile and its ground-support equipment must be designed as a system, and the ground equipment must be built, installed, and tested with as much care and precision as the missile itself. At the Plattsburg site, the final F-type installation, a force of 4,200 people were employed in the construction and installation. The missile contractor was responsible for establishing the technical criteria for the design of the launch sites, integrating the installation of the ground-support equipment, checking out and activating the complexes, and assisting in the training of Air Force crews. The Air Force employed firms of architects and engineers to convert the technical criteria into

Figure 2   The Atlas family of operational ICBMs poised and ready for launch. The Atlas-D (*lower left*) is deployed in a soft site in which the ICBM is stored horizontally. The semihard site (*top left*) contains the Atlas-E, still housed horizontally, but all underground. This complex, near Fairchild, Washington, is difficult to build but gives considerable protection to the missile and crew. The most difficult to construct is the Atlas-F silo, 174 feet beneath the surface of the earth. It is invulnerable to all but a direct nuclear attack. In this silo, near Plattsburg, New York, the Atlas-F is stored in an upright position with fuel on board. (General Dynamics-Astronautics)

detailed drawings and specifications. The Corps of Engineers of the Army were responsible for awarding the contracts and supervising the "concrete and steel" phase of base construction and activation.

MICROWAVE RADIO–RELAY SYSTEM (TD-2)

Telephone communications in the United States are provided by a network of interconnected local systems, nearly all of which are owned and operated by the operating components of a single corporation, the

American Telephone and Telegraph Company. The local systems and the long-line systems connecting them are known collectively as the Bell System. This section presents a summary of the development and introduction into service of the microwave radio—relay-telephone system in which the conventional long-distance coaxial cables were replaced by a series of radio-repeater stations between terminals connected to the local telephone systems. (See Chap. 5 concerning communications.)

The American Telephone and Telegraph Company (AT&T) is composed of three functional elements, namely, the Bell Telephone Laboratories (BTL), which conducts basic and applied research in telephony and designs new telephone equipment; the Western Electric Company, which manufactures telephone equipment; and 21 Bell System operating-affiliate companies, which buy and install this equipment to provide telephone service to millions of customers in the United States and Canada. Western Electric manufactures or purchases equipment according to designs submitted by Bell Telephone Labora-

Figure 3 Schematic diagram of Atlas-F missile, silo, and launcher. (General Dynamics-Astronautics)

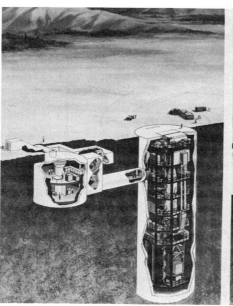

tories and does not change these designs without BTL approval. On the other hand, BTL designs must be satisfactory to Western Electric in terms of manufacturing feasibility and to AT&T and the operating companies in terms of cost, service features, reliability, and quality. These component organizations are each very large. The joint execution by them of a major, novel engineering project requires effective communications and smooth coordination of the engineering groups representing the three functional constituents—design, manufacture, and operations.

Large engineering projects require large numbers of people to carry the work through from design concept to a working system. The organization of these people into groups of manageable size and the effective direction and coordination of their work may affect substantially the cost, the elapsed time, and the value of the result. Many patterns of organization have been employed successfully, and there is no one "best" plan, but it is instructive to examine the organization and the procedures followed successfully by large organizations. The TD-2 project organization is a good example.

Within the BTL, the Systems Engineering Department performs these functions in relation to the conception, initiation, and execution of new systems development projects; namely, it (1) follows closely both the telephone equipment needs of the Bell System and the scientific and technological possibility of filling these needs; (2) analyzes possible new systems in terms of technical feasibility and economic desirability; (3) formulates and recommends to management the objectives and requirements for the development of new systems; and (4) evaluates development programs both during and after their execution. In effect, this department is responsible for the synthesis of "what is possible" from the standpoint of science and technology and of "what is needed" by the Bell System into concepts which are economically and physically feasible and which yield a profit in some form—lower costs, greater reliability, better service—sufficient to justify the investment.

The Bell Telephone Laboratories is well known among scientists and engineers for the excellence of its scientific work. Not so well known is the fact that BTL spans the range of activities described earlier, ranging from truly basic research to the design of equipment. The origins of the laboratory may explain this unusually broad scope under one management. Shortly after the first successful telephone demonstrations, Alexander Graham Bell established a small laboratory in Boston in 1876. In 1907, this laboratory was moved to New York where it became the Engineering Department of AT&T. The Western

Electric Company had establishd its own engineering department and two laboratories, one in New York and the other in Chicago. In 1925, AT&T combined its own research laboratory with the engineering department of Western Electric under a separate corporate entity, the Bell Telephone Laboratories. In 1919, the AT&T Engineering Department had been divided into two entities, the Operations and Engineering Department and the Development and Research Department. In 1935, the Development and Research Department was transferred to BTL and later became the Systems Engineering Department of the Laboratories. This long-standing close association between engineers and scientists engaged in basic research, development, and equipment design is believed to have been a major influence in the outstanding success of the organization. In 1941, BTL moved from New York to a 300-acre site at Murray Hill, New Jersey. In 1959, the staff of the laboratory included a 3,500-person professional staff, 3,800 statisticians, laboratory technicians and mechanics, draftsmen, and other technical assistants, and 3,400 administrative and clerical personnel.

A basic policy of BTL has been not to begin the development of a specific new system until the technology basic to its successful accomplishment is available from fundamental research or exploratory development. This policy does not require that all the technical problems associated with a novel development be solved before design for manufacture is undertaken, but rather that their solution does not require fundamentally new concepts. This policy is intended to assure efficient progress once a major development is started, because the rate of expenditure mounts steadily during this phase and unexpected bottlenecks, requiring a return to the research laboratory for basic or exploratory research, can be very costly.

Electromagnetic radiation was discovered by Heinrich Hertz a few years after Bell demonstrated the telephone. In 1894, Marconi began his experiments on the application of electromagnetic waves to wireless telegraphy and soon after began sending and receiving messages in Morse code; his work was the beginning of the radio industry. There was much speculation about the use of Hertzian waves for transmitting messages by others than Marconi, and unsuccessful efforts at message transmission had been attempted by AT&T as early as 1892. In 1914, the company started experiments on the possibilities of transatlantic radiotelephony, and in 1915 *speech* messages were broadcast from Arlington, Virginia, to the Canal Zone and to Paris. These early radiotelephone experiments were carried out at a frequency of 60 kc, corresponding to a wavelength of 5,000 meters. Regular radiotelephone service was initiated between New York and London in 1927 at 60 kc frequency. By 1928, the New York–London link was operating at 10 and 18 Mc (30 and 16 meters wavelength). Other applications of the radiotelephone were made between 1920 and 1941 in locations where cable laying was difficult, as between Long Beach and Catalina. During this period, BTL was active in the development of the electron tubes and related equipment required for radio transmission. A multichannel radiotelephone link had been in service at the Virginia Capes for some time, and planning had been started on a microwave radio system when World War II interrupted normal commercial development.

The term *microwave* applies to the electromagnetic spectrum above 1,000 Mc, which corresponds to a wavelength of less than one foot. These waves can be focused into a narrow beam by small parabolic antennae, and consequently offered the possibility of line-of-sight transmission at low power and without interfering with other communication channels. Furthermore, experiments had shown that this region of the spectrum would be relatively free of noise, interference, and other disturbances. There was then the attractive fact that the microwave region had not been utilized and that a wide band of frequencies was available for telephone traffic. Although line-of-sight transmission would require relay stations at frequent intervals, it would also permit reuse of the same frequencies at other geographical locations.

During World War II, BTL developed the AN/TRC-6, a mobile, multichannel, microwave radio–relay communication for the Signal Corps. The klystron developed by Varian a few years earlier was the oscillator used in this system. AN/TRC-6 provided eight 2-way message channels in the range of 4,350 to 4,800 Mc. The eight channels were obtained by a pulse-position modulation, in which all eight channels share the time of one transmitter and receiver in sequence, each channel sending a short burst transmission. Messages in the two directions were separated in frequency. Eighty-four sets of this equipment were produced, and some saw combat service. World War II was a period of intense activity in many applications of microwaves, the best known being radar.

Prior to World War II, AT&T had installed a nationwide network of multichannel coaxial cables for telephone service. Television had been developed to the point of production and commercial use when the war effort deflected all electronic capacity to military requirements. With the end of the war, television broadcasting, at very high frequencies and necessarily at line-of-sight distances, expanded rapidly, and there was a strong demand for intercity transmission of the programs. The potential magnitude of this demand is indicated by the fact that a television broadcast requires a channel capacity equal to that needed for approximately 500 voice channels. Studies of the growth in telephone traffic and of the steeply rising demands of the television industry showed that a large increase in intercity capacity would be an urgent need at a very early date. Prior to the end of the war, AT&T had planned to expand its transcontinental coaxial-cable system, and, when the war ended, began installation of the cables. However, earlier technical-economics studies had indicated the possibility that use of a microwave relay system in place of cables would bring a substantial reduction of the cost of installation. Solution of many technical problems and reliable data on the cost per telephone channel were essential before the decision to install a transcontinental network could be made. To resolve these questions, AT&T decided as early as 1943 to build and operate a microwave relay link between Boston and New York (TD-X), and to conduct experiments at several locations on radio propagation, fading, and other phenomena which might affect such a system.

The TD-X link, designed in 1945, was based on the available technology—a philosophy fundamental to BTL development programs. The basic oscillator and amplifier tubes were klystrons similar to those used in the AN/TRC-6. Antenna designs were novel but were derived from earlier development programs of the Research Department. An early phase of the design was the installation of a "bread board" model of the system to permit simulation of the actual TD-X operating conditions. Relay stations were located at the AT&T building in New York City and at BTL in Murray Hill, a distance of 21 miles, and this test system was put into operation in May, 1946. By double-looping messages sent through the test relays, it was possible to simulate the repeater conditions to be expected on the New York–Boston link. These experiments led to the decision to design the link with transmission bandwidth of 4 Mc with a capacity of 480 telephone messages or 1 television program. The decision was also reached to use frequency modulation to separate the voice channels in place of the time-sharing system employed on AN/TRC-6.

The TD-X link was completed in November, 1947, two years and ten months after the design group had been assigned to the project. The cost of development, design, construction, and experimental operation was $2.6 million, exceeding the original estimate made in 1944 by 30 percent. During the same period, the construction-cost index rose by 42 percent. The TD-X experimental system was put into commercial service for television relay in 1948 and was used for several years.

Although the TD-X experimental program was being carried through on a "crash" basis, television broadcasting had grown so rapidly that AT&T was faced with the necessity of expanding its cable system or proceeding with the microwave system without waiting for the completion of the TD-X tests. Another pressure for early decision was the growing demand for channels in the microwave region by many other users. The Systems Engineering group began design studies and cost comparisons in 1947, and by the end of that year provided an engineering comparison of the microwave relay and coaxial-cable system costs. The conclusion reached was that the radio relay system, used either solely for long-distance television transmission or for mixed telephone and television transmission, would be lower in first cost than the coaxial cable. It was estimated that the annual costs for radio relay would equal approximately the cost of cables. The question of the relative value of the two systems was reduced to the technical question of how much bandwidth could be realized and utilized in the radio relay system. The results of the TD-X tests would be required to answer this question, but the decision was reached to proceed with studies of a New York–Chicago microwave link prior to the availability of TD-X results. Television networks needed added transmission facilities by 1948, if possible, and at the latest by 1950. Various plans were studied, ranging in concept from a conservative design, which would include only those changes in the TD-X design that would make it suitable for this 1,000-mile link with a bandwidth of 3,900 to 4,200 Mc, to a more risky design involving more development effort but a system concept suitable for transcontinental transmission and a bandwidth of 3,700 to 4,200 Mc. It was believed that the conservative TD-X approach could be put into operation in 1949. However, it was also concluded that the greater bandwidth would be needed to handle the traffic. Another consideration was that the Chicago–New York link should be the first step in a transcontinental system, but the TD-X type of equipment would probably not be suitable for distances greater than 1,000 miles because the klystron amplifiers used in TD-X could not transmit over very long radio relay chains without excessive amplitude and phase distortion.

Tube technology had advanced around the klystron and magnetron concepts because of the extensive use of these types in military radar. The triode was the type of tube which, in principle, would provide the characteristics needed for TD-2, but triodes of the size and capacity required had not been developed. The technical problem was that tube dimensions decrease approximately linearly as frequency increases, and microwave frequencies require very small tubes. This potential need had been recognized earlier, and studies were under way on a triode design proposed by J. A. Morton of the BTL staff to operate at 4,000-Mc frequency. This design required a spacing between the cathode and the grid of $\frac{3}{10,000}$ in. and a grid consisting of wire $\frac{3}{10,000}$ in. in diameter with 1,000 turns of wire per inch. Nothing like these dimensions and precision had ever been achieved previously in production tubes, but laboratory models had been tested successfully.

The decision was made to proceed with the design of the TD-2 Chicago–New York relay chain, using the Morton triodes for the broadband frequency modulation and amplification required. The laboratory-proven tubes were thought to be manufacturable in quantity in spite of their extreme requirements; as a "back-up," a considerable team was assigned to development of this tube and to the related manufacturing problems.

A signal is processed through a TD-2 repeater station in the following manner: The incoming signal at 3,730 Mc is focused on the wave guide by the antenna and lens, and travels through it to the first modulation stage where the signal is mixed with a slightly offset frequency produced by a microwave generator. This mixed frequency is modulated by crystal converters to an intermediate frequency of 70 Mc. This signal then passes through many amplification stages. When the 70 Mc signal has been amplified to the necessary power level, it is again mixed with a microwave signal, and this mixed signal is modulated by the Morton triode to yield an output at microwave frequency. The outgoing signal is offset to 3,770 Mc to avoid mixing it with the low-power incoming signals at 3,730 Mc. The 3,770 Mc signal next passes three microwave amplification stages, each employing the Morton triode, then through a wave guide to the transmitting antenna and on to the next repeater station.

The Chicago–New York segment of the TD-2 system was completed and put into operation in June, 1950. The system has since been expanded to serve nearly every portion of the United States; the repeater stations have become a familiar feature of the landscape for almost every major highway. The figures of Chap. 5 picture some aspects of this system.

The TD-2 project, particularly the Morton triode development phase, is an example of the way in which technical advances are achieved. Knowledge and sound judgment based on experience set difficult but achievable goals; skill and a determination to succeed frequently achieve these objectives. The risks are great if the advance sought is beyond the existing state of the art and should be assumed only if the potential gain justifies the cost, but the alternative is to advance technically at only a slow pace. Rapid advance requires a team of imaginative, resourceful, and knowledgeable engineers and scientists whose talents span the gamut from conceptual design to production, construction, and system test; also required is the support of top management willing to take a chance and not to "panic" when the technical group encounters difficulty. Clearly, the basis for the TD-2 project had been developed, in advance of the project dates mentioned, through many years of basic and applied research in fields which *might* apply to telephone communications, and the broad, forward-looking program had provided both the knowledge and the knowledgable people that were synthesized in this program.

TENNESSEE VALLEY DEVELOPMENT

In 1933, Congress created the Tennessee Valley Authority (TVA) to develop the resources of the Tennessee River basin, an area of 41,000 sq miles in portions of 7 states. This multipurpose development is a good example of the complex influences—social, political, financial, and technical—that determine the objectives and scope of major systems in the public works area of engineering practice. The scope of this project included improvement of navigation on the Tennessee River and its tributaries, control of destructive floods in the Tennessee and Mississippi Valleys, generation of electric power, development of new forms of fertilizers and promotion of this plant food in a practical system of agriculture, and studies and recommendations to Congress and to the states regarding the development of natural resources for economic welfare in this region. (See Chap. 4, entitled "Resource Engineering.")

The TVA program required no discoveries in science or technology for its realization. Although contemporary advances in technology have been incorporated into the TVA system to reduce cost or to improve service or reliability, the state of the engineering-design art in 1933, and subsequently, has been adequate for the design, prediction of cost, and construction of the physical components of the TVA system. A combination of social, economic, and political factors—government spending on public works during the depression of the 1930s, a desire to bring the benefits of electric power to an underdeveloped area, a political philosophy of public ownership and operation of power production, and other nontechnical considerations too numerous to recount here—established the objectives of the TVA. Engineers knew what was possible in the way of dams, locks, spillways, turbines, generators, transmission lines, and other equipment and could predict the cost and performance of these components in a system; the Congress and the Administration then in office made the decision regarding the economic feasibility of the project.

Hydrology is the science of natural waters. The *hydrologic cycle* is the term used to denote the cycle of evaporation from oceans and lakes, movement of the moisture by air masses across the earth's surface, condensation as rain or snow, precipitation on the earth's surface, runoff in streams, or percolation as ground water back to the evaporating surfaces to complete the cycle. The components of this cycle show variations daily, seasonally, annually, and in longer cycles in any region on the earth's surface. Although theoretical and experimental studies have yielded quantitative explanations of many aspects of the hydrologic cycle, the principal facts about hydrology upon which engineers must base their plans for river developments are observational and statistical. In brief, past records of the duration and intensity of rainfall over the region under study and of the resulting runoff in the streams must be analyzed to yield the probable frequency and volume of future river flows: the maximum, average, and minimum flows at all critical points on the main river and its tributaries. The theory of probability is an important tool in this analysis.

The rate of flow (cubic feet of water per second) as a function of time over a period of many years, say several centuries, at critical points on the main stream and major tributaries would provide the ideal basis for planning and design. Unfortunately, adequately extensive flow records are rare and must be constructed. The questions asked by the engineer about river flow will depend on the project objective, such as the following:

1   Flood control will require a knowledge of the maximum rates of flow and the corresponding river stages. At what rate of discharge does the river begin to overflow its channel (*bank-full stage*)? What is the maximum flow on record? How frequently have lesser flood stages occurred? What flood stages are likely to occur *in the future?* In 10, 20, 50, or 100 years? The objective is to prevent flood *damage;* the economic feasibility of a flood control project requires a comparison of project cost now with the probable damage to be prevented in the future.

2   River navigation requires that some *minimum channel depth* be maintained. Meeting this requirement will depend on the minimum river discharge and its duration. Even when the river level is controlled by dams, navigation locks pass water through the dam on each lockage, and this rate of flow must be available. Flood flows also affect navigation, at least to the extent of causing stronger currents; spillway capacity must be sufficient to pass the maximum flow. What artificial works will be necessary to maintain the project channel depth at all times?

3   *Hydroelectric power* may be generated at dams or natural falls in proportion to the product of the rate of flow and the drop in level (the *head*). Dams, penstocks, turbines, generators, transformers, and switching equipment require an investment and an annual charge for capital; the return from power sales will depend upon two factors, namely, the flow available and the concurrent demand for power. Storage of energy in electrical form is not yet feasible so that the rate of generation must equal the rate of consumption. However, potential energy may be stored as water in reservoirs to be passed through the generators at rates matching the hourly, daily, and seasonal power demand. The head available at a dam varies with the river flow, the variation being greatest at low dams. *Firm power,* that is, power which is guaranteed to be delivered on demand, is more valuable than secondary power delivered as available. The variability of stream flow may be compensated in several ways, including reservoirs to store peak flows and release water at low flows and supplementary steam plants operated on fossil or nuclear fuel. Thus, power generation tends to focus attention on the average flow of a river, on variations from the average, and on means of reducing these variations.

4   *Irrigation* requires water at times and places when the natural rainfall is inadequate. Thus demand tends to be seasonally out of phase with supply; storage of peak flows and release in dry periods, extending possibly over several years, is desired.

5   *Recreation,* wildlife conservation, and mosquito control also affect river development. For example, maintenance of a stable water level in reservoirs during the summer vacation period is desirable, but this requirement will limit the other uses.

These multiple purposes not only place emphasis on different aspects of the hydrology of a river basin; they are mutually conflicting first in the design, and later in the operation, of a river project. Furthermore, the conflict is not confined to different users in the area in which the engineering works are located. For example, dams for flood control may reduce flood heights and damage to cities and agricultural lands hundreds, and even thousands, of miles away; however, the reservoir created by the dam may inundate rich agricultural land which was the productive base for a local economy. Irrigation needs dictate that water be held for release in dry seasons, whereas optimum return from installed power-generating capacity exerts pressure for steady flow throughout the year. Extreme storms may follow each other in quick succession as at Dayton in 1912; flood control dictates that reservoirs be drawn down after a flood as rapidly as the downstream channel capacity will permit.

The criterion that engineers seek to apply in the design of a river system is the achievement of the maximum ratio of benefits to costs—and in all cases a ratio greater than unity. The costs are usually measurable in dollars, but what benefits are to be included? What value is to be attached *now* to protection against a flood stage forecast to occur, say, once in fifty years? What benefits are to be credited to flood control? Is lack of damage to future buildings by a flood which will be prevented a measurable benefit? Should the enhanced value of land in the flood plain be included in the benefits? Is the benefit of power measured by the income from power sales or is some credit to be given for industry made possible by this power? What is the benefit to be credited to river navigation? Should the reduction as compared with railroad rates be considered a clear benefit? The benefits mentioned here are concentrated on those involving direct use of the waterway, but the costs are diffused through taxation of many sources, including the railroads.

What benefits? What costs? Who gains the benefits? Who pays the costs? Questions of this nature could be multiplied almost without limit about the engineering development of a major river system. The answers will reflect conflicting social, political, economic, and geographical considerations; the engineer cannot resolve these issues, but he can contribute substantially to their solution through sound design and reliable estimates of costs and of the effectiveness of the works proposed.

Returning to the Tennessee Valley development, the Federal government had built a hydroelectric plant at Muscle Shoals during World War I to supply power for the fixation of atmospheric nitrogen and the production of fertilizer. Technological advances and lessened demand left this plant a surplus after the war, and it became the focal point of a movement which resulted in the creation of the Tennessee Valley Authority. There were many controversial issues involved, the most publicized being that of public power versus private power and the creation of a so-called "yardstick" for the reasonable cost of power in other areas. Whatever may have been the validity of the arguments for and against this project, the TVA system of dams, locks, power plants, and transmission lines is one of the finest examples of American engineering practice.

Figure 4 shows the Tennessee Valley Region and a profile of the main stream. The hydrology of the Tennessee Valley can be sum-

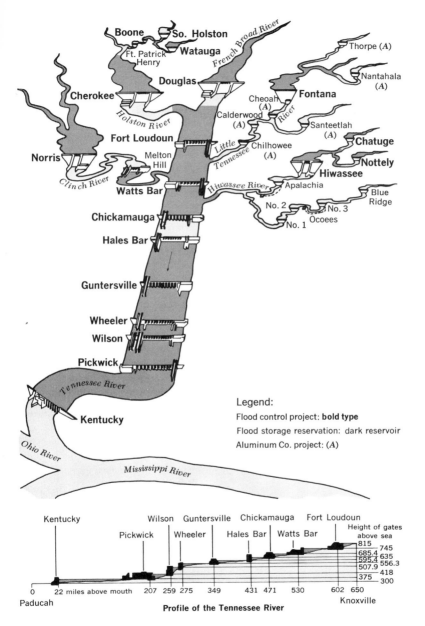

Legend:

Flood control project: **bold type**

Flood storage reservation: dark reservoir

Aluminum Co. project: (A)

Figure 4 Tennessee Valley region.

marized in overall features as follows: Mean annual rainfall, averaged over the entire watershed, amounts to about 51 in., but has varied from a low of 38 in. to a high of 65 in. The heaviest precipitation (rain and equivalent snow) occurs in the mountainous headwater areas of some tributaries where it reaches 80 to 90 in. annually. Other portions of the Tennessee Valley show mean annual precipitation as low as 40 in. The average runoff (the amount of water flowing in the streams) from the valley as a whole equals 42 percent of the precipitation on the area. These figures are mean values over the period of record. Heavy storms move across the valley between December and April; between June and October cyclonic and local storms and decaying hurricanes may cause intense rainfall.

The maximum intensity, location, area covered, total rainfall, and runoff produced by each storm vary in an unpredictable manner; the problem of the engineer is to examine the records available and to reach a conclusion regarding the most probable values of those flow regimes which are critical to his problem; in the case of a multiple-purpose project, the whole range of flows must be studied and forecast. Although the flow in the channels is the variable directly pertinent to design, rainfall data are usually more extensive in time, thus providing a real coverage, and can be used to extend the stream-flow measurements.

The unregulated river flow at Kentucky Dam, the lower end of the TVA project, has varied from a maximum of 500,000 cfs (cubic feet per second) in 1897 to a minimum of 4,500 cfs in 1925, with an average of 65,500 cfs. At Fort Loudoun Dam, above the mouth of the Little Tennessee River, the corresponding figures were a maximum of 300,000 cfs, a minimum of 1,600 cfs, and an average of 13,500 cfs. At Mile 480, the recorded low-water elevation was 635 ft; the crest in March, 1867, reached 688 ft, a range of 53 ft.

Such, in brief, are the random inputs to this complex flood control–navigation–power system.

The major features of the TVA system (1962) are as follows:

Navigation	Nine dams and locks on the Tennessee River maintain a minimum draft of 9 ft from Paducah to Knoxville, a distance of 650 miles.
Power	*a* Thirty-one major hydroelectric plants, including nine dams on the main river, have an installed capacity of 2,900,000 kw.
	b Ten steam plants have a capacity of 8,070,000 kw.
	c Interconnected hydroelectric plants of the Army

Engineers and the Aluminum Company of America have an installed capacity of 1,020,000 kw.

Total installed power capacity—12,000,000 kw approx.

Flood control   Achieved by storage of flood flows in the reservoirs behind the dams built also for power and navigation.

At Chattanooga, the location of greatest flood hazard, the regulation was achieved primarily by storage reservoirs on the tributaries which control 63 percent of the drainage above this point. The reservoirs on the main stream have only limited storage capacity, but it is sufficient, in conjunction with full regulation of the tributaries, to hold flood stages to acceptable levels. The greatest flood at Chattanooga since completion of the reservoir system was that of January, 1957, which, it is estimated, would have reached a stage of 54 ft without regulation. The actual measured stage was 32.2 ft. The estimated monetary saving through prevention of flood damage plus the resulting enhanced land values, as estimated by TVA, are shown in Figure 5 and Table 1. Estimates of this type are a matter of judgment, primarily because the existence of flood control induces a drastic change in the character of the development along the river. Whatever the correct figure may be,

Figure 5   Flood control benefits, TVA multipurpose system.

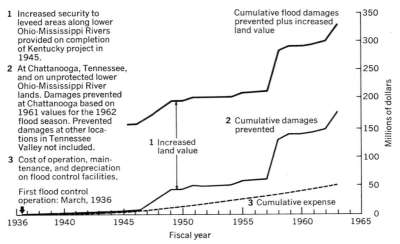

1 Increased security to leveed areas along lower Ohio-Mississippi Rivers provided on completion of Kentucky project in 1945.

2 At Chattanooga, Tennessee, and on unprotected lower Ohio-Mississippi River lands. Damages prevented at Chattanooga based on 1961 values for the 1962 flood season. Prevented damages at other locations in Tennessee Valley not included.

3 Cost of operation, maintenance, and depreciation on flood control facilities.

First flood control operation: March, 1936

Cumulative flood damages prevented plus increased land value

1 Increased land value

2 Cumulative damages prevented

3 Cumulative expense

350
300
250
200
150
100
50
0

Millions of dollars

1936   1940   1945   1950   1955   1960   1965

Fiscal year

Table 1 FLOOD DAMAGES

Date of actual flood	Damages from actual flood	Damages from natural flood	Damages averted *
Mar. 29, 1936	$170,000	$ 2,100,000	$ 1,930,000
Apr. 9, 1936	21,000	700,000	679,000
Jan. 4, 1937	5,000	24,000	19,000
Dec. 30, 1942	35,000	1,100,000	1,065,000
Feb. 19, 1944	0	8,000	8,000
Mar. 30, 1944	5,000	330,000	325,000
Jan. 9, 1946	200,000	12,000,000	11,800,000
Feb. 11, 1946	0	415,000	415,000
Jan. 21, 1947	5,000	11,500,000	11,495,000
Feb. 14, 1948	160,000	13,100,000	12,940,000
Nov. 29, 1948	0	360,000	360,000
Jan. 6, 1949	0	500,000	500,000
Feb. 2, 1950	0	3,400,000	3,400,000
Mar. 15, 1950	0	30,000	30,000
Mar. 30, 1951	0	350,000	350,000
Jan. 22, 1954	0	7,600,000	7,600,000
Mar. 22, 1955	0	400,000	400,000
Feb. 4, 1956	0	17,000	17,000
Apr. 17, 1956	0	185,000	185,000
Feb. 2, 1957	20,000	66,000,000	65,980,000
Apr. 5, 1957	0	2,000	2,000
Nov. 20, 1957	0	710,000	710,000
Apr. 30, 1958	0	†	0
May 10, 1958	0	3,000	3,000
Total	$621,000	$120,834,000	$120,213,000

* Status of date of flood—1953 status used since that date.
† Included in following flood.

the improved flood situation justified a considerable expense for flood control.

The volume of traffic on the Tennessee River, largely barges loaded with coal and bulk cargo, has grown steadily since the river was improved and regulated. Figure 6 shows the traffic in ton-miles per year and the estimated annual savings to shippers.

The TVA Act requires TVA's Board of Directors to allocate the cost of completed multiple-use facilities to the multiple purposes served. The cost of facilities installed exclusively for a single purpose is assigned directly to the particular purpose served; the cost of those

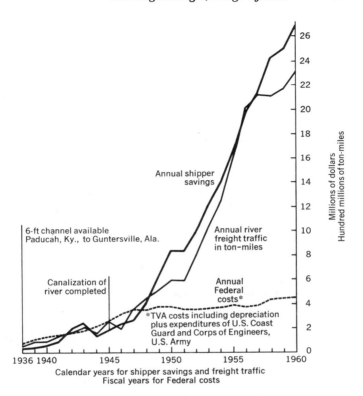

Figure 6   Tennessee River navigation, TVA multipurpose system.

portions of the projects which serve power, navigation, and flood control jointly is allocated to the three purposes as follows: 42 percent to power, 27 percent to navigation, and 31 percent to flood control. The total investment in multiple-use dams at the end of 1962 was as shown in Table 2.

Behind these numbers lies a considerable technical-economic problem because the basis for such allocation is basically an arbitrary policy decision, whatever may be the rationale stated. Should the project be designed and should cost be estimated separately for each purpose? Should a major purpose be selected, say, that involving the major cost, and should design and cost of the project be estimated first for this purpose alone and then determined for the incremental

Table 2

	Investment (millions)			
	Power	**Navigation**	**Flood control**	**Total**
Direct investment	$248	$ 84	$ 56	$377
Multiple-purpose investment	173	111	128	411
Total	$421	$195	$184	$800

costs of other purposes in succession? Should the costs for each purpose be allocated in proportion to the use made of the storage capacity for each purpose? These questions could, if answered fully, generate a tremendous volume of design work and cost estimating without, in the end, providing more than a guide to a policy decision. When applied to a single, isolated structure, allocation of multiple-use costs is difficult; when an interrelated system of dams and reservoirs serves multiple purposes, allocation of costs becomes a question of reasonableness in the relationship between allocated costs and the benefits derived from each purpose.

The TVA power system has become the dominant aspect of the TVA program, ranking in generating capacity with the largest utility systems in the United States. Power is sold wholesale to private utilities, power cooperatives, electrochemical plants, and other large users. As the market for power in the TVA area grew, the variability in amount of available hydroelectric power, due to the annual cycle of stream flow and the obligation to operate the system with primary attention to navigation and flood control, led to the need for "firming up" the hydroelectric power with steam power in order to make up the difference between the demand on the power system and the amount of power available from the regulated river flow.

The Tennessee Valley is located near large coal deposits, and steam power can be generated at low cost. The production of aluminum, calcium carbide, and many other metallurgical and chemical products requires large amounts of electric power, and numerous producers were attracted to the TVA system by the low rates available for large blocks of power. As a consequence of these uses plus the added demand generated by the growth of population, the demand for power grew beyond what could be supplied from hydroelectric power merely supplemented by steam power. Today the generating capacity of the steam stations is almost three times the hydroelectric capacity. The magnitude of the TVA power system is best illustrated by the accumulated capital investment at the end of 1962 and the operating costs and income during the year 1962.

Completed plant	$2,084 million
Accumulated depreciation	464 million
Construction and investigations in progress	288 million
Total fixed assets, Dec. 31, 1962	1,908 million
Operating revenue (1962)	252 million
Operating expenses (1962)	145 million
Depreciation (1962)	52 million

The TVA Office of Engineering plans, designs, and constructs the hydroelectric and steam-electric plants, the navigation and flood control structures, and all other facilities of the TVA system. It also regulates the flow of water in the system of 31 dams on the Tennessee and its tributaries. A separate Office of Power operates and maintains the power system; plans, designs, and constructs the transmission and communications system; and markets the power.

TVA is unusual among public works agencies in that the Office of Engineering acts as its own contractor, employing engineers, technicians, and skilled and unskilled workers directly on its own payroll to design and construct all structures, including the steam-electric power plants, and to install all purchased equipment. For this reason the total force in the Office of Engineering fluctuates with the construction volume. At the end of 1962, the number of employees in the divisions of the Office of Engineering was:

Office of Chief Engineer	21
Rotation Training Program	40
Division of Water Control Planning	425
Division of Design	625
Division of Navigation	37
Division of Construction	6,794
Total	7,942

In 1942, when 7 dams were under construction at the same time, the corresponding total figure was approximately 30,000, all under the direction of the Chief Engineer. The expenditure for power facilities in 1962 was $171 million.

TVA buys its turbines, generators, boilers, and other mechanical equipment on a competitive basis. The rapidly growing demand for power has justified the installation of large incremental steps in generating capacity, and TVA engineers have utilized the latest advances in the turbogenerators. The 500,000-kw unit at the Widow's Creek plant is the largest in operation in the world; a second unit of the same size is being installed. The Bull Run steam plant, now under construction, will include a single turbogenerator having a generating capacity of 900,000 kw.

TVA began in 1951 to design its hydroelectric plants for operation by remote control, and such equipment had been installed in 61 units by the end of 1962. Automation of the steam plants was initiated in the design of the 500,000-kw Widow's Creek unit where a high-speed data-collecting system scans the critical sensors, particularly those measuring temperature and pressure; abnormal readings are printed out at regular intervals. At the Paradise (two 650,000-kw units) and Bull Run (900,000-kw) plants, the design provides for almost complete automation; in addition to the alarm, logging, and calculation functions, the computers will be used to control the boilers and turbines and some of the auxiliary equipment.

The Office of Engineering was assigned responsibility for assisting the Oak Ridge National Laboratory (ORNL) in a study for the Atomic Energy Commission of a nuclear power plant having a net electrical output of 750,000 kw. TVA responsibilities include development of the conceptual plant, preliminary drawings of the project, and design of the conventional portions covering the turbogenerator, condensing and feedwater cycle, electrical systems, and utilities. ORNL is responsible for developing the design and costs of the reactor, steam-generating equipment, and all nuclear portions of the project. The purpose of this joint study, called Gas-Cooled Reactor 3 (GCR-3), is to determine whether gas-cooled, graphite-moderated reactors using enriched uranium fuel can produce power in the foreseeable future which would be competitive with conventional steam-electric generating stations using coal, oil, or gas as fuel. GCR-3 is an advanced version of the EGCR (22,000 kw electric) project now under construction at Oak Ridge, which TVA will operate.

ANALYTICAL TECHNIQUES

The mathematical, graphic, and experimental techniques employed in the analysis of large engineering systems have been dealt with in many books and professional papers. Only brief mention of some commonly used techniques and of a few recent developments will be made here.

A distinction which should be stressed more than it has been is the distinction between systems engineering and systems analysis. Engineering, including systems engineering, is the whole process of creating working "hardware" which did not before exist, including all the steps from synthesis of the concept to successful operation. Systems analysis is one of the tools of systems engineering—but a most important tool in the engineering of large and costly systems. As stressed earlier, the engineer seeks to minimize the risk in advance of commitment to a particular approach by thorough analysis of the overall design concept and of the subsystems, components, and parts.

In principle, all of the analytical techniques employed in analysis utilize a model of some kind to represent the full-scale system, or prototype. The simplest form of model is the block diagram showing qualitatively the subsystems and major components and the interrelationships between them. Mathematical models convert the block diagram into a set of quantitative relationships. Analogue models take advantage of the fact that identical equations describe different physical phenomena and that some phenomena, primarily electrical circuits and fields, are more convenient to deal with experimentally than others. Dynamical models represent the same physical phenomenon as the prototype but to a different size, usually smaller than the prototype.

DYNAMICAL MODELS

These may be employed to study many electrical, hydraulic, and mechanical problems. Scaling laws for transferring data from model to prototype are derived from the physical phenomena involved. As an example of the derivation of the scaling laws, consider the flow of water with a free surface exposed to the atmosphere, for example, flow over the spillway of a dam. The analysis may proceed from the equation representing frictionless fall from rest under gravity.

$$v = gt$$

$$s = \tfrac{1}{2}gt^2$$

$$v = \sqrt{2gs}$$

Here, s is the vertical distance traveled, g is the gravitational force per unit mass, and v is the velocity. The spillway and the adjacent channels of the prototype are modeled to a scale ratio R, yielding a geometrically similar model; the water level in the pool, measured above the spillway crest, will be controlled so that the depth at geometrically similar points also follows the same scale ratio R. What are the applicable ratios of velocities, of rates of flow, of times of transit, and of other performance values? Indicating quantities in the model by the subscript m, and making all comparisons at *geometrically similar points,* the ratios are:

Velocity

$$\frac{v}{v_m} = \frac{\sqrt{2gs}}{\sqrt{2gs_m}} = R^{\frac{1}{2}}$$

Rate of flow: Velocity × area (cubic feet per second)

$$\frac{q}{q_m} = \frac{v}{v_m}\frac{\text{area}}{(\text{area})_m} = \sqrt{R}\,R^2 = R^{\frac{5}{2}}$$

Time intervals: $\dfrac{\text{Distance}}{\text{Velocity}}$

$$\frac{t}{t_m} = \frac{s/v}{s_m/v_m} = R^{\frac{1}{2}}$$

If a geometrically similar model is built to a scale of 64, the velocities and times of transit would be reduced by a factor of 8, and the rates of discharge would be smaller by a factor of 32,768. It was assumed that the horizontal dimensions were scaled in the same ratio R as the vertical dimensions. Is this restriction necessary, or might the horizontal-scale ratio differ from the vertical? To test this point, consider the factors governing horizontal movement of the flow.

Distance: Velocity × time interval

$$\frac{L}{L_m} = R^{\frac{1}{2}}\,R^{\frac{1}{2}} = R$$

The horizontal scale must be the same as the vertical.

In the preceding derivation, it was assumed that the flow in the model would be frictionless. In reality, motion of the water along the solid surfaces will induce frictional resistance and one must investigate the possible effect of this phenomenon on the accuracy of the model. The loss of energy in hydraulic friction may be represented by the equation

$$h = f\left(\frac{L}{D}\right)\frac{v^2}{2g}$$

Here, h is loss of energy per pound of fluid due to friction, L is a distance in the direction of flow, and D is a dimension of the cross section. If the model and prototype are geometrically similar,

$$\frac{L}{D} = \frac{L_m}{D_m}$$

$$\frac{h}{h_m} = \frac{f}{f_m} \frac{v^2}{v_m{}^2}$$

Substituting $h/h_m = R$ and $v/v_m = R^{1/2}$, the ratios required by the model laws, it follows that the losses due to friction may satisfy the model laws provided that $f = f_m$. This requirement can be met approximately in many practical design problems of the hydraulic engineer, and models of this type are utilized extensively as an adjunct to design. In general, f is a function of a quantity called the Reynolds number. It is nearly constant in a flow regime called *fully developed turbulent flow*. Fortunately, many of the model tests needed by the civil engineer fall in this regime.

The principle demonstrated by the preceding example is that the use of dynamical models requires quantitative rules for the transfer of data from model to prototype. These rules, or *model laws*, are derived from the equations describing the major physical phenomenon involved; they must be analyzed to discover the possible causes of discrepancy between model and prototype by both theory and experiment.

The electrical engineer is fortunate in that his systems are generally linear and may be modeled to an arbitrary scale, chosen for convenience to match the equipment or instruments available. This flexibility of the electrical systems, as well as the ease of assembling and operating them, has led to the use of electrical systems as analogue models of other phenomena—heat flow, vibrations, fluid flow, and so forth.

ANALOGUE MODELS

Another type of model depends upon the analogous behavior of different physical systems. For example, the two-dimensional flow of heat in a conductor may be studied by using the electrical analogy, as suggested above. The basic equations governing these two phenomena are:

Heat: $q = -k \dfrac{\Delta T}{\Delta X}$

Electricity: $L = -c \dfrac{\Delta E}{\Delta X}$

where Δ = a difference
$\qquad q$ = flow of heat per unit area
$\qquad k$ = heat conductivity
$\qquad T$ = temperature
$\qquad X$ = distance
$\qquad L$ = electric current per unit area
$\qquad c$ = electric conductivity
$\qquad E$ = voltage

An analogy is said to exist because these equations have the same form; E replaces T as the driving force to induce a flow of electricity rather than heat. An example will serve to illustrate the principle. Suppose that an engineer needs to know the temperature distribution in a sheet of copper exposed to a high temperature at one end and to a cold contact along a portion of one side. The copper sheet is slotted at a number of points and contains several "cutouts." The copper plate is to be covered on both sides by good insulating blankets, so that heat can enter only at the high-temperature side and leave at the cold surface. This problem could be modeled directly by building the unit as described, applying a temperature difference, and measuring the temperature at points on the sheet. An analogue, frequently more convenient, is to represent the heat-flow problem by the analogous problem of an electric conductor, such as a shallow pan of salt solution, and to represent the slots, the cutouts, and the entire geometry of the heat-flow problem by islands of nonconducting material. A uniform voltage is applied at electrodes where high and low temperatures would exist in the heat-flow problem. With a voltmeter connected between one electrode and a movable probe, one can trace out a map of lines of equal voltage. The resulting map of lines of equal voltage is analogous to the map showing lines of equal temperature in the original problem. The advantage of this analogy method is in its simplicity and cost.

The *analogue computer* is a generalized model applicable to engineering systems problems which can be represented by analogous electric circuits. Appropriate combinations of resistances, capacitances, and inductances are arranged in series and parallel to represent fluid flow, heat conduction, mechanical vibrations, and other systems in such manner that the electric input-output relationships, both of the overall and of the subdivisions of interest, bear a known quantitative relationship to the corresponding quantities in the analogue. After this quantitative correspondence has been established, the electrical analogue offers a more convenient means of studying the effect of changes in a system than by altering the mechanical system itself.

ALGEBRAIC MODELS

These models differ in a fundamental way from the models previously discussed. In principle, the difference is that the physical models previously described required only a knowledge of the different equations describing the phenomenon on a microscopic scale; the model provided a means of solving these equations for particular, complex boundary conditions. However, some systems problems may be represented, at least in essence, by sets of algebraic equations which may be solved numerically to obtain system input-output relationships. This technique has been greatly facilitated by the availability of large-capacity, fast computers. A further step is to use the computers to solve the differential equations describing a physical phenomenon for particular boundary conditions; here, the differential equations are replaced by finite-difference equations which are solved by steps to the desired accuracy by choosing the degree of fineness of the steps. The computer performs repetitive calculations until the solution matches the specified boundary conditions. Still other specialized methods of mathematical modeling especially suited to the high-speed computer are rapidly being developed.

CONCEPTUAL MODELS

The preceding examples of engineering models dealt with situations for which the basis of model design was a physical law. Engineers encounter problems of another type for which an algebraic model may be an aid to design. For example, bridge engineers need to forecast the traffic, and the growth of traffic with time, over a bridge not yet in place. Suppose that a toll bridge is contemplated as the replacement of a ferry. What will be the future travel over the bridge? Will the bridge change the ratio of travel by private auto to public transportation? How will traffic vary as a function of the toll charged? What will be the peak rate of traffic flow over the bridge? The physical design of a major bridge and its foundations and approaches presents a challenging problem but one usually lying within the state of the design art. Forecasting the cost is not routine, but the methods and facts with which to do it are available. However, forecasting the traffic is a more intangible and difficult problem.

As an example of the approach used, consider the question of the flow of highway traffic between two populated areas. The number of daily trips to or from an area is probably proportional to its population. The fraction of the population making a trip will depend upon (*1*) the attraction of the other area and (2) the difficulty of a trip, measured in time, distance, or, cost. These considerations may be represented algebraically by the expression

$$T_{12} = K \frac{P_1 P_2}{d^n}$$

Here, T_{12} is the daily number of trips, P_1 and P_2 are the two populations, and d is the distance between the centers. This equation will be useful only if generally valid values for K and n are found from an analysis of statistics on travel. One can speculate further on the factors which will affect the value of K and organize the statistical work in order to determine its value for certain patterns of attractiveness. For example, if the two centers are a suburban town and a nearby metropolitan center, the flow of traffic will probably be proportional to the population of the suburban town, but the attractiveness of the metropolitan center for these people is not its population but its activity, as measured by job opportunities, shopping centers, sports, and cultural activities. Clearly, the problem is not as easy as the simple equation implied. Nevertheless, there is value in the use of such models because the problem is reduced in scope from a mass of data to a study of the factors affecting the values of K and n.

The large-capacity, fast digital computers mentioned earlier have become an essential element in the analysis of large engineering systems; in fact, computers are relied on so extensively that one wonders whether these modern systems could be designed at all without the extensive input-output analysis, cost-effectiveness–trade-off studies, and other analytical support which the speed and capacity of the computers make possible. A much wider range of conditions may be explored analytically than was possible by earlier, less powerful methods. The systems designer may thus narrow the range of problems requiring component experimentation or prototype test.

PROBABILITY AND STATISTICS

These topics are the subject of an extensive and complex literature. They are presented here in skeleton form as background for the following section on reliability, and because they have come to be used in many other ways in modern systems analysis.

Games of chance provide an illustration of the theory of probability. In throwing dice, each die has six numbered faces; if the dice are not defective, there is an equal chance, or probability, that any one of these faces will show when a die is thrown. There are 6 possible events when a single die is thrown, but only 1 can occur, and the probability that a certain number, say 5, will appear is 1 in 6. These events are random; having thrown one 5, the same probability exists that a 5 will appear on the next throw. What then is the probability of throwing two 5's in succession? There are 36 possible events but only 1 combination 5-5; the probability of obtaining this pair is then 1 in 36. The probability of occurrence of a certain class of random events is thus the ratio of the number in this class to the number of possible events.

An example of the application of probability theory to physical problems is the analysis of errors of measurement where the objective is to determine the magnitude of a quantity, such as the horizontal distance between two points on the earth's surface or the radar cross section of an airplane. The instruments are calibrated, readings are made with care, and the result should be precise. However, if the measurements are repeated, successive values do not agree exactly. What is the true value of the quantity measured? A mathematical model of this situation was devised by Gauss who assumed that (*1*) positive and negative random errors are equally likely, (*2*) small errors are more likely than large ones, and (*3*) very large errors do not occur. Conforming to these assumptions, Gauss proposed the equation now given his name, namely

$$y = \frac{hN}{\sqrt{\pi}} e^{-h^2 x^2}$$

Here, y is the frequency of deviations of magnitude x from the arithmetic mean of N measurements. This curve has its maximum value of y at $x = 0$ and is symmetrical. The value of h determines the shape of the curve, a large value yielding a sharp peak on the line of symmetry. A small value gives a flat curve and a more gradual decrease with increasing x. The quantity h may then be called the index of precision since a large value indicates a small spread in the measurement errors. Properties of this equation are to be found in standard mathematical tables. Note that this model applies only to random variations in the measurement of a presumably constant quantity. The area under the curve of y between $-\infty$ and $+\infty$ embraces all possible random errors; the chance that a single measurement will fall in the interval x and $x + \Delta x$ is the ratio of the segment under the curve between these values and the total area.

Prior to the availability of large computers, engineering analysis tended to concentrate on a deterministic, unique cause-and-effect relationship in dealing with physical systems; this assumption does not always conform to the real situation in which the relationship between the components of a system is subject to statistical variation because of environmental changes, differences between components in replicas of the same system, wear of parts, or other unavoidable random causes. Until high-speed computers become available, analytical treatment of problems including statistical variations was unacceptably burdensome and costly. Analysis by digital computer allows one to inject into the computation values of these variables chosen at random from a population of values representing the real frequency-distribution curve. Each point in the system, at which statistical variations may occur, is thus represented. The computer repeats cause-and-effect–input-output calculations a thousand, or even a hundred thousand, times and thus develops a statistical input-output relationship for the system as a whole.

RELIABILITY OF LARGE SYSTEMS

There is the possibility that engineering equipment will fail to perform its function because of improper fabrication, carelessness of an inspector, overload, inattention or fatigue of the operator, wear in service, environmental conditions outside the design range, and other causes. These unpredictable contingencies account in part for the "factor of safety" introduced into engineering designs. After the event, these causes of failure are usually identifiable. In addition, there are failures of unidentified cause which follow a random pattern. For example, Fig. 7 is representative of tests showing this effect; a large batch of parts, made and inspected to close standards, are exposed to repre-

Figure 7   Survival of parts; time to failure.

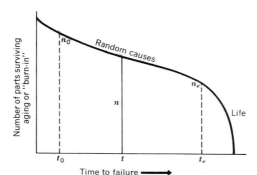

sentative operating and environmental conditions until they fail. There is an initial period of high casualties called the "burn-in" period during which some parts fail due to improper assembly, contamination, or other causes. At the end of the test period, an abrupt increase in failures may occur; this last phenomenon represents the ultimate life of the parts. Between t_0 and t_e, the rate of failures may be approximately of the form

$$\Delta n = -np\Delta t$$

Here, p is the probability of failure at time t and Δn is the number of failures among n parts in the time interval Δt. The value of p is obtained from test data such as shown in Fig. 7. The probability of survival in the period during which failures are essentially random (t_0 to t_e) is of the form

$$s = \frac{n}{n_0} = e^{-p(t-t_0)} = \text{fraction surviving at time } t$$

If the rate of failure is low and the total number of failures small (or the interval $t - t_0$ is short), the value of p may be obtained with sufficient accuracy from the equation

$$p = \frac{1}{n_0} \frac{n_0 - n_e}{t_e - t_0} = \text{probability of failure}$$

$$1 - p = \text{probability of survival}$$

Suppose that p is 0.001 per hr, how many out of a batch of 200 parts would be expected to *fail* in 3 hr?

$$0.001 = \frac{1}{200} \frac{\Delta n}{3}$$

$$\Delta n = 0.6$$

A part either fails or survives; the fractional answer indicates that one part may be expected to fail after approximately three hours in this example.

The reasoning about p is the same as that about the probabilities in throwing a certain number at dice. A number of events are possible, N_0, and events of the type of interest, namely failures, have occurred in the past to the extent $N_0 - N_t$ in the interval $t - t_0$. We do not know in advance which event, failure or survival, will occur in the next test of a single part, but if the part is of the same manufacture, is subject to the same load, and is selected from the survivors after a burn-in period, we conclude that the probable future behavior of such parts is like the past.

Suppose that M parts are connected in series to form a system; the system fails if any component fails. What is the probability that the system will survive for a certain period of time? The basic equation for the survival of a *single component* for a time Δt is

$$S = e^{-p\Delta t}$$

The system survival requires the concurrent survival of m parts, the same problem essentially as that of throwing the same number on two or more dice, discussed earlier. The system survival probability is

$$(e^{-p\Delta t})^m$$

Suppose that the probability of survival of each of 5 parts for 10 hr is 0.9, the probability of survival of the system is $(0.9)^m$ or 0.59. Clearly, if a system is made up of a large number of parts, all essential to the functioning of the system, the probability of survival of the individual parts must be very high. As an example, consider a system made up of 10,000 parts, each having a failure rate of 10^{-6} failures per hr (i.e., one failure per million hr). What is the probability of survival of the system for 100 hr?

$$\begin{aligned} S &= (e^{-p\Delta t})^m = e^{-mp\Delta t} \\ &= e^{-(10^4 \cdot 10^{-6} \cdot 10^2)} \\ &= e^{-1} = 0.37 \end{aligned}$$

The assumed accuracy of the parts was high, but the large number of parts in series reduced the system probability of survival to a figure which would be unacceptable for many purposes. Often, there are mitigating factors such as the fact that not all parts function all the time; parts may be replaced at scheduled intervals; failure of some parts impairs but does not interrupt system operation; and so forth. The primary means of improving system reliability are by improving the reliability of the individual parts and by designing the system for minimum vulnerability to parts failure.

Reliability may be improved by inserting identical parts in *parallel* and arranging for the parallel part to operate when its counterpart fails. This technique is called *redundancy*. There are factors which make this approach less of a panacea than it appears to be at first glance, but it is a valuable tool. The essence of the principle may be illustrated by considering two identical electrical components wired in parallel in such fashion that the spare part takes over when the first part fails. The probability of *survival* of each component for a specified period is S. The probability that both will *fail* in the same period is $(1 - S)^2$. For example, if the probability of survival of one part is 0.9, its probability of failure is 0.1 and the probability that both would fail is 0.1^2 or 0.01. In general, the probability that m redundant parts will all fail is $(1 - S)^m$ and the survival probability of the redundant group is $[1 - (1 - S)^m]$.

Redundancy has the disadvantage that the redundant parts add to the cost, weight, and space required. If means of sensing failure and switching to the redundant parts are required, the sensors and switches have a failure probability which counteracts the effect of redundancy in some degree. Failure and switching may introduce a transient overload and decrease the survival probability of the transient part. As in all engineering design, the trade-offs between the gain and the cost of redundancy must be analyzed to find a solution compatible with the reliability requirements of the system.

Large systems, containing many in-line parts, components, and subsystems, must include reliability as one of the design parameters. Figure 8 shows schematically and ideally the progress of development of a novel concept. The point of intercept with the vertical axis represents a simple design which will perform the desired function, but at a performance short of the theoretical limits and less than is deemed acceptable. Let us assume that this simple design represents maximum system performance that can be expected by improving com-

Figure 8   Performance and reliability of parts.

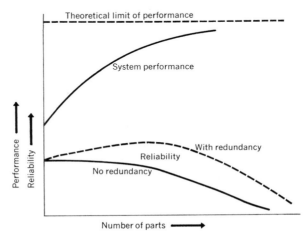

ponent performance, and that the only method discovered to improve the system performance is by the addition of refinements which increase the number of parts. The performance does increase but at the expense of reliability, assuming no redundancy. One can counteract the effect of the number of parts to some degree by redundancy, but this technique has its limitations. It sometimes turns out that no design can be found which has the desired performance and reliability; when this fact is established empirically by building the system and then discovering its low reliability, the cost can be very great.

This discussion of reliability covers only the bare elements of the problem. The examples are oversimplified, and imply a degree of quantitative analysis which cannot yet be applied in many design problems. Judgment based upon experience is an important element in design for reliability—but judgment may be aided by applying quantitative analysis. Reliability analysis and design for reliability have become major components in the design of large systems.

ORGANIZATION AND MANAGEMENT

Organization and management of the engineering work required to carry through a large-system project from concept to working reality have been studied extensively in recent years in an effort to discover such basic principles and criteria as might be effective in reducing the cost or shortening the time. The results of these studies have been helpful to engineers responsible for directing this work, but they cannot be stated quantitatively, like the results of scientific research, and they are meaningful primarily to the initiated. In these notes, attention will be directed to a few points which may be helpful to prospective engineers in understanding better the environment in which they will work.

Large engineering projects require large numbers of people—engineers, scientists, technicians, skilled labor, and specialists of many kinds —whose efforts must be planned, coordinated, and reviewed. True, an individual or a small group may originate the concept on which the system is based, and not many more individuals may be necessary to analyze the concept and to judge its feasibility, but there is a difficult and costly path between the identification of a feasible concept and the realization of an operating system. This path requires the efforts of large numbers if the goal is to be reached in reasonable time. The work and the workers are divided in accordance with the functions to be performed. To the maximum extent possible, these functional groups are given the responsibility and authority to carry out a discrete portion of the whole in accordance with the overall plan and schedule. Interactions between these groups must be intimate and continuous as the project is carried through the sequence of engineering steps previously described.

A major problem for the individual professional engineer and for the management of the organization is the proper balance between freedom and discipline in the execution of engineering work. Creative imagination, initiative, and a willingness to accept the risks inherent in pioneering must be encouraged if substantial technical advances are to be made; on the other hand, the effort must be directed toward the project objective, avoiding attractive "nice-to-know-about" side issues which are not essential. Referring to the sequence of steps from concept to working "hardware" through which an engineering project passes (Chap. I, p. 13), we see that the degree of freedom permissible becomes progressively restricted. In the initial phase of analyzing the feasibility of a concept, all possible alternative concepts should be cast up for screening, and the imagination can be given free rein. As the project proceeds, the range of technical choice is restricted to a narrowing scope, but within these limits there is opportunity and need for creativeness and initiative. More specifically, the preliminary design group chooses from among alternative concepts, defines feasible input-output characteristics, and specifies the type and characteristics of at least one set of subsystems and major components likely to yield the desired system characteristics; the component designers, working within this framework, study alternative designs and ultimately prepare detail drawings and specifications; the manufacturing engineers analyze these designs for manufacturing accuracy and cost; and so it continues, on to the machinists who make the parts and assemble them and to the engineers and technicians who test the system.

Not only is there opportunity for an imaginative approach to the task emerging at each level, but there is also the desirability of "feedback" to the earlier steps to reduce cost, improve quality or reliability, eliminate investment in special tools and equipment, and other reasons. Some engineering organizations occasionally dictate the details of engineering work too rigidly; others err in the direction of allowing too much freedom in technical work, resulting frequently in good components which nevertheless are not optimized for the system. The young engineer, viewing this process from the bottom of the pyramid of authority, may feel frustrated when his suggestions for improvement or change are not adopted; he should not give up thinking about improvements, but should realize that his ideas must be judged against the background of the project objectives, status, and schedule. Engineering offers opportunities for individuals having a wide range of talents, interests, and experience; the young engineer should gain early experience in all phases of the engineering work for which he is best suited. Fundamental to success in engineering practice is the deep-rooted drive to produce tangible, useful results, on time, within a budget and without being distracted by side issues, however interesting. Practically speaking, this criterion means that the engineer must come to regard the problem his organization poses for him as a challenge, and he must discipline himself to apply all his knowledge and ingenuity to the solution of *that problem*—not some other problem that he happens to find more interesting, unless his job is in exploratory research.

Engineering organizations are often referrered to as *functional organizations* or *project organizations.* The difference is one of emphasis because convenience of management of a large engineering force leads inevitably to grouping around functions. When an engineering organization is created to execute a single project, the individuals required for each step from concept to operating system are employed, perform their portion of the work, and are discharged. Each phase of the work builds up to a peak and then tapers off gradually; production or construction uncovers difficulties which require redesign; and redesign may require consultation with the preliminary design group. In some branches of engineering in some localities, different organizations in the same field do grow and decrease as described, but the more usual situation is that each organization seeks new projects, ideally projects out of phase, so that each functional group may transfer its attention to a new project as the old one passes its peak demand. Thus, a group of engineers develop special competence in a particular function, for example, in the design of compressors for jet engines, and they apply to each new project the knowledge and experience gained on earlier work. This plan is efficient because it conserves competence and avoids the delay and cost of recruiting and training for each project. However, there are two major problems which arise when a functional organization undertakes several projects at the same time. In the first place, each project has a unique set of quantitative objectives to meet, and each component must be designed to optimize the system as a whole; someone must represent these overall objectives in appraising the work of the functional groups. Secondly, each project has its own schedule and budget, and someone must give attention to coordination of these aspects of the work. The solution has been to appoint project managers or project engineers to represent the needs of the several projects. Urgent military projects, such as the Polaris Submarine development and the Atlas ICBM, are frequently organized as independent entities in the contractor's organization. Unfortunately, the inherent characteristic of a project is that it presents a temporary demand for specialized personnel who must be relocated when their phase of the work has been completed in the one project.

The appropriate balance of emphasis between project organization and functional organization depends primarily upon the maturity of the product or the system being designed. When an engineering organization is engaged in the design of a succession of new versions of a well-established concept—say an automobile with an internal-combustion engine—the feasibility of the concept and the systems engineering of the relationship between the components have been established, and each functional group has the problem of designing improved or different components compatible only with altered specifications of this established concept. A novel concept, or one novel to the organization, can seldom be undertaken successfully by a functional organization built around some other concept. For example, an engineering organization successful in designing automobiles would probably be incompatible with the design of an airplane, no matter how competent the individuals in it might be. This example is perhaps extreme, but it is true that industrial development organizations do frequently undertake new projects involving a mix of science and technology different from what they have undertaken in the past, and these differences must be recognized in the way in which the engineering work is organized. The strict functional organization may be suitable for a project in one stage of development, and the tight project organization may be required for another phase.

These remarks about functional and project organizations are made to warn the young engineer that he should expect to be involved frequently in organizational changes in an active development organization because a different balance of emphasis on the two types of organization is frequently appropriate to different phases in the life cycle of a project.

SCHEDULING AND CONTROL

Engineers perform their technical work in a framework of restraints imposed by time and cost. Their work, and all the related work of fabrication, assembly, and test, must be completed to a schedule. Parallel and concurrent efforts must mesh at the point of final assembly or installation. A delay in the date of completion and operational use is costly because, once the organization is in place, the expenditure required to support it is almost proportional to the time elapsed. Scheduling engineer work and estimating its cost is not new to engineering practice, but some recent innovations are noteworthy as an indication of the degree of scheduling and control necessary on large projects and, incidentally, as an example of systems analysis applied to the management of engineering itself.

The development of the Polaris Fleet Ballistic Missile was assigned by the Navy to a special agency created for the purpose called the Special Projects Office (SPO). There was an urgent need for early availability of this submarine-launched missile, and the SPO was given the authority and responsibility to complete the project at the earliest possible date. The enormous number of subsystems and components, and the complete novelty of many of them, posed a planning and scheduling problem of unusual complexity. To handle this project, the SPO devised a system known as PERT (Program Evaluation and Review Technique) which is now applied generally in the Department of Defense and also in many industrial projects.

The progress of an engineering project may be broken down into a series of observable events which must be completed in series or parallel; precise specifications must be written for components and subsystems; drawings must be prepared for fabrication; performance must be demonstrated by test; contracts must be written: personnel must be recruited and organized; buildings and test facilities are needed; components must be assembled in sequence; and so on through all the chains of events which must occur. Examination of these many events will show two characteristics, namely, (1) that there are parallel paths from beginning to end, and (2) that there are interconnections between these paths. As an example, consider the total requirement for personnel. There will be a buildup in numbers to a peak and a tapering off; and this number will be made up of many specialists required in different phases of the work. Engineers must be recruited or transferred in time to become thoroughly familiar with the special problems involved; technicians must be trained and qualified for special tasks of fabrication, assembly, inspection, and tests; and each of the contractor organizations has this type of problem. One could list a series of dates at which each part of the overall organization must have "on board" both numbers and varieties of specialists. However, before the personnel are put in place there must be contractual coverage of the costs, and these contracts must specify the characteristics of the product and the delivery date; negotiation of these many contracts requires time, and this work, a not inconsiderable task, must be scheduled and completed on time if the work covered by the contracts is to be undertaken. Each contractor must deliver equipment to specifications compatible with the overall system. Consequently, the system design must be completed before the subsystem and component specifications can be prepared. The situation need not be described further to demonstrate that it is complex indeed, and that the "chicken and egg" type of problem involved can be resolved only by a series of approximations, starting from a simple listing of the essential events and their relationship, in time and with each other, and then assigning numerical values and elapsed times to each as the data become available. There is a considerable feedback from component design to system analysis as the design studies proceed, and this process must be allowed for in the schedule. The performance targets are difficult, almost by definition, in a truly advanced project, and there is no assurance at the outset that they can be met. Slippages in performance or in completion dates must be discovered early and allowed for in the system appraisal, if they cannot be corrected. Such is the nature of the problem.

The mechanics of the PERT system are illustrated in Fig. 9 which shows a network in which the key events are indicated by the letters *A, B, C,* etc., and the progress of time is from left to right. Each path, such as *AB*, represents a task to be performed to reach an identifiable goal, such as *B*; for example, completion of preliminary design of the guidance system or rocket-motor test stands checked out and available for test. The original PERT concept identified only the events and the related time. A modification called PERT-cost adds the cost of performing each task. The estimates of cost and time are obtained from those responsible for the work, and the original estimate of time includes the shortest, the probable, and the longest time interval for

Figure 9   PERT-cost diagram.

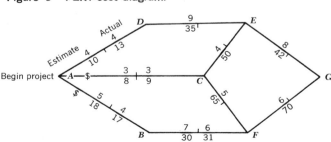

Estimate: *ADEG* — 21 weeks (critical path)
  ACEG — 15 weeks
  ACFG — 14 weeks
  ABFG — 18 weeks

each task; these data are adjusted with varying degrees of refinement to obtain an expected time for each task. All the events along all of the paths must be completed to reach G and, in addition, tasks leading to each intermediate interconnection must be in the sequence shown. Considering the original estimates of expected time, shown above each line and to the left, the longest elapsed time between A and G, the path *ADEG*, is called the *critical path* because these events control the date of completion. Clearly, a slippage in the time required to complete any of the tasks may shift the critical path to another series of events.

The diagrams of Fig. 9 may be regarded as the gross network of a project showing only the key events—but *all* of the cross-connections between paths. Each link in the network may be broken down into a hierarchy of degrees of detail, with each level of complexity following the same pattern. A major project will involve thousands of components and many times that number of events. The PERT-cost system may be programmed for a computer, and the information in the system may be continually updated by inserting the facts about completed work and the revised estimates of tasks remaining to be done.

COMMUNICATIONS AND THE SIZE OF WORKING GROUPS

The design and construction of major engineering systems require large numbers of workers for the many interrelated functions of planning, design, production or construction, finance, legal matters, marketing, special facilities design, testing, and so forth. Their work must be directed toward achieving the desired objectives at minimum cost and within a limited time. Even when the technical aspects of a large project fall within "the state of the design art," the organization and management of a large project present a major problem. When the objective is the development of a novel concept not previously reduced to practice, the design objectives will be altered by concurrent scientific research or exploratory development as the work proceeds and, under these circumstances, the problems of organization and management become correspondingly more complex.

The organization and management of engineering development programs comprise too complex and extensive a subject for discussion in any detail here, but the nature of the problems involved will be illustrated by some idealized situations. The primary problem is that of communication—upward, downward, and laterally within the organization, and between the organization and the total environment in which it works.

R. C. Raymond [5] has formulated mathematical models of the process of communication in an organization. Although these models have been idealized in order to focus attention on the elements of the problem and although the numerical values assumed may be questioned, they do illustrate the nature of the problems of communications in large organizations. One learns from these models, and from the real situations which they idealize, that large organizations differ from small ones not only in mere size and cost but, more importantly, in the very nature of the problems which they pose. Failure to recognize this difference, and to reflect it effectively in organization and procedures, has frequently been the cause of wasted effort and lost time when organizations grew to undertake tasks of greater magnitude.

Raymond considered first this simple situation: A group of N individuals are engaged in technical analysis; the work of each individual is related to that of all others. Each individual divides his time between working, talking to $N-1$ others about the work he has completed, and to hearing what $N-1$ have done. Under these circumstances what is the net output of the average individual and what is the aggregate output of the group? Reporting one's own work and hearing of the work of others might be achieved in two-way conversations, in oral reports to $N-1$ others in groups, or by written communication. Considering first two-person conversations between each individual and $N-1$ others, the distribution of each worker's total time would be

$$T = \frac{w}{a} + \frac{(N-1)w}{b} + \frac{(N-1)w}{b}$$

$$= \text{working} + \text{talking} + \text{listening}$$

where $w =$ work produced in time T by the average individual

$a =$ rate at which individuals work

$b =$ rate at which an average individual reports his work orally *and* the rate at which he listens

The total work output of the group is $W = Nw$ in time T, and their rate of working is

$$\frac{Nw}{T} = \frac{W}{T} = \frac{Nab}{b + 2a(N-1)}$$

If N becomes very large $(N \to \infty)$

$$\frac{W}{T} \to \frac{b}{2a}$$

[5] Dr. Richard C. Raymond, unpublished report, Advanced Technology Services, General Electric Company.

Raymond takes the rate a as unity and assigns the value 16 to the relative rate of oral reporting or listening, and obtains $W/T = 8$ as the *rate* of working of a very large group, as compared with $W/T = 1$ as the rate for an individual working alone (group $N = 1$). As the group grows in numbers, each individual spends more time in communication and less time on productive work, with the result that the increment of work produced by the addition of the $(N + 1)th$ worker is progressively smaller and approaches zero in the limit.

The preceding example is not without significance in engineering work in which oral communication is common and in which at least one individual, the supervisor, must communicate in two-way conversations with all his direct subordinates—and the subordinates must communicate their work results to each other. A model similar to the preceding one might be constructed for a supervised group but, as it stands, the model given illustrates the trend for such a group. Assuming a group of eight individuals including the supervisor, the rate of net output would be

$$\frac{W}{T} = \frac{Nab}{b + 2a(N - 1)} = \frac{8 \cdot 16}{16 + 2 \cdot 7} = 4.27$$

Eight individuals working without comunication but with an assumed "ideal" coordinating mechanism would have produced 8 units. Coordination of effort in the manner assumed reduced the net output by approximately half—a price which small organizations may be able to afford to achieve their objectives.

Clearly, two-person communication of *all* work results is feasible only in small organizations. Raymond's analysis considers the effect of several measures to reduce the burden of internal communication, such as (1) communication orally of all results to the $N - 1$ others in group meetings, (2) written communication of all results, (3) written communication to each individual of only that fraction of the total work which is relevant to his work. The algebraic analysis of these alternatives is left to the reader.

One obvious conclusion regarding the working of large organizations is that the communication technique of sending copies of everything to everybody may slow down rather than speed the work. Written communication, with filtering in order to communicate only what is relevant, is essential if the group is large. The optimum *span of control*, the number of subordinates a manager can effectively direct, is determined primarily by the nature and extent of the communications involved. The organization can be represented as a triangle with the individual workers as the base and the effective head of the organization as the

Figure 10 The familiar freeway interchange is a component in our modern highway transportation system. Its design must take into account the properties of construction materials, the behavior of motor vehicles, the psychology of drivers, the cost of the land utilized, and the statistics of traffic flow. (Ewing Galloway)

apex. The number of layers of organization between the base and the apex, and the number of individuals through which instructions and data must pass upward and downward will *increase* as the *span of control* of individuals at each level *decreases*.

The last model, representing written communication of relevant material, applies to communication in scientific and technical fields. There was a time when an individual scientist could know about nearly all of the science of his day and could correspond with most of his contemporary scientists. However, the steady increase in the *rate* of scientific advance has forced scientists to reach a decision regarding the distribution of their time between working themselves and reviewing the work of their contemporaries. *Relevance* in this case is enhanced by specialized meetings, journals, and societies organized around a limited subject.

Since communication plays a major part in a large project, it may well determine the type of organization—functional or project—discussed earlier. The principle of relevance here also is the key issue in the decision. Finally we should stress the tool used by individuals in assuring precise, clear, and complete information flow within and between the organizations engaged in the engineering of a large system. The engineers must develop the skill to write the necessary letters, reports, and specifications so clearly that they cannot be misunderstood. The first step in acquiring this skill is to learn to speak and write the English language accurately; English is as important a technical tool as mathematics or graphics in the practice of engineering.

PARKINSON'S LAW AND THE "WATTLESS COMPONENT"

It is difficult to forecast the number of engineers and supporting personnel necessary to carry out a proposed project or even to appraise the effectiveness of an organization already in being and at work. Such questions as: Could the completion date be advanced by increasing the force? Is progress being impeded by superfluous numbers? can be answered only qualitatively. Factors other than the communications problem just discussed must be considered. A humorous but fundamentally valid analysis of this problem for "white collar" work in public service brought the conclusion that "Work expands so as to fill the time available for its completion [Parkinson's law]." [6] The quantitative basis for this conclusion was the growth of the administrative staff of the British Admiralty and the British Colonial Office during periods of peace, when the size of the fleet and the number of colonies were actually decreasing; in fact, Parkinson concluded that this growth would have occurred whether the work to be done increased, decreased, or remained constant.

Although amusing to the point of seeming facetious, Parkinson's analysis of the tendency for administrative or overhead personnel and costs to increase is valid for all types of organizations, including engineering projects, unless there is a strong counteracting force exerted, usually by limited funds. The pressure for this growth is always present. For mass-produced items, competition between organizations, under stress of the price competition in the market for engineering products, serves to limit the engineering effort and the related administrative overhead. However, for urgent and large "one-of-a-kind" projects, or for subsidized functional organizations, these natural controls may be absent.

[6] C. Northcote Parkinson, "Parkinson's Law," Houghton Mifflin Company, Boston, Mass., 1957.

Why should Parkinson's law be a factor in the engineering of large systems? The unnecessary expense of superfluous work, either administrative or technical, obviously increases the total project cost. More important, however, is its effect of slowing down and possibly diverting the core of engineering work. One can imagine, at least, an optimum project force—optimized to achieve minimum project cost, least time to completion, or system performance—and then visualize functions and people added beyond this optimum, for example, to audit progress, to prepare reports, to brief visitors, to control expense, to plan, to schedule, to explore parallel technical ideas, and so forth. The functions just mentioned are useful, and to a certain degree are necessary in the execution of large projects, but they can also be detrimental because there must be communication with the engineering force—taking their time and attention—and because project management must give them some direction.

When the engineering force itself is enlarged beyond the optimum core essential to the technical objectives—and no one can state with certainty just how large it should be—the effect is to generate superfluous tests and studies, all of which seem related to the problem at hand and some of which may turn out to have been valuable insurance against unforeseen difficulties. Engineers and scientists of the type employed on advanced projects are ingenious individuals, and they will apply their talents to work which they regard as interesting and important. The effect of too large a force may be not only to impede the project by the demands on facilities, engineering management attention, and communications with the core engineering group, but to divert the project to interesting side issues or constantly changed objectives. This internally generated work, not contributing to the final result, has been referred to in electrical engineering terms as a "wattless component."

If a project group grows beyond the numbers and competence essential to its job, cutting back is extremely difficult because no one is idle; all are busy on tasks apparently related, though sometimes remotely, to the objectives of the project. Division of the work into specialized tasks makes difficult the elimination of individuals by combining jobs. Few functions can be eliminated completely. Supervisors have been appointed, and contraction usually reduces the numbers of supervisory positions justified. These and other factors exert strong pressure to avoid a drastic reorganization and to maintain the present numbers, especially when rapid completion of a project is required. Nevertheless, the constant goal must be to minimize "the wattless component" of large organizations.

BIBLIOGRAPHY

ALEXANDER, J. E., and J. M. BAILEY: "Systems Engineering Mathematics," Prentice-Hall, Inc., Englewood Cliffs, N.J., 1962.

Aviation Week, July 6, 1959, p. 27.

CARNOT, SADI: "Monograph on the Second Law of Thermodynamics," 1852. (Contained in translation by W. F. Magie, "The Second Law of Thermodynamics; Memoirs by Carnot, Clausius and Thomson," Harper and Brothers, New York, 1899.)

FRIIS, H. T.: Microwave Repeater Research, *Bell System Technical Journal,* vol. 27, pp. 183–246, April, 1948.

GODDARD, ROBERT H.: "A Method of Reaching Extreme Altitudes," Smithsonian Institution Publication, no. 2540, Washington, D.C., 1919.

GOSLING, W.: "The Design of Engineering Systems," Heywood & Co., Ltd., London, 1962.

HALL, A. D.: "A Methodology for Systems Engineering," D. Van Nostrand Company, Inc., Princeton, N.J., 1962.

KERSHNER, RICHARD B.: *Proceedings of the Workshop on Systems Engineering, IRE Transactions on Education,* vol. E-5, no. 2, June, 1962.

LANCHESTER, F. W.: Aircraft in Warfare, *Engineering,* Oct. 9, 1914.

PARKINSON, C. NORTHCOTE: "Parkinson's Law," Houghton Mifflin Company, Boston, Mass., 1957.

PECK, M. J., and F. M. SCHERER: "Weapons Acquisition Process," Graduate School of Business Administration, Boston, Mass., 1962.

ROETKEN, A. A., K. D. SMITH, and R. W. FRIIS: The TD-2 Microwave Radio Relay System, *Bell System Technical Journal,* vol. 30, pp. 1041–1077, October, 1951, part 2.

VON NEUMANN, J., and O. MORGENSTERN: "The Theory of Games and Economic Behavior," Princeton University Press, Princeton, N.J., 1944.

10

Women in Engineering Careers

by Irene Carswell Peden

Irene Peden is Associate Professor of Electrical Engineering at the University of Washington—the only woman faculty member in Engineering there. She has also been a successful engineer in industry, working with the Delaware Power and Light Company, the Stanford Research Institute on antenna problems, and the Stanford Microwave Laboratory on measurement techniques in microwave circuits. She has several publications on these subjects. Her B.S. degree was from the University of Colorado, and her M.S. and Ph.D. degrees were from Stanford University.

Dr. Peden is Vice Chairman of the Seattle section, Institute of Electrical and Electronics Engineers, and was a former chairman of the Professional-Technical Group on Microwave Theory and Technique of that Institute. She is active in the University YWCA and does a good deal of career counseling in high schools, especially with respect to engineering and science careers for women. She serves on the Education Committee of the Governor's Commission on the status of women.

Dr. Peden, with her lawyer husband, likes swimming, water skiing, and boating on beautiful Lake Washington. Other hobbies include music and clay modeling. She likes cooking, which may be considered work or hobby depending upon which facet you look at, housewife or engineer.

269

THE WORLD OF ENGINEERING has long been considered a male stronghold. It is still true that engineers are out in the field building bridges and dams and working with heavy machinery, but these activities are now in the minority. Engineers also work in a host of other areas requiring brains, a high level of technical competence, and no more physical exertion than it takes to lift a slide rule. It seems fairly obvious, after one has thought of it, that women with the same interests and training can work in these areas too, and yet 0.8 percent of all the engineers in this country are women. At a time when engineering enrollments are decreasing while the need for trained people continues to rise, this figure is almost startling. It implies that nearly half our technical potential is not being used. From a more personal standpoint, it implies that a number of women who could enjoy the many advantages of an engineering career are missing them. We are going to explore the matter from the point of view of some of the women who have established themselves as engineers in this world, which is not closed to them at all.

There is no longer any question that women *can* be engineers, by the way. There are over 7,000 in this country. According to recent information [1] 29.6 percent of the engineers in the Soviet Union are women, although that country counts engineering technicians and other subprofessional workers as engineers, and we do not. We are certain that many of the Russian women are graduate engineers in responsible positions, however. In 1956 a letter to the editor of *Soviet Women* requesting an article about women engineers was answered by the (female) chairman of machine-building technology at the Moscow Chemical Machine-Building Institute and head of the U.S.S.R. Cutting Tool Research Institute.[2] She described the accomplishments of a number of Russian women engineers in her institute, including the heads of the metallography laboratory, the hard-alloys laboratory, and the chemical laboratory, and reported that more than half of the personnel at the institute were women including seven department heads and six laboratory heads. The numbers are much smaller elsewhere, with England claiming 149 women as members of the chartered engineering societies in 1962; there are even fewer in other countries.

By the turn of the century, there were less than 100 women engineers in this country. Edith Julia Griswold was the first pioneer of

[1] Beatrice McConnell, Deputy Director, Women's Bureau, U.S. Department of Labor, Private Communication.
[2] Letter to Olive Mayer from Yelizaveta Nadeinskaya, *Society of Women Engineers Newsletter,* November, 1956.

whom we have any record. She studied civil, mechanical, and electrical engineering as well as law, and established herself in New York City in 1886 as a specialist in patent office drawings. One by one, interested and determined young women enrolled in the all-male engineering schools after that. The way was not easy, and they all encountered some degree of alarmed opposition from their teachers and fellow students. Those who persevered in their studies had difficulty in finding engineering positions, although the outlook was not completely black. Bertha Lamme got a job. She worked on the design of large motors and generators for the Westinghouse Electric Corporation after earning her electrical engineering degree from Ohio State University in 1893. She eventually married a fellow engineer and retired to the role of homemaker—a familiar course of events in the history of women engineers and one about which we shall have more to say later.

Wars have served to open new doors to working women, and World War I was no exception. A few more women began to enroll in engineering during the period 1919 to 1920. The late Edith Clarke was one of these. She had graduated after studies in mathematics and astronomy and had taught, without being entirely satisfied with her choice. She entered the Massachusetts Institute of Technology in the spring of 1918; just one year later she received the first Master's degree in electrical engineering ever given to a woman by that institution. During her next 26 years with the General Electric Company, Miss Clarke contributed original theory to symmetrical-component and circuit analysis and long-distance power transmission. After her retirement she served as professor of electrical engineering at the University of Texas. In addition to her published papers, some of which won prizes, she held two patents and wrote a well-known textbook for electrical engineers.

A well-loved figure in the world of women engineers is Dr. Lillian M. Gilbreth, President of Gilbreth, Inc., industrial engineering and management consultants. She is the famous mother of 12 in "Cheaper by the Dozen" who pioneered with her husband, Frank Gilbreth, in the field of motion study from which the profession of industrial engineering has evolved. Dr. Gilbreth has applied motion study and scientific work analysis to simplify and improve work methods and to aid the handicapped and disabled. She has written many books, technical papers, and articles on management and psychology, has held professorships at two universities, and has been Chairman of the Personnel Relations Department at a third.

Women engineers have made significant contributions to their fields in the relatively short time they have been on the scene. Dr. Irmgard

Flügge-Lotz, for example, is an internationally known figure in the field of theoretical aerodynamics and automatic control. Her 1931 paper on the computation of lift distribution of wings represented a major contribution to modern aircraft design; the method she described has been widely used in many countries. She and her graduate students at Stanford University, where she is Professor of Engineering Mechanics and of Aeronautics and Astronautics, are currently working on missile and satellite control problems and problems of heat transfer and drag of fast-moving vehicles.

Rebecca Sparling of General Dynamics is a materials specialist with degrees in chemistry; her background and active interests are in metallurgy and nondestructive testing. She was a coauthor of the first paper on immersed ultrasonic testing, and pioneered the use of a dye-penetrant inspection technique.

Dr. Esther Cornwell is Scientist-in-Charge of the Electronic Materials program at the General Telephone and Electronics Laboratories, where she heads a group of some ten to fifteen physicists, engineers, and technicians. Her group does research in solid-state physics on materials and phenomena that are currently or potentially useful for electronic components. Her own work, which is theoretical, has been mainly in the field of semiconductors, the material from which transistors are made.

Women engineers are executives as well as contributors to technology. Dr. Beatrice A. Hicks has been significant in the design, development, and manufacture of pressure- and gas-density controls for aircraft and missiles, and is the inventor of the gas-density switch, a key component in systems using artificial atmospheres. She is also President and Director of Engineering of Newark Controls Company in Bloomfield, New Jersey.

Among the women who received the 1963 Federal Woman's Award are a pioneer in the development of sounding rockets to probe the upper atmosphere and a world-renowned expert on concrete who heads the Army Corps of Engineers' waterways-experiment station. A woman holds a patent on a process used in manufacturing the type of printed circuit found in transistor radios; another helped develop the underwater missile launcher for the United States Navy's Polaris. Another became Section Chief responsible for all ground and airborne surveillance radars used for range clearance prior to firings at the Air Force Missile Test Center covering Cape Kennedy. Still another is working with the Peace Corps and UNESCO to revise the electrical engineering curriculum in a university in West Pakistan and to help put a communication system into a neighboring village.

Figure 1 Exemplary women scientists and engineers must surely include Elizabeth Zimmerman, research specialist at Philco's Advanced Technology Center in Blue Bell, Pennsylvania. Her work has contributed to high-frequency germanium devices, negative resistance diodes, parametric amplifiers, and active elements used in microelectronic circuits.

More routine engineering work occupies most of the women in the field, of course, just as it does their male colleagues, and this is an important point for prospective women engineers and for their teachers and counselors. One can be inspired with a great deal of admiration and awe by a recital of outstanding accomplishments, but this goal is not always primary in motivating students to try the field themselves. It is important to think of women engineers as real people doing real jobs which the students could do, too. The success of the women described above, and many more who might equally well have been introduced, is indicative of what can be achieved by the highly motivated and talented individual. Perhaps not all girls who are attracted by the possibilities in engineering could reach such goals, but many more have the potential than are realizing it now.

It is another important point for engineering that the work can be done at several different levels. Engineering is traditionally a four-year curriculum; the bulk of the work is done by engineers with the Bachelor's degree. It is interesting, varied, well paid, and responsible to the degree that the individual is mature and capable. More interesting jobs are available to the engineer with the Master's degree in return for the investment of another year of time and energy. Many engineers, both male and female, hold this degree. The strongly motivated person who is interested in teaching or research will want to work for the Ph.D. degree so that he can express himself at the upper levels of his field where engineering and applied science overlap. The personal sacrifices are undoubtedly greater for women than for men, although there are a number of women who have earned doctorates and are leading full and well-rounded lives. The point for engineering, in contrast to the pure sciences like physics and chemistry, is that we have a choice. We can pursue it to the Ph.D. degree with all the dedication and personal commitment that implies, if circumstances make it possible; on the other hand, we can do valuable and rewarding work after four or five years of study.

Psychologists tell us that intelligence and special abilities seem to be distributed approximately normally in each sex. There are sex differences in interests, however, and several masculinity-femininity scales have been constructed on this basis. Men are generally more interested in scientific activities, mechanics, physical activity, etc., than women, while women show the greater interest in people, social and clerical work, teaching, etc. It makes sense that these differences should be of importance in making vocational choices. It makes just as much sense that the general results do not apply to all individuals in each category, and that these apparent sex differences are artifacts of a system of social training; this latter conclusion has been drawn from a study of the occupational interest of boys and girls in the 6- to 16-year-old age group.[3]

Whether mechanical aptitude is inherently masculine or whether this interest is the result of cultural conditioning, it is no longer the most important talent for the prospective engineer, anyway. University vocational counselors are familiar with the worried and frustrated student who comes to them because he is doing poorly in engineering school. He is good with mechanical things and has always known that he should be an engineer; his analytical ability is weak, however, and herein lies the key to his difficulty. The broad face of engineering has been changing through the years as the level of our technology has moved upwards. The successful engineering student of today is good at mathematics; he or she is near the top in intelligence and has almost exclusively intellectual hobbies.

Psychologists have something to tell us about the sex distribution of ability in arithmetic reasoning.[4] Test scores have been plotted separately for boys and girls; the resulting curves approximate the normal distribution but both are skewed so that the means are significantly different. Much has been made of the result that the mean score for boys is the higher of the two. What is more important in this context is that the curves are completely overlapping. The median student should not be advised to go into engineering or any mathematics-based field in either case. It is the student with high achievement who can be productive and happy, and there are many girls as well as boys in this category. Due to the skewing of the curves, the distribution at the upper levels is not 50–50, but it is very much greater than the number of women engineers would indicate. If the ratio were only 2 to 1 and if this test were the determining factor, we could still have many more women engineers than we have now. What is more to the point, mixed groups of high school students have been given basic aptitude tests with the result that 6.3 percent of the boys and 4.2 percent of the girls showed an aptitude for engineering.[5] According to a 1961 study made by the National Science Foundation,[6] an average of 72,000 engineering graduates per year will be needed to meet the nation's requirements

[3] Anne Roe, "Psychology of Occupations," John Wiley & Sons, Inc., New York, 1956.

[4] *Ibid.*

[5] Emma C. Barth, Engineers in Skirts, *National Business Woman,* April, 1962.

[6] "The Long Range Demand for Scientific and Technical Personnel," National Science Foundation Study, 1961.

for professional engineers by 1970. The above tests suggest that 28,800 of these should be girls, but the total number of women enrolled in engineering schools in 1961 was only 1,486. It should be pointed out that the total number of students currently enrolled in engineering falls substantially below 72,000.

The number of women engineers rose from about 750 to 6,500 in the decade between 1940 and 1950 as women responded to the country's need for engineers and to the opportunities that this need opened to them.[7] Perhaps they will respond again as they become more aware of the current shortage and of its implications for them.

Studies also suggest that as the minority group in the engineering world, women might have a particular contribution to make, caused in part by their slightly different way of looking at the problems.[8] This ability to see things differently is the cornerstone of creativity, a quality to be sought and developed wherever possible. The missing percentage of our technical potential may have greater contributions to make than we have realized.

Rebecca Sparling has some sound and "down-to-earth" advice on the masculinity-femininity question. In her words [9] "There's nothing inherently feminine about mixing a given batch of materials, exposing it to a definite temperature for a definite time and producing a cake. There's nothing inherently masculine in mixing a batch of materials, exposing it to a definite temperature for a given time and producing iron castings. I've done both, and find them satisfying occupations." This kind of thinking is heartily endorsed by women engineers in all fields.

Electronics is a good field for women. The problems usually lend themselves to mathematical analysis at all levels, from the simple to the very sophisticated. The fact that trained women can do theoretical work as well as men is obvious. But much of the experimental work in this field is well suited to women. It tends to be precise, and the equipment it involves is clean, small, and lightweight. Of 7,211 women em-

[7] Stella P. Manor, Opportunities for Women Engineers During the Decade. Women in Engineering—Past, Present and Future, "Women in Engineering," Published findings of a conference held under the auspices of the Executive Office of the President of the United States and sponsored by the University of Pittsburgh and the Society of Women Engineers, April, 1962.

[8] Anne Roe, *op. cit.*

[9] Rebecca Sparling, Women in Engineering, text of a speech, private communication.

ployed as engineers in 1960,[10] 1,474 were working in some branch of electrical engineering. The largest number were industrial engineers (2,069); 808 were in aeronautical engineering. Civil engineering, that traditionally male stronghold, had 880 women; it would seem from available information that the top women in this field have tended to stay in structural design. Chemical engineering, another area open to women, had 389 in 1960. An outstanding member of this group is Dr. Margaret Hutchinson, a consulting chemical engineer who specializes in design work on units and equipment for chemical plants and oil refineries and in research in the field of commercial distillation (*fractionation*) equipment. Women are found in all branches of engineering including mining and sales.

There are some women engineers who do physically hazardous jobs. The Department of Labor has this to say about them: [11] "Individual women are known to work at jobs in which they test planes under exceedingly hazardous conditions, or to climb into oversized machinery to inspect it. These women undertake such tasks by choice, and are undoubtedly more physically fit to execute them than many men." Dynamic Dot Merrill, an engineer-executive who owns her own firm, believes that the statement about climbing into oversized machinery may refer to her. The firm sells all kinds of power equipment—boilers, turbine generators, diesel engines, motors, switchgear, compressors, etc., and tiny Dot has had occasion to inspect coal mines, turbine generators, and boilers from the inside. She says she can do it in half the time it would take some of the oversized boiler inspectors she knows.

Physical stamina is no limitation, then, to the woman who wants to go into engineering; neither is mechanical aptitude. Certainly salaries are attractive; engineering is probably one of the highest-paying professions open to women today. Women have their full share of the intelligence distributed to the human race, and engineering does not require more of it than any other profession. Interest and aptitude seem to be the most important features, just as they are for any other career, and just as they are for men.

A girl is not likely to choose a career field disapproved by her parents, teachers, classmates, and friends. All of these people have been generally discouraging in the past. They would seem to be responding in part to an erroneous but popular image of the woman engineer as a

[10] Beatrice McConnell, Deputy Director, Women's Bureau, U.S. Department of Labor, private communication.
[11] "Professional Engineering—Employment Opportunities for Women," *Women's Bureau Bulletin*, no. 254, U.S. Department of Labor.

cold, hard, overintelligent and aggressive female who trudges through life in her flat-heeled shoes without a man in sight (away from the job). This image is strictly not true. No one would deny that there are women in the profession who prefer tailored suits and low-heeled shoes; so do some nurses, librarians, and housewives. Many women engineers are very attractive; most represent a perfectly normal cross section of femininity. The only way that this image can be brought into line with reality, of course, is by way of personal contact. Few women engineers would refuse an opportunity to talk with interested girls and their parents and teachers. The Society of Women Engineers, with over 700 members and with chapters in 16 cities and 14 colleges, has the counseling and encouragement of students as one of its primary goals. Its members are their own best public relations experts.

A girl who has the aptitude and interest for an engineering career must be willing to work hard, and must be sure that she really likes the work. In high school she can use her feeling about problem solving in mathematics and physics as a measure of interest. This is a realistic guide; the problems will become harder and more interesting if she goes on into science or engineering, but she will continue to tackle them because she enjoys this activity and finds real satisfaction in solving such problems.

Almost all engineering schools admit women, and serve as a valuable testing ground in many ways, including the technical. Here the student will meet most of the problems of an engineering career and can decide, without "getting in too deep," whether this is the best career for her. She either resolves the problems to her own satisfaction or decides that another major would suit her better. The drop-out rate after the first year of engineering school is very high for both men and women, for various reasons including unrealistic student goals and impatience with the freshman curriculum which cannot provide the excitement of higher-level engineering problems. Most students who change their minds do so before or during the sophomore year, and without loss of credit. The freshman curriculum in science and mathematics is a fine background for other work, and the hours will fill elective requirements in any other curriculum. In other words, one cannot "get in too deep too fast" by enrolling in engineering school. And certainly a girl can get out gracefully anytime with no loss of face. How many of her friends would be surprised if she didn't like it?

There certainly are some problems which need to be faced as soon as possible. How much they bother the individual student depends on her own makeup and internal resources. She will find herself an object of curiosity, and she will have to cope with this when she goes to work unless there should be a sharp increase in the number of women engineers in a very short time. She is "spot-lighted" in a sense—not always a comfortable situation. It is rather lonely at times even under the best circumstances. The girl who is going to be troubled by this will meet and deal with it almost immediately after enrolling in engineering school. A girl in her sophomore year of electrical engineering at the University of Washington has remarked that the boys were pretty stand-offish until they were sure that she was serious about her studies—and then she became just an unusual member of the group. This course of events is quite typical on the job as well. Getting the job in the first place is usually the major hurdle for the woman engineer, and one which sometimes requires courage and patience. Once established, she usually has little difficulty becoming an unusual and valuable member of the group.

No honest person can deny that women engineers have met with discrimination along the way. The early trail blazers found it everywhere; nowadays we find it in some branches of engineering more than in others, in some companies, and in some supervisors. Attitudes have changed markedly during the working lifetme of most of the women active today. The negative attitudes can be expected to decrease, particularly as the need for engineers continues to exceed the supply. The generally increasing acceptance of working women in our society may be expected to contribute as well.

Significantly, it is the women engineers of higher accomplishment who report that they have been least affected by prejudice. There are several possible reasons for this. In the first place, real accomplishment in the world of technology is very concrete and cannot be denied. Admiration for a job well done can be counted on to outweigh other attitudes from employers and colleagues; the resulting satisfaction can help to compensate for other feelings which might have been troublesome. In the second place, these women have no doubt been more devoted to their work for its own sake than some of their sisters. This kind of one-pointed interest can "mask out" problems in the office or laboratory. It is also quite possible that they have chosen fields in which women can work most effectively without artificial barriers—research is one of these—and have found job situations in which discrimination was minimized. We could not go far astray in assuming that they have combined technical competence with feminine tact and charm to produce an unbeatable set of job qualifications.

In general it may be said that the person who has too many problems on the job is a person who has problems. It would be impossible to separate career adjustment from general adjustment to life, or career satisfaction from satisfaction with life. Each is a measure of the other. It seems only sensible to assume that the well-adjusted person of either sex in any job classification will either accept some difficulties in the working situation and find his satisfactions away from the job, or else he will "adjust" himself in another office or laboratory where the climate is more favorable. The first women engineers had very little alternative; undoubtedly they found enough satisfaction and sense of accomplishment in the work itself to carry them through. At least they had to be aware that a free choice had been made and that they must support the consequences of their own decisions. Today, however, the situation is quite different. There are so many choices as engineering expands and grows in scope, and so many job opportunities, with nearly 90 percent of the engineering jobs confined to desk, computer, or laboratory, that it would seem unnecessary for any woman to remain long in an unfavorable situation.

The fact that women do the childbearing and child-caring has certainly affected the hiring policies for women in all job categories. Much has been made of the fact that women leave their jobs to care for their families and relatively little of the fact that men leave jobs rather often either for advancement or for change. It is interesting that another physical fact has had relatively little effect in the job situation, viz., that women live longer than men on the average. There may have to be a reconsideration of the retirement age as the age of our population increases. It seems quite likely that this difference between the sexes might receive more attention in regard to the employment and training of women. In any event, so many women are working now that such problems have to be faced and solved by society no matter what careers women choose.

Promotion policies have traditionally been more favorable for men than for women. The Boeing Company's Maxine Mitchell takes a "down-to-earth" view of the situation. As Supervisor of Technical Data for Flight Test, Maxine Mitchell is responsible for 60 people. She believes that if a man and a woman of exactly equal qualifications were up for promotion to the same job, the man would win. She adds that she has never seen a situation that equal. Nevertheless, it is a matter of record that many women engineers rise to administrative positions, but more do not. To what extent this is the conscious or unconscious preference of the women themselves we do not know. Some of our earlier reasoning might be used again to predict that the situation will become more favorable in time.

Some recent statistical work by the Society of Women Engineers, based on a survey of its own membership, has revealed the following important result: "that most women engineers marry and raise happy active families—just as do most women everywhere. They do tend to mary late, often in the late twenties to early thirties, but once married they also tend to stay married." [12]

They tend to marry professional men—other engineers, doctors, lawyers, etc. Many have worked a few years while their husbands were in graduate school and have then retired either temporarily or permanently to raise their families. The salary a woman engineer can command has provided a better standard of living for the couple during the graduate school period than is usual under the circumstances.

Those who retire in favor of homemaking do so with a greater sense of security than the untrained, who rush from uncompleted schooling into marriage. There is something interesting and worthwhile that the woman engineer has learned to do; the fact that it was difficult to learn and to do well contributes to her feelings of self-worth in an important way. Her training is accorded a good deal of prestige by her friends. Personal security and self-esteem are vital to us all; they are very important indeed in the world of diapers and dishpans. It is rare for a woman who has mastered the engineering curriculum to regret her training, whether she has used it temporarily or not at all.

Those who consider their retirement temporary have several avenues open to them. They can try to keep up during the retirement period; this can be rather difficult, especially in some of the rapidly advancing fields. Some have been able to do it, some have not.

They can plan a comeback for the time when the children are a little older and they can earn enough to accommodate the cost of household help and baby-sitters. Technical writing is a good field for women; the woman with an engineering degree has special advantages in this area, whether she is a recent graduate or not. The work can sometimes be done on a part-time or free-lance basis.

Computer programming is another possibility. The Boeing Company's Maxine Mitchell is an authority on this subject; her supervisory responsibilities include 15 computer programmers. Programming requires a background in mathematics, with engineering training desirable in many contexts, including that of her company. She believes that the future in this field is very bright, either for the person who has been out of school awhile and wants to get back into technical work, or for the newly graduated student.

Partial retirement is often possible. The woman who is highly trained and well established in her field may be able to "keep her hand in" by consulting; chemical engineer Margaret Hutchinson is among the

[12] "Profile of a Woman Engineer," pamphlet prepared by the Statistics Committee, Society of Women Engineers, New York, May, 1963.

women who have done this. Rebecca Sparling has worked at home quite profitably during a period when her son was convalescing from a serious illness. Lectures can be written at home, and sometimes research of a theoretical nature can be done there by the women in teaching and research; part-time appointments are likely to be available to them during these years. It is worthwhile to point out again that it is the untrained women in our society who are at a disadvantage in trying to match jobs to family needs.

Some women hire housekeepers and continue to work while their children are small. There is evidence that this solution is not as harmful to the children as is popularly believed, at least in the case of the children of working mothers in the general population.[13] There appear to be no studies which have determined whether or not the employed woman would be a different mother if she stayed home; in particular, published results of studies involving professionally trained women and their children seem to be lacking.

When mother is practicing her profession, and the family is not in need of her income, it would seem to make sense that she has a strong need for self-expression which is not met in her role as housewife. The woman who successfully manages home, motherhood, and career is doing so because she is intensely interested in her work and feels that she cannot do otherwise. Occupations have become very important in our culture because so many personal needs are satisfied by them; they give us status and feelings of personal esteem, and they satisfy our needs for self-expression.[14] If some women cannot fill these needs at home, it would seem to be appropriate that each one works it out in her own way with the cooperation of her husband. Engineers do, physicists do, and so do lawyers, physicians, secretaries, and beauticians. The woman with the same strong needs and motivations who has not trained herself for the career of her choice will very likely devote herself to club work or community service.

Seattle's vivacious Patricia Corwin is a striking example of what can be accomplished right at home. Pat has seven children, a Master's degree in ceramic engineering, and a laboratory at home where she designs ceramic transducers on contract. Both Pat and her husband, also a ceramic engineer, work on the components; she does the production and testing while he is away at his own job; he works at home in the evenings. They specialize in the design of unusual items which

---

[13] Lois Meek Stolz, Effects of Maternal Employment on Children: Evidence from Research, *Child Development*, vol. 31, no. 4, December, 1960.

[14] Roe, *op. cit.*

are often used in the customer's own research; oceanographic and fisheries research are principal end users. On occasion, their work has led to a commercial product such as a fathometer transducer [15] for boats, used to detect rocks, schools of fish, etc.

When Pat is working to meet a contract deadline, the whole family organizes to help. The oldest child does simple testing of the ceramic, other older children go on a pay scale for baby-sitting with the younger ones. The children keep their own accounts and present their claims to Pat when the check arrives. She says that the children watch the mailbox avidly when a check is due, and that throughout the whole operation, there is a very strong feeling of working together for a common cause.

Pat feels that she could not possibly earn as much working outside her home, even if this were possible. Furthermore, she can work or not as needed or convenient for the family. She believes, as so many women engineers do, that her training is a very effective insurance policy for her family. She is able to provide for them, if that should ever be necessary, and she is not out of touch with her field while the children are young.

It seems that the very small percentage of women in engineering careers is due in part to several factors which have affected students, teachers, and counselors alike. There is an unfortunate and unrealistic image of the woman engineer which could be dispelled by more personal contact. There has been some prejudice, which is decreasing and which is hardly felt today by many women engineers. The problems are not really different from those of other careers or from those of all women who work; they seem to be sometimes intensified when they do occur. Most women engineers agree that for every difficult situation they have found, there have been many others that were favorable and rewarding. There has been a lack of true information about the scope of engineering jobs, viz., that they are not confined to construction and railroading. And finally, there has been a genuine lack of realization that engineering is available to women, and that it is a field of wide-open opportunity for them. Probably the only limitations are ability and willingness to accept responsibility.

A girl who is enthusiastic and creative will be welcomed by many professions, and should be encouraged to give careful consideration to all the doors which may be open to her. If she likes mathematics

[15] This transducer is an electroacoustic device which converts electrical energy to mechanical energy and transmits pressure waves at audible frequencies to the water surrounding the ceramic element.

and science and has a real aptitude for engineering, she should be encouraged to try out her abilities in engineering school with an eye toward an exciting and rewarding future. She should take seriously the opinion of Dr. Mervin Kelly, former president of the Bell Telephone Laboratories: [16] "I am often asked, 'Can girls make a go of engineering?' The answer is a resounding 'Yes'."

BIBLIOGRAPHY

BARTH, EMMA C.: Engineers in Skirts, *National Business Woman*, April, 1962.

KELLY, MERVIN J.: Should You Be an Electronics Engineer? *Career Opportunities*, New York Life Insurance Company, September, 1962.

Letter to Olive Mayer from Yelizaveta Nadeinskaya, *Society of Women Engineers Newsletter*, November, 1956.

"The Long Range Demand for Scientific and Technical Personnel," National Science Foundation Study, 1961.

MANOR, STELLA P.: Opportunities for Women Engineers During the Decade. Women in Engineering—Past, Present and Future, "Women in Engineering," Published findings of a conference held under the auspices of the Executive Office of the President of the United States and sponsored by the University of Pittsburgh and the Society of Women Engineers, April, 1962.

"Professional Engineering—Employment Opportunities for Women," *Women's Bureau Bulletin*, no. 254, U.S. Department of Labor.

"Profile of a Woman Engineer," pamphlet prepared by the Statistics Committee, Society of Women Engineers, New York, May, 1963. (Society of Women Engineers, 345 E. 47th St., N.Y. 17, N.Y.)

ROE, ANNE: "Psychology of Occupations," John Wiley & Sons, Inc., New York, 1956.

STOLZ, LOIS MEEK: Effects of Maternal Employment on Children: Evidence from Research, *Child Development*, vol. 31, no. 4, December, 1960.

---

[16] Mervin J. Kelly, Should You Be an Electronics Engineer? *Career Opportunities,* New York Life Insurance Company, September, 1962.

11

Engineering Growth and the Community

by F. E. Terman

Frederick Emmons Terman, Provost of Stanford University, has been one of the great influences in the radio and electronics industry through his work in education, government service, and his cooperation with the electronics industry. He has been Professor of Electrical Engineering at Stanford, Executive Head of the department, and Dean of the College of Engineering there. His books on radio engineering are classics and are used in universities throughout the world. During World War II he directed the Radio Research Laboratory at Harvard University, which was responsible for this country's effort on radar countermeasures. He has chaired and served on countless advisory boards for the Department of Defense and other government agencies. His work with the electronics industry, especially in the Palo Alto area, led to the large growth of the aerospace industry in that area and formed a pattern which has been followed in many of the industrial parks of the country.

Dr. Terman was son of the well-known psychologist, Lewis Madison Terman, of the famous Terman-Benet "IQ" tests. He received his B.A. and E.E. degrees from Stanford University and his Sc.D. from the Massachusetts Institute of Technology. He holds honorary degrees from Harvard University, the University of Brit-

ish Columbia, and Syracuse University. He is a former
president of the Institute of Radio Engineers, and holds
most of its major awards. He holds the Medal of Merit
from the United States, the Medal of Honor from the
Institute of Radio Engineers, and a medal from the
British government.

SINCE WORLD WAR II there has been an unprecedented expansion of
industries emphasizing research and development. Examples include
electronics, missiles, space, computers, nuclear power, chemical and
pharmaceutical industries, instrumentation, automation, etc. Such industries are often referred to as "growth industries" because so many
companies specializing in these fields have had remarkable growth records during the last fifteen years.

Growth companies of this type are based on the exploitation of new
developments and new knowledge in science and technology. Their
characteristic growth is a result more of the creation of new or improved products than it is of expansion of markets for old products.
They depend upon a sophisticated technology and they live close to
the frontiers of science and such technology. For this reason they are
sometimes called "glamour companies."

Such companies are characterized by the fact that a high fraction of
the value of their output is the result of ingenuity, originality, and
sophisticated engineering. As a result, an unusually large proportion
of their employees are college graduates in engineering or science.
Moreover, many of them have training at graduate level, including
usually a generous sprinkling of Doctor's degrees. It is not surprising
that companies of this type have also been called "egghead" companies.

In these egghead companies, technical men with advanced degrees
in engineering or science are invariably prominent in the top management of the company, in capacities other than director of research and
chief engineer. If the company started business during or since World
War II, the founder, or at least one cofounder, is probably an engineer
or applied scientist. There is usually at least one technical man on the
board of directors; not infrequently the board also includes one or two
college professors of engineering or science.

These growth companies are the antithesis of the "mass-production"
companies. In the latter, most of the employees are concerned with
production activities and perform simple repetitive tasks requiring only
limited skills. The engineering costs then represent only a small fraction of the value of each article produced, and competition is based

more upon manufacturing efficiency and marketing than upon creative contributions by the engineering staff. In this connection it is to be noted that electronics includes both "mass production" and "research and development" types of activities. Thus the production of standard television sets is not a growth activity in the sense of this discussion; the total number of sets manufactured in the country does not vary greatly from year to year, and a large increase of sales by one company decreases the sales of other television-set manufacturers. In contrast is the continual development of tape recorders for use in satellites, telemetering, instrumentation, computers, television broadcasting, educational television, etc.

GROWTH INDUSTRIES AS AN IMPORTANT ECONOMIC FACTOR

The growth industries have become a major factor in the economic life of the nation and promise to be even more significant in the years ahead. Their total sales and services are now a significant fraction of the gross national product and are increasing far more rapidly than is the total gross national product.

Egghead companies are particularly important to certain communities. Thus in New England in general, and the Boston area in particular, the future once looked dismal as the textile, shoe, and other mass-production industries moved to locations that were closer to markets and raw materials and to cheaper and more abundant factory labor. Now, with Boston perhaps the liveliest center in the country for growth industries, business was never better or on a sounder basis. Again, the tremendous population growth of the San Francisco Peninsula since World War II has been supported largely by the development of a highly creative electronics and space industry in the general vicinity of Stanford University. Other areas, for example, Phoenix, have for the first time experienced the stimulus of industrialization as a result of the influx of growth companies.

THE ROLE OF THE ENGINEER IN THE GROWTH INDUSTRIES

The work of the engineer is essential to these glamour industries.[1] The ideas leading to new products sometimes originate with a research engineer, sometimes with a scientist, but in either case the engineer does

---

[1] An exception is in the chemical and pharmaceutical fields where the chemist has the central role. The subsequent discussion of the work of the engineer excludes these chemical fields.

most of the work required to transform the raw idea into a product that is useful, practical, and reliable. In carrying out this work, the engineer must often gain a deeper and broader understanding of the device and the principles involved than did the research engineer or scientist responsible for the original discoveries that made the device possible. In acquiring an understanding of how best to handle the new principles and concepts to obtain the desired result, the engineer frequently must perform additional research to find needed answers for new problems that arise.

In general it can be said that the more sophisticated the ideas with which he is working, the greater is the demand on the engineer and the challenge to him; the contribution that he can make to the total program is likewise greater. Thus an intercontinental ballistic missile (ICBM) or a manned satelite, with its multistage rocket power plant, its complex guidance system, electronics instrumentation, and nuclear warhead (or capsule), is fundamentally the work of the engineer. While scientific discoveries made the achievement possible, it was the engineer who did most of the work entailed in bringing a workable device into existence, and each successful flight is a triumph for the engineers involved.

GRADUATE TRAINING FOR ENGINEERS

Since the growth industries deal with advanced and complex concepts, they place a real demand upon the competence of the engineer. Graduate training, at least to the Master's level, has become almost a necessity for the man who wishes to make full use of his ability in these challenging new fields. The nature of these growth fields is such that practical "on-the-job" experience is not a substitute for formal training. The necessary training beyond the Bachelor's degree is best obtained in the classroom, although home study of academic subjects is a possible alternative. In addition, old knowledge becomes obsolescent with the passage of time, and as new technologies are developed a man with even the best of academic training must constantly study if he is to continue to be a contributor. Graduate work provides the best foundation for this process of lifelong learning. Because of the importance of high-level knowledge and training, industry recognizes graduate training, or its equivalent in competence gained through self-study, in terms of salary and responsibility.

In response to this situation, engineers in increasing numbers have since World War II continued their education to the Master's and

Doctor's degrees. At the present time about 25 percent of all engineers who graduate with a Bachelor's degree carry their formal training to a Master's degree, and 4 percent receive a Doctor's degree. It is expected that over 10 percent of the engineers graduating in 1970 will continue their education to the Sc.D. or Ph.D. degree. By way of contrast, before World War II only a small percentage of the engineers went as far as a Master's degree, and engineers with Ph.D.'s were rare indeed.

It is the engineers, particularly those with advanced training, that carry most of the responsibility for progress in the growth industries. While physicists and others make important contributions, by far the largest part of the work carried on is performed by engineers, if for no other reason than that there are far more engineers than physicists or mathematicians. In 1961 to 1962 the universities awarded over six times as many Bachelor's and Master's degrees in engineering as in physics and twice as many Ph.D. degrees.

The type of graduate training now available in engineering emphasizes the more fundamental and scientific aspects of engineering; it deemphasizes empirical knowledge, routine design procedures, and details of industrial practice. The result tends to produce a true engineer-scientist, who possesses the intellectual tools required to understand the new and sophisticated concepts and new developments so characteristic of the research-oriented industries. With such training, the engineer is also adaptable; he can move from one area of advanced technology to another without undue difficulty of adjustment. The depth and breadth of his background make it easy for him to grasp the new concepts that must be understood to keep up with an advancing technology.

CONCEPTION OF GROWTH INDUSTRIES IN PARTICULAR AREAS AND LOCALITIES

The creative work associated with growth industries is concentrated in particular areas of the country, rather than widely dispersed. There are, for example, notable concentrations in the Boston area, the San Francisco Peninsula, Long Island, and around Washington, D.C., greater Los Angeles, etc. At the same time there is an obvious lack of creative work being done in some regions, including those where a large volume of standard electronic equipment and parts are manufactured on a mass-production basis.

In order to understand what has led to concentrations of growth industries in particular localities, we note that the factors determining the location of a factory have traditionally been the availability of a large supply of inexpensive labor, closeness to markets or raw materials, cheap or quick transportation, etc. None of these factors is important in the growth industries. Here the products produced typically have a high value per pound, so that shipping costs both for raw material and the finished product are relatively unimportant. As to labor, it is the quality and skills available that are more important than quantity or cheapness.

What counts most in a growth industry is brains. As a result the most important consideration in location is nearness to a source of brains, which means either a university or an existing concentration of growth industries. Brains are mobile and can move about easily. Accordingly, the engineer and the scientist with interests and abilities in the newly developing technologies tend to gravitate to firms in communities where living conditions are attractive. This means locations where other people like themselves, with similar training, interests, and ambitions, are also present. Although engineers and scientists are not as social as some human beings, they are in their own way very gregarious. They need intellectual contacts with like-minded individuals; they need the opportunity to attend technical meetings, to participate in discussions, and to live in a professionally stimulating environment. An engineer or a small group of engineers isolated from outside contacts will generally go stale and lose both their creativity and their zest. Advanced and highly technical activities do not flourish in an intellectual desert.

Growth companies favorably located in intellectually challenging environments will be most successful because they attract the most capable and the best-trained minds. In contrast, companies less favorably located will on the average be less successful because they find it harder to recruit and hold the best employees. The end result is that creative activities in the growth industries concentrate increasingly in particular communities that for one reason or another have an appeal for people with intelligence. Let us now examine further the elements that contribute to this concentration.

A NEW KIND OF COMMUNITY OF SCHOLARS

In medieval times scholars tended to concentrate in particular locations where the principal attraction was the presence of other scholars. Where there were scholars, there came students typically from many countries. In this way the center of learning, or *universitas,* came into being. Teaching was done in Latin, and as a result scholars and students could maintain rapport with each other irrespective of the country in which they happened to be or of the nationalities of the individual students and scholars.

Students would commonly move about, attending lectures at first one center and then another. In the beginning this was all very informal. There were no curricula, admission procedures, grade-point averages, degrees, or even typewriters. Individuals set themselves up as scholars and offered lectures as they pleased. If they could attract students who were able to pay fees, they prospered, and could become famous, influential, and even well-off financially. Some of these *communities of scholars* became famous as centers of learning, and many great universities of present-day Europe are their direct descendents. Examples are Oxford, Bologna, Heidelberg, Salamanca, Paris, Gottingen, and Cambridge.

A new counterpart of these medieval communities of scholars has in recent years begun to take form in our modern society. This consists of great universities which have strong programs in engineering and science, surrounded by companies emphasizing research and development, under conditions where there is continual interaction among all of the components—some formal, some informal, some organized, others unorganized.

This modern version of the community of scholars is still embryonic in character, having developed in the last twenty or so years. However, the trend is clearly present, and is becoming more distinctive each year. The largest and best-defined of such modern communities of scholars is in the Boston area, where one has both the Massachusetts Institute of Technology and Harvard University in a community that includes many, many growth companies, some large, some small. Also included are a number of large research and development laboratories supported by the government, which add further stimulation and diversity to the community. Another example is the San Francisco Peninsula around Stanford University. This particular "community of scholars" is particularly noteworthy in that at the end of World War II in 1945 there was almost no industry of the growth type there. Yet in less than twenty years it has become one of the liveliest and most creative centers in the country. Other examples of this phenomenon exist to varying degrees at many places around the nation.

In these modern communities of scholars there is a continuous ferment which makes them intellectually stimulating for people having the qualities that contribute most to growth industries. A great university is first and foremost a center for brains. The members of its faculty are highly trained and knowledgeable experts. It brings bright students in from all over the country to interact with each other and with the local intellectual environment. Upon completion of their college work these young people become available for employment, and represent the most important raw material that goes into the growth industries.

The faculty members of a university that is part of such a modern community of technical scholars live in no "ivory towers." They have numerous contacts with stimulating, highly creative individuals in industry. They typically do some consulting with one or more adjacent growth companies on subjects in which they have professional expertness, and often they sit on a board of directors. Many professors also serve on government advisory committees of one kind or another. As a result they bring to the classroom a broad background because they are truly men of affairs.

The creative individuals doing interesting work in local companies will give frequent talks to seminar classes at the university. Here they are not only on exhibition to the students, but are also subjected to their critical questions. Junior employees of local companies will in many cases enroll in classes at the university; some will even do doctoral research at the university on subjects that are of interest both to the employer and to the university faculty member with whom they are associated.

Original ideas coming out of the research activities of the university which have practical possibilities will be picked up and exploited by the local industry. In turn, the activities carried on by local industry react on research work being done in the universities, contributing to its progress and in some cases influencing the direction in which it goes. Thesis projects by students which have industrial implications are often moved at the completion of the Doctor's degree from the university into a local company, and modified to become part of a commercial development.

Such an environment is stimulating, is conducive to the development of new ideas, and in general maintains intellectual activity at a high tempo. It is in such an environment that new companies are born and older companies, if they are well managed, grow rapidly. This is the twentieth- and twenty-first-century form of the honored and ancient community of scholars. It represents a new and distinctive force in our society.

THE ROLE OF THE UNIVERSITY

The growing importance of industries based on science and technology has given the university a new role in national life. This is touched on in the previous section but can well stand further examination. Increasingly, each significant center of growth industries finds need for educational facilities at university level. In turn every university with a sound program in engineering and science, including at least some graduate work, is a potential center for growth industries if it is not already such a center.

Universities are thus rapidly becoming more than mere places for learning. They are becoming major economic influences in the nation's industrial life, affecting the location of industry, population growth, and the character of communities. They have in brief become a natural resource just as are raw materials, transportation, climate, etc. Dr. James R. Killian, former President of the Massachusetts Institute of Technology (MIT), has described the university-originated "common market of ideas" resulting from MIT, Harvard University, etc., as the principal economic force in the present economy and prosperity of New England. Again, Clark Kerr, President of the far-flung University of California with its many campuses, has publicly argued that engineering programs must be established on new campuses in order that the University of California may adequately serve the industrial needs of a growing California.

The hunger that growth industries have for a university is apparent in situations where such industries were established at locations lacking a nearby university. One type of case is represented by situations where isolated locations have been dictated by the nature of the work being done; examples are the atomic energy installation at Hanford, Washington, the missile base at Huntsville, Alabama, and the Naval Ordnance Test Station at Inyokern, California. At each of these locations, and also at many other similar installations, on-premise educational programs are provided under the sponsorship of the state university.

When growth companies do creative work in cities that do not have an adequate local university, major efforts are often made to remedy this lack. Such efforts can take several forms. At Hartford, Connecticut, companies have banded together to support a graduate campus of Rensselaer Polytechnic Institute. On Long Island, the Brooklyn Polytechnic Institute is establishing a branch campus adjacent to the plant of Republic Aviation. Growth companies in Phoenix, Arizona, persuaded the state to establish undergraduate- and graduate-level programs in applied science at Arizona State College, formerly a teachers' college. Even the Bell Telephone Laboratories, which has the largest research laboratory in the country and would appear to be self-sufficient, has an arrangement with New York University to provide graduate-level degree programs of instruction on the Bell Laboratory premises at Murray Hill, New Jersey.

This is a very different situation from that which existed as recently as a quarter of a century ago. Then most engineering schools operated in splendid isolation; their ivory towers were sullied by the world around only if the institution happened to be located in a large city, and most of the institutions were not. Students came to these schools eager to learn, and after their four years they left to work in factories around the country as graduate engineers. Most universities were then little worlds in themselves, largely isolated from the hurly-burly of everyday life.

These days are now gone, and with them our beloved Stanford has changed. Once known as the "Farm" because of its rural setting with a 9,000-acre campus, Stanford University is not what it used to be. It is now the center of a major industrial activity. The students sit at the feet of professors who typically have consulting connections with a local industrial laboratory, and who miss some classes every term because of being invited somewhere to give talks on their research, or as a result of having to fly to Washington to sit on a government committee and advise the government on how things should be run in the country. Also in seminars and colloquia the students no longer have the same old succession of familiar professors and graduate students. Instead, they see and hear a series of men from industry who are doing interesting, impressive, and important things. Moreover, when the students obtain their degrees, now commonly a Master's or Doctor's degree instead of just a Bachelor's degree, they do not go off a thousand or more miles to work in some distant plant. Rather, a high proportion of them take a job in a local company, stay on in the Stanford community, and keep coming back to the university to see their old professors and sit in at seminars, and to give talks themselves to the next generation of students. The lively university of today no longer means the same thing to the engineering student or to its faculty members that it did a quarter of a century ago.

COMPETITION BETWEEN COMMUNITIES
FOR GROWTH INDUSTRIES

Egghead companies are attractive to communities interested in growing or in strengthening their economic base. Such companies are characterized by high average educational level of their employees, and by high average income as a result of the emphasis on intellectual abilities of the white-collar workers and upon high levels of skills on the part of the blue-collar workers. They are also clean, quiet, and have status. Moreover, employment in such companies tends to be stable; in particular it does not follow the "hire, layoff, and fire" pattern so common in mass-production industries.

Growth companies generally occupy attractively landscaped plants with modern architecture, which differ greatly from the old-fashioned and depressing "factory." This comes about because these companies are in competition for the best brains, and the people they want can be and are "choosey" about the surroundings in which they work.

As the attractive features of these growth companies have become generally appreciated, communities all over the country have sought to induce such companies to settle down within their own boundaries. Private promoters, politicians, chambers of commerce, and even nonprofit organizations are all in the act.

In this wooing of growth companies, there are several factors that contribute to success. First and most important is the availability or lack of availability of a university with an acceptable graduate program in engineering and science within commuting distance. The lack of such an institution is not absolutely fatal, but its presence is a great help.

The second factor, and one of almost equal importance, is whether or not there already exists a stimulating technological environment. If there are already activities in the community that have brought together a nucleus of engineers and scientists, the problem of attracting industry that needs people of this type is made much easier. The situation in this connection compares to that with fissionable material: There is a critical size below which nothing much happens, but above which things take off rapidly. A community ambitious to be a center for growth companies finds that its principal problem is to get up to this critical size; after that things are easy.

The third important factor is the cultural atmosphere of the community. This environment is particularly important in the early stages, before the growth companies have made their impact. In general, communities having a high proportion of professional people are more attractive and have a greater chance of becoming centers for activities with a high engineering and science content than communities where the initial population has a low vocational and educational level. Communities not too far from major cities have advantages because they combine the opportunity for suburban or rural living with the cultural opportunities associated with a major city. This is one of the reasons that Long Island, the San Francisco Peninsula, and Route 128 outside of Boston have become so popular.

Major cities are, however, not in themselves particularly attractive locations for growth industry. Even when the city has a major university in its downtown area the large population and diverse activities of the city simply overwhelm the growth companies located in a metropolitan area. Thus in the greater New York area, one finds the growth companies on Long Island, in New Jersey, and up the Hudson River rather than in New York City proper. Again the growth companies in the Boston area tend to be located either in Cambridge in the immediate vicinity of MIT and Harvard, or in the suburbs.

The Los Angeles area might appear to be an exception to this rule, but close examination reveals that it is not really so. The growth companies in that great city, and there are many of them, are scattered around the outskirts at locations where the employees can live fairly close to where they work, in a home having a green lawn and a patio with orange trees. This is not really city living.

THE EFFECT OF GROWTH COMPANIES UPON A COMMUNITY

When growth companies concentrate in a particular community, their presence has a profound effect upon the sociological characteristics of that community. One of the first and most obvious effects is that these companies tend to grow, and as a result they force their community, and also the adjacent communities, to grow similarly. This process distresses many of the older inhabitants and produces continuing problems related to the expansion of school systems, zoning policies, traffic congestion, etc.

Another obvious effect comes from the fact that the economic status of the employees of growth companies is relatively high. This level affects the character of the homes, the shops, the community attitudes, and community politics. The type of employee who makes up the growth companies is in general very much concerned about education and the character of the community in which his children grow up. There is great interest in the public schools, and in such community matters as parks, zoning, etc. In particular, communities that have come under the influence of growth companies are prepared to pay for good schools, but in return they really expect their school systems to be superior and are very active and vocal in this respect. This attitude is particularly evident in connection with school boards. Thus in recent years nearly every school board in the communities surrounding Stanford University has included at least one engineer; this is not atypical.

THE FUTURE

In conclusion, a few words are in order about where all of this is leading the engineer and the country. It can be said with assurance that growth industries, although important now, will become proportionately even more important with the passage of time because they are the industries of the future. The creative activities of such industries will concentrate increasingly in specific locations. The importance of the great university in this scheme of things will become better understood, and as a result will become even greater than it is now. Also, as the true implication of the "community of technical scholars" becomes better understood, such centers will become more numerous and even stronger than they are now.

Finally, the engineer will have a central role in this entire operation, a position which he will achieve by having on the average carried his education to increasingly advanced levels. As a result he will be able to exploit the opportunities in the new and interesting world in which he lives, will grow with the times, and will be in a position to take advantage of new opportunities as they develop.

Epilogue: A Word about History

Civilization, as we know it today, owes its existence to the engineers. These are the men who, down the long centuries, have learned to exploit the properties of matter and the sources of power for the benefit of mankind. By an organized, rational effort to use the material world around them, engineers devised the myriad comforts and conveniences that mark the difference between our lives and those of our forefathers thousands of years ago.

The story of civilization is, in a sense, the story of engineering—that long and arduous struggle to make the forces of nature work for man's good. The story of engineering, pieced together from dusty manuscripts and crumbling relics, explains as well the state of the world today as the accounts of kings and philosophers, generals and politicians.[1]

[1] From "The Ancient Engineers" by L. Sprague de Camp. Copyright © 1960, 1962, 1963, by L. Sprague de Camp. Reprinted by permission of Doubleday & Company, Inc.

WE HAVE STRESSED recent engineering developments in this book at
the expense of history. Engineers know too little of the origins of their
profession, and as is the case for all history, knowledge of the past
should help in planning for the future. Yet the history of science and
engineering is a large subject and one difficult to glimpse briefly without distortion. It is hoped that many readers will follow it more carefully in the references cited at the end of this Epilogue. A few comments follow, and some dates are set down. These dates are neither
complete nor fully representative, but they will serve as beginnings.
Concentration is on that line of events which most affects our present
technological activities.

PREHISTORY AND ANCIENT HISTORY

The first engineering projects were undoubtedly agricultural engineering—irrigation and the improvement of the tools of farming—enabling
the land to support larger populations and freeing many persons for
specialized occupations. One of these occupations was war; thus military engineering was also one of the earliest developments. In fact,
the ingenious "engines" of conquest and defense brought about the
name *ingeniator,* the antecedent of the name we now use for the profession. These activities encouraged improvements in materials, both
metals and ceramics, and the stress on specialized materials gave names
to certain of the early "ages" of history. Transportation, especially shipbuilding, was important. Yet the most dramatic and enduring symbols
of early engineering were the large structures, and it is significant that
all the seven wonders of the ancient world fall into this class.

It may be argued that little of science or quantitative skills was used
in these structures, but specialized knowledge and skills were required,
and the "master builder" of that period enjoyed a standing in his society never since equaled. Measurements of distance, weight, and
time were made, and the methods of making these were improved.
All of this provided some of the impetus for science, along with the
natural curiosity of the philosophers who felt the need to ask Why?
Some dates are:

6000–3000 B.C.	Food production revolution in Nile and Tigris-Eu-phrates basins
3000–2000 B.C.	Growth of urban cultures
2980 B.C.	Imhotep's first great pyramid (at Sakkara) for King Zoser

ca. 1500 B.C.	The Rhind Papyrus, the first engineer's handbook
1100–600 B.C.	Military engineering of Assyrians, using iron
691 B.C.	Aqueduct of Jerwan in Mesopotamia
ca. 600 B.C.	Phoenician perfection of shipbuilding
ca. 600 B.C.	Beginnings of formalized science by Thales of Miletus
530 B.C.	Great tunnel of Samos, 3,300 feet long, 900 feet underground
ca. 500 B.C.	Artificial harbor with breakwater ¼ mile long, 120 feet deep
ca. 500 B.C.	Silver mines of Mt. Laurion, Greece
ca. 300 B.C.	Euclid's organization of mathematical knowledge of the time
ca. 200 B.C.	Archimedes' contributions to shipbuilding, hydraulics, mechanics, and military devices
ca. 200 B.C.	Hero's descriptions of steam and other heat engines

THE ROMAN EMPIRE

All of the above activities were carried on during the several centuries of the Roman Empire's strength, but with stress on the "how" and little on the "why" of the procedures. The great engineering contributions were the aqueducts, roads, and public buildings, some of which still stand and a few of which are still used. The name *architectus* was used for the skilled designer of that period. Some dates are:

ca. 30–10 B.C.	Agrippa's planning of aqueducts, the Pantheon, and the Pont du Gard at Nimes for the Emperor Augustus
ca. 15 B.C.	Writing of *De Architectura* by Marcus Vitruvius Pollio
41–138 A.D.	Building of harbors, aqueducts, roads, and buildings under Emperors Claudius, Trajan, and Hadrian

THE MIDDLE AGES

There was more engineering activity in this period than might at first be supposed. The structures included the massive fortresses on the one hand and the beautiful and structurally ingenious cathedrals on the other. New engines of war were devised. Alchemy, with its false goal, set the stage for some advances in chemistry and metallurgy. Shipbuilding continued, extending the skills of the naval architects and building the basis for the coming age of exploration. Meanwhile, in

China there was the building of the Great Wall (not really an engineering achievement in the design but perhaps in the management), the invention of gunpowder, and the use of the compass.

200–1000	Improvement in catapults, battering rams, and engines of war
ca. 1000	Evolution of the fortress and walled town
1137	Beginning of the first consistent Gothic cathedral at St. Denis
1200–1300	Exploitation of water and wind power (known earlier), Dutch dykes and polders.

THE RENAISSANCE AND THE GROWTH OF SCIENCE

The beautiful architectural and structural designs of Michelangelo and the ingenious machines of Leonardo for war and peace are usually thought of as the symbols of this period. There was a resurgence of experimentation and questioning and a period of conflict between such activities and established religion. Bacon, near the end of this period, set down a methodology for enquiry which still makes sensible reading today whether or not it affected much the great scientists who followed.

1434	Brunelleschi's great dome for Santa Maria del Fiore (Florence)
1454	Printing of Gutenberg's Bible
1470	Foundations of trigonometry (*Regiomontanus*)
1482–1519	Leonardo's military machines and other inventions
1530	Michelangelo's building of St. Peter's in Rome
1564–1642	Life of Galileo, who made contributions to mechanics and structural design as well as to astronomy
1578	Besson's screw lathe
1595	Veranzio's arch and chain-metal bridges
1600	Gilbert's treatise on electricity and magnetism
1605	Publication of Bacon's "Advancement of Learning"
1614–1620	Napier, logarithms, and the adding machine
1625–1650	Progress in hydraulics by Torricelli, Pascal, von Guericke
ca. 1640	Development of analytic geometry by Fermat and Descartes
1650–1700	Major scientific contributions of Boyle, Hooke, and Huygens
1680	Differential calculus (Leibniz)
1687	Publication of Newton's *Principia*

THE INDUSTRIAL REVOLUTION TO THE PRESENT

The tremendous activity of the period that started at the beginning of the eighteenth century is usually symbolized by the machine, but the focus should be placed upon the new sources of energy harnessed, first by heat engines and later by electrical machinery. The results stimulated the search for better materials, permitted larger structures, and led to the rapid and intricate transportation systems of a modern society. It is no coincidence that three of the most important educational steps for engineering were made in this period: (*1*) the start of separate engineering schools in France, (*2*) the marvelously productive *Technische Hochschule* of the Germanic countries, and (*3*) the century-old land-grant movement in this country. Civil engineering separated from military engineering during this period, and from it grew all the specialties discussed in Chap. 1.

It can be argued whether the present is just an extension of the Industrial Revolution, different only in degree, or whether the growth of electrical communication and the advent of nuclear energy, automation, electronics, and space exploration justify a new name. Our age has been called the Age of Automation, the Scientific Revolution, and the Space Age, among other things, to denote more than a change in degree. That argument, and the right name, will be left for experts in history to debate and for a later age to settle. Only a few of the many significant dates can be set down. Those shown are largely selected from "Techniques and Civilization," by Louis Mumford, and are chosen because they will be recognized whether or not they are the most significant ones.

1705	Newcomen's atmospheric steam engine
1708	Wet-sand casting (Darby)
1736	Commercial manufacture of sulfuric acid (Ward)
1747	Establishment of École Nationale des Ponts et Chaussées in France to stress technical subjects (largely military engineering)
1749	Euler's contributions to ship hydrodynamics and structures
1756	Cement manufacture (Smeaton)
1765–1786	Watt's perfection of the steam engine as a prime mover
1785	Interchangeable parts for muskets (Le Blanc)
1787	Iron boat (Wilkinson)
1790	Manufacture of soda from NaCl (Le Blanc)
1791	Gas engine (Barker)

1793	Whitney's cotton gin
1800	Volta's battery
1802	United States Military Academy as first engineering school in United States
1818	Whitney's milling machine
1822–1831	Principles of electric motor and dynamo (Faraday)
1823–1843	Calculating machines (Babbage)
1824	RPI founded as first nonmilitary technical school of this country
1825	Technische Hochschule at Karlsruhe
1833	Magnetic telegraph (Gauss and Weber)
1838	Electromagnetic telegraph (Morse)
1840	Engineering started at University of Glasgow
1858	Open-hearth (Siemens) and Bessemer furnaces
1859	Oil mined by digging and drilling (Drake)
1862	Morrill Land Grant to stimulate "instruction in the arts and sciences related to agriculture and the mechanic arts"
1864	Maxwell's theory of light and electricity
1867	Dynamite (Nobel)
1867	Reinforced concrete (Monier)
1869	Periodic table of elements (Mendelejev and Lothar Meyer)
1876	Electric telephone (Bell)
1877	Compressed-air refrigeration (J. J. Coleman)
1877	Phonograph (Edison)
1887	Polyphase alternator (Tesla)
1887	Demonstration of electromagnetic waves (Hertz)
1893–1898	Diesel's heat engine
1895	X ray (Roentgen)
1896	Radio telegraph (Marconi)
1898	Radium (Curie)
1900	Quantum theory (Planck)
1900	Einstein's principles of relativity, showing equivalence of mass and energy
1903	Wright brothers' first man-carrying powered flight
1904	Fleming valve
1906	De Forest audion
ca. 1940	World War II, development of microwave radar, jet aircraft, nuclear fission weapons, and German rocketry
1950	Development of nuclear fusion weapons (Teller et al.)
1954	Announcement of maser by Gordon, Zeiger, and Townes
1957	Launching of Russian satellite "Sputnik"
1960	Demonstration of first operating laser (Maiman)

BIBLIOGRAPHY

DE CAMP, L. SPRAGUE: "The Ancient Engineers," Doubleday & Company, Inc., Garden City, N.Y., 1963.

FINCH, JAMES KIP: "The Story of Engineering," Doubleday Anchor Books, Garden City, N.Y., 1960.

KIRBY, R. S., S. WITHINGTON, A. B. DARLING, and F. G. KILGOUR: "Engineering in History," McGraw-Hill Book Company, New York, 1956.

MUMFORD, LEWIS: "Technics and Civilization" Harcourt, Brace and Company, Inc., New York, 1934.

Newcomen Society: periodic publications.

SINGER, CHARLES (ed., with E. J. HOLMYARD, A. R. HALL, and T. J. WILLIAMS): "A History of Technology," vols. 1 to 6, Clarendon Press, Oxford, 1954–1958.